"Because there is really nothing in your three-dimensional world that can help you to understand completely who and what I am, you all try to figure me out in different ways. However, of all the ways human beings perceive me, or the names they call me, the Eternal Life Force – or the ELF – is the closest to what I really am. I am the Force that creates and sustains all life, and I am eternal."

The ELF

GO TO ELF!

Connecting with the Eternal Life Force

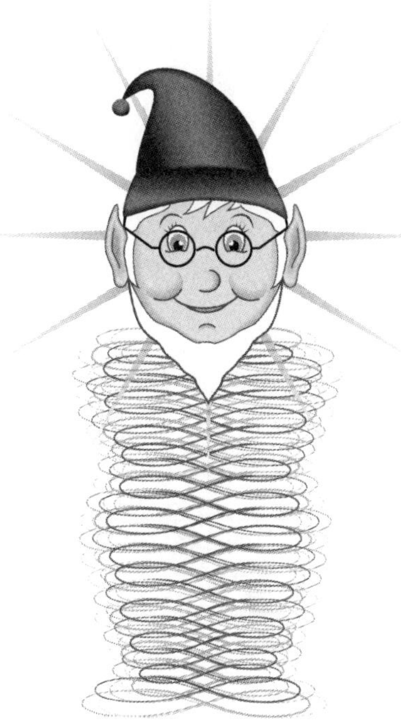

Lauren McLaughlin

Awareness Expansion, Inc.
Publishers

*"A friend sent me a copy of **Go to ELF!** and I just read it! This book has been a powerful help to raise my consciousness of peace, well-being, and trust that all is well! I love the simplicity of the book! I have written down the steps to getting what I want from the book and am integrating the affirmations."*

– Michael L. Jones, Manager

*"**Go To Elf!** was amazing and shifted my core family from angst to oneness! Everyday I remember to **Go To Elf!** 2012 was trying and the ELF helped us through! My husband and I both read it and now refer to it when in need of a new attitude or perspective. Going to Elf always works for us."*

– Paulette OShaughnessy, Teacher

*"I must say that I love **Go To Elf!** The story is delightful and keeps you engaged. More importantly, the processes that Tony and Frankie used to create a life they each wanted to have really do work. Since reading **Go To Elf!** I have made it a regular practice to create the Life Design for what I want in my life and then follow the ABC's = Ask, Believe and Collect."*

– Margaret Martin, Author – *The Chatter That Matters*

*"I just finished reading **Go To Elf!** and wanted to tell you how much it meant to me. I have always been told that, "Everything always works out for you." Or, "You have an angel on your shoulder." Now I know. Thank you for re-inspiring me to stay connected to my eternal life force, expect that good things will happen, and be grateful for my many blessings."*

– Gina Leigh Duncan, Author – *Attraversiamo – "Let's Cross Over"*. *A Story of Gender Transition*

"I used the "Life Design" exercise in this book to create two big opportunities in my sales branches. The process was simple and straight-forward, and positive results began to appear within just one week. I've seen firsthand proof that this stuff really works."

– John C., Sales Manager

***Go To Elf!** is a marvelously engaging, dramatically appealing, spirited story with direct universal messages. I am walking within your book! Thank you!"*

– Caryl Loper, Graphic Designer

This book is just so powerful...a story that talks about the Eternal Life Force (The ELF) in a way that has just not been done before. How creative! How delightful! It sounds so simple. And Truth is simple."

– Dorothy Ann Jackson, Minister Emeritis – Unity of Sarasota

*"Loved **Go To Elf!** Have been telling everyone about it and will be giving it for Christmas gifts. Best book I've read in years!"*

– Sheila Ross, Counselor

*"I have been meaning to tell you how much I loved **Go To Elf!** Reading it was one of those energy shifting, life changing experiences for me. In fact, since reading it, I have been writing music with such ease that it almost seems like taking dictation. It has been this amazing experience of feeling like all the songs in the universe already exist, and all I have to do is "tune in" to the right frequency to hear them and bring them into this plane. So cool. So... Thanks!"*

– Debra Hart, Music Teacher

"The sooner every person in this Universe reads this book and understands it, the sooner we will live in peace and happiness. Well done!"

– Eric Wolf, Sales Representative

*"I loved **Go To Elf!** I read it twice already and will read it again. It felt so real, like the characters were my friends and ELF's messages inspired my soul... helping me follow my own passion...thank you Lauren I can't wait for **Go To Elf! 2**!"*

– Bea Timpanaro, Author – *Did I Kill My Mother?*

*"Last night I finished this fantastic book, **Go To Elf!** Your book really helped me. My son Jonathan was in the hospital last week with pneumonia. He slept most of the time and I read. The characters are very well developed. They are likable and reading your book, it is hard to put it down. You have also developed your story around real point of needs at the current time. Starting with the hopelessness of someone that is almost on the brink of bankruptcy, going back to childhood issues and the pain, talking about reinventing yourself, and those that go from rejecting love to finally excepting it. It is also injected with good business advice, You present Truth in a beautiful way.*

– Christopher Ian Chenoweth, Minister – Positive Christianity

*"**Go To Elf!** is a wonderful read, offering a collection of valuable insights for living–with simple, yet powerful techniques for spiritual growth and emotional healing that are shared within the telling of a story of self-discovery. The techniques for creating a happy, prosperous, and love-filled life are explained clearly and concisely through the characters' lives and the ELF's conversation –showing the reader how easy it can be to create a new life with direction and focus. This is the next **Celestine Prophecy**."*

– Joy Katzen-Guthrie, Cantor

"I love this book so much! The characters were so real to me, that I feel like I know them and wish I did. I loved the ELF throughout the book, especially the way his body shimmered. The Epilogue made me laugh! In fact the entire book struck so many emotions. I laughed and cried, and was educated with spiritual practices through the entire story. I didn't want it to end. The last time I read a book that I was sad to finish was ***Eat, Pray Love****."*

– Sandy Cromp, Graphic Designer

"I have to tell you that my favorite part of the book is when Tony is processing his childhood pain with the ELF. It is SO real. It brought up a lot of emotion in me. I think this section is really going to help readers relate to their own childhood pain, and then be able to release and heal their "I'm not good enough" from the past, no matter what it is. So beautifully written. Thank you!"

– Susan Carr

Go To Elf! *is comfort food for anyone dancing with new-thought principles. You'll love the presentation, and if you haven't been to St. Petersburg, ELF and his protégé's will make you want to visit! Throughout the story and wonderful characters, Lauren writes in a way that makes the law of attraction easy and practical."*

– Sharon Jebens, Book Store Manager

"I loved this book! Read it in 2 nights after work and didn't want it to end. Fell in love with Tony & Frankie and their life challenges and success'. I have been "Going to ELF" more and more each day, told everyone I know about the book and shared my own experiences with many. Thank you for the gift!"

– Helen Harvey, Realtor

"I finished ***Go To Elf!*** *last night. It held my interest until the last word was read. I enjoyed it more than anything I've read in ages and I can't wait for the next one in this series."*

– Nancy Rubino

"I love the book, ***Go To Elf!*** *I finished it in two days and I could not put it down. It is a fantastic opportunity for all to learn about oneself! It has all the teachings combined into one."*

– Melissa Tart

Awareness Expansion Inc., Publishers
Po Box # 4965
Clearwater, Florida 33758

ISBN# 978-0-9829464-1-1

"Go to ELF! - Connecting with the Eternal Life Force" by Lauren McLaughlin

First Edition 2010; First Printing 2010
Second Edition 2013

Book design, illustration and photography by Sandy Cromp of Sunshine Design Studio.
Edits and revisions by Carole Harris Barton

A Story of sELF Realization

~TABLE OF CONCEPTS~

This book is dedicated, with great love and appreciation to
Abraham, Michael and John

GO TO ELF!

Connecting with the Eternal Life Force

Lauren McLaughlin

A story of sELF realization.

FOREWORD

Did you ever hear the word "edutainment"? A few months after I published the first edition of *Go to ELF!*, Lauren's self-help book disguised as a novel, I was sitting in a hotel lobby in Tampa with Bruce Lipton, a mentor and teacher for many years and someone I much admire. Naturally, I was bragging about *Go to ELF!* He leafed through it, noted the storytelling style, and said, "You know, John, this kind of teaching is called 'edutainment' because it educates and entertains the reader all at the same time. And it's really big right now."

The word intrigued me – edu-tainment: a combination of the elements of education and entertainment through storytelling. I certainly was familiar with the concept of using storytelling to teach important lessons. Master teachers from the ancient realm, including Aesop and Jesus, were skilled at it. More contemporary writers, including Og Mandino and Richard Bach, were brilliant at it. James Redfield's *The Celestine Prophecy* falls into the genre of edutainment. And I had recently been enthralled with Morgan Freeman's superb storytelling skills as he narrated the intricacies of quantum physics in the Science Channel's "Through the Wormhole." The edutainment format provides the reader with a nonintrusive platform from which to personally observe what might otherwise appear to be complicated practices and principles, and suggests ways to apply them to his or her life.

Clearly, Lauren is on to something here, because *Go to ELF!* did indeed edutain me, bringing home practices and truths that, even though I had known and taught them for years, seemed to seep into my consciousness in an even more significant way. As if by osmosis, I found myself literally experiencing not only the teachings in the book, but what I had been teaching others for years. Now that was an interesting experience!

As you read *Go to ELF!*, you will find yourself taking a journey with Tony Celentano and Frankie Doerrer, each of whom was born into a very troubled and dysfunctional family. As teens, both boys struggled to understand and deal with the violence raging within their own homes. Then, through a twist of fate, they met in the middle of a small patch of woods in St. Petersburg, Florida. There they forged a boyhood alliance that made it easier for them to deal with their individual and collective lives, and they have remained best friends throughout their adult lives.

This book is about the struggle we all have in overcoming the beliefs we unquestioningly accepted about ourselves in our early childhood. Even if we had relatively good parenting, these unconscious and often limiting beliefs can hold us back from being who we really are and who we want to become. Ninety-five percent of our current belief system was formed between the time we were born and the age of twelve, and we are still functioning on the unconscious information we internalized about ourselves at that very early age. Those early impressions create the essence of our personal belief system or, as I like to call it, our personal B.S. These impressions have left a deep imprint on us. It never occurs to us to examine, let alone question, these hidden beliefs running our lives, because we have forgotten they are even there.

In *Go to ELF!*, as Tony approaches his fortieth birthday and faces financial ruin, he has a truly mystical experience during which, in a moment of deep despair; he conjures up the ELF, an apparition that had helped him when life overwhelmed him as a teenager. An acronym for the Eternal Life Force, the ELF represents Tony's spiritual nature, his inner being, his higher self – the same energy that is his (and our) personal connection with the creator and sustainer of all life. We each have our own ELF, our own internal guidance system, but like Tony, most of us have forgotten how intimately we are connected to our spiritual nature, or how to access this spiritual nature for our own benefit when we need it.

The insight the ELF provides for Tony also allows the reader of *Go to ELF!* to see how this internal guidance system works. And with that realization comes the most important message of all: Life doesn't have to be so hard.

The ELF explains why and how making life less hard is as easy as A-B-C, and living a happy life is as simple as 1-2-3. And just as you will be inclined to do, Tony argues with the ELF when he hears these things. "I find it hard to believe it can be that easy," he says.

"Well," replies the ELF, "I'm really sorry, Tony, there's just nothing I can do to make it more complicated for you."

If you're weary of your complicated life and if, like most of us, you long to understand the rules so you can live a more peaceful, joyful life, then you're the perfect reader for *Go to ELF!*

– John McLaughlin
Creator of "MIND IS YOUR OWN BUSINESS"

CONCEPT 1

Realizing . . .
The ELF is right inside YoursELF

CHAPTER ONE

Tony Celentano stepped onto the balcony of his eleventh floor condominium just as dawn was breaking over Tampa Bay. Dressed in the black silk boxers and t-shirt he'd worn to bed the night before, he stood still for a moment, testing the outside temperature. The morning air was clear and cool but comfortable enough, he decided. He set his coffee mug onto the glass-topped table, settled his body easily into a canvas deck chair, and stretched out his long legs.

I wonder what my world would be like today if Denny had lived? It was an unanswerable question, and not the first time Tony had considered it.

He pushed the thought away and looked out with some interest at an all-grey world. As light began slowly to creep through the inky night sky, the dim outlines of the buildings below were shrouded in grey, the mist rising from the waters of the bay was grey, and because he wasn't yet totally awake, even his thoughts were grey. He found it comforting. His whole world was still shrouded in possibilities.

Tony let his mind drift to nothing in particular until the sun came closer to the horizon and brilliant colors overtook the sky, reflecting onto the water and turning the bay a glistening pink. To the south, Tony could see the city of St. Petersburg awakening. The morning light tripped the sensors on the city street lights, turning them dark. The whooshing brakes of a city bus blended with the dim voices of people on the street below, and the traffic moved slowly as people who worked nights headed home and people who worked days started early.

Tony closed his eyes and opened his mind and heart to memories he seldom bothered to visit anymore. On this particular morning when so many things in his life were changing, he wanted to remember clearly how he got here, hoping it would help him see clearly where he should go next.

Tony's first conscious memory was of his eighth birthday. He knew that many people could remember further back than that, and occasionally a shadowy picture of some earlier event would play at the back of his mind. But his first clear memory was of a day a little more than thirty years ago: March 6, 1980, his birthday and the day the Celentano family moved into their own house.

The two-story, white frame house with its wide, welcoming front porch greeted the world from a shallow front yard. The brick-lined street, like many in the northeast section of St. Petersburg, was bracketed by sidewalks of hexagonal tiles that zigzagged for blocks. The grassy back yard contained a clothesline, Tony remembered, and had plenty of room where he could play catch with his dog, Lazy. A single-car garage faced the alley that ran behind the house. The family didn't own a car, but Tony imagined he could store his bike in the garage.

Tony's pregnant mother was visibly excited and his father quietly proud as they led him from room to room, all the while chattering about their plans to turn the house that looked so huge to Tony into their new home.

The furniture that had been delivered that morning was scattered sparingly throughout the large space, and because the Celentanos had moved from a very small apartment, most of the rooms were almost empty or seemed to be. But when Luca and Helen took Tony upstairs to his room, he discovered that for his birthday, they had bought a new bed, a new dresser, and a new desk for him, and even a new bed for Lazy. Even better, his father told him he could choose any color paint he wanted for his room, and together they would paint the walls that same afternoon.

He and Luca took a bus to the paint store, and after sorting through dozens of samples, Tony chose a color called Sailor Blue. Then, just as Luca had promised—because his father never broke a promise—Tony went to sleep that night in his new bed, in his new room, in his new house, happily inhaling Sailor Blue paint fumes from the walls they had just finished painting.

The next weekend, Helen sewed bright red curtains for his windows and a blue bedspread scattered with sailboats for his bed.

It was the last time Tony could remember his parents' attention being focused solely on him.

He didn't remember anything about how the rest of the house was furnished or decorated, except for Denny's room. Shortly after Tony and his father finished painting the nursery Sunshine Yellow, the baby was born.

Funny how little details like those paint colors stick in your mind for thirty years, Tony thought. But those were the happy years, which may explain why he had clung to the memory.

Denny had blond hair and blue eyes like his mother's, and Tony had dark hair and black-olive eyes like his father's. Tony adored Denny and never grew tired of entertaining him. As soon as Denny was old enough to toddle, he and his brother were inseparable. When Tony wasn't in school, he was playing with Denny—right up until the day Denny was killed.

Tony's stomach knotted the way it always did when he remembered that day.

When the weather was nice enough, which in St. Petersburg was most of the time, Tony, his mother, and Denny always went out to the front yard at about four-thirty in the afternoon to play on the grass while they waited for his father to come home. Luca Celantano never did like to drive a car, which may explain why the family didn't own one, so he took the bus down Fourth Street every day to his job at the St. Petersburg Times, and took the bus back home again at night. Like clockwork, every night at five-fifteen his father came strolling down the street whistling. People watching him often said, "There goes Luca Celentano. Now there's a happy man."

It was a beautiful spring day, and Tony was sitting in the grass rolling a ball back and forth with Denny, who sat across from him grinning from ear to ear. Helen sat with them, clapping for Denny every time he caught the ball.

The phone rang, and Helen took Tony's place in the game when he ran into the house to answer the phone. It was a wrong number. "Don't worry about it," Tony told the caller.

Just then he heard a squeal of brakes, a second squeal, and then his mother's blood-curdling scream.

By the time Tony ran to the street, Denny and Lazy were lying lifeless about six feet apart on the bricks. Crying hysterically, Helen was bent over Denny as Luca ran full-bore toward them from a block away.

Before Tony could speak or even see his brother one more time, a neighbor whisked him away from the scene and into her house, where he stayed for what seemed like forever. The worst part was that no one told him why Denny and Lazy were in the middle of the street or why they were dead.

Finally, almost a week later, his father came for him, took him home, and told him what Luca had just barely been able to figure out.

Apparently, Lazy had come into the front yard just as Tony went into the house to answer the phone. Denny and his mother were sitting on the lawn petting Lazy when a squirrel ran down a tree and into the street. Lazy took off after the squirrel, and before his mother could grab Denny, he ran after the dog and directly into the path of a delivery van.

The impact tossed Denny high into the air, and he died the minute his little body hit the street, just seconds after a car going in the other direction hit and killed Lazy.

Tony was ten when it happened.

Now, at almost forty, Tony understood that shock and grief can change a person in an instant. But he hadn't known anything about that then, and he hadn't understood why, in a matter of just a few minutes, he had lost his mother, his brother, and his dog all at the same time.

Life from then on was as different as a little boy's life could be. Oh, his mother was still with him physically, but mentally and emotionally, she was a different person. She was angry, crude, and violent, and if not, she was so exhausted from her frequent tirades that she was dead asleep.

Countless trips to countless hospitals, recovery centers, and mental health programs failed to pierce the veil of guilt with which she fortified herself. And when it came to blame, she had enough to go around for herself, Tony, the dog, the squirrel, the van driver, and for some reason, especially for her husband.

Luca did all he could to cope with the hand he had been dealt. For eight long years, he withstood Helen's relentless rages while he did all he could to provide some sort of sensible life for himself and Tony. They could never figure out why, even though she yelled at Tony when he was in the house, she did much worse to Luca. In an instant, she would fly into a rage and begin pitching things—lamps, dishes, kitchen utensils, and furniture—and she always aimed them at Luca. His body constantly bore a black and blue mark somewhere, but he did nothing but try to soothe his wife when she was in a rage. If anyone had asked Tony, he would have said his father was a candidate for canonization.

Luca never let his wife's cruel temper tantrums stop him from doing anything that had to be done. He went to work at the same time every day, came home at the same time every night and, with Tony's help, saw that they were all decently fed, wore clean clothes, slept on clean sheets, and lived in a clean house.

Luca helped Tony with his homework when he needed to, and he went to most of Tony's basketball and baseball games and weight lifting tournaments. But at the end of every day when all was done that needed to be done and Helen was finally asleep, Luca shut himself in his study with his books, his television, and his knitting until it was time for bed. The next morning, he began a new day without complaint—a day that Luca could count on to be much like all the days before and all the days to come for as far into the future as he could imagine.

Tony found out later that while all the drama was playing out at home, Luca was climbing an invisible corporate ladder at work. He had started work in the print room of the Times when he graduated from high school at the age of eighteen, sweeping floors and helping to roll the huge rolls of newsprint into place on the presses. He had done this job with care as he watched and learned. Eventually, he began to repair the huge presses when they broke down.

The Times was a family-owned company as loyal to its employees as the employees were to the paper. So when his supervisors became aware of Luca's innate intelligence and inventive nature, not to mention his loyalty and decency, they began to offer him more responsibility. Thirty years later, an integral part of the management team at the paper, he had retired at the age of forty-eight with a pension that would support him the rest of his life.

Tony's childhood, at least from the age of ten, would have been described by most people as dysfunctional. It was, but it could have been much worse. Not only did he have his father as a role model for creating order in the midst of chaos, but he also happened to love school. He did well in his studies, and he was good at sports. The thing he liked most about sports was the way his body responded to the regular workouts. He grew muscular and well-toned, and this gave him a sense of security about himself.

For a few years, from the time he was about fifteen until he was seventeen, Tony also had the wise and gentle friendship of Bill Lee. From one of the men Luca worked with at the Times, he had learned about Big Brothers, a non-profit organization that matched stable, young adult men with teenage boys considered "at risk."

Luca knew that most of the Little Brothers came from single-parent families, but he went to the agency and explained that Tony, in effect, had no mother— certainly not one who could support him emotionally—and that Luca was sometimes just too used up to give Tony as much attention and direction as a young boy needed. So Luca asked them to make an exception and match Tony with a Big Brother.

When Luca explained to Tony that he had arranged for a man neither of them knew to come see him so Tony would have another adult to talk with, Tony wasn't particularly keen on the idea. He didn't like to talk about his home life, and he wasn't sure he wanted someone coming to his house in case his mother went off while the man was there.

But Tony's interest peaked when a nice-looking man knocked on the door the next Saturday morning and introduced himself as Bill Lee. Bill was the first Asian Tony had ever seen up close. He was nearly six feet tall, Tony guessed, and his skin wasn't yellow the way Tony had heard some adults describe Asian skin, but just a bit darker than Tony's. Bill had almost black, fairly straight hair cut below his ears; dark brown, slightly almond-shaped eyes; an undefined nose; and a killer smile. But what really grabbed Tony's attention was that after Bill introduced himself, he asked if Tony would like to go with him to the auto show at the Dome.

In spite of, or maybe because of, no one in his family ever having owned a car, Tony was nuts about cars. He spent at least half of every month's allowance on car magazines, and when he made extra money mowing lawns for the neighbors, that money usually went toward buying car magazines, too. His collection of magazines was impressive, and not coincidentally, his knowledge about cars also was impressive, especially for a kid who had seen the inside of an automobile only once or twice in his life.

Bill drove a nice little 1980 Triumph TR7 with a deep, aqua metallic finish, its leather seats the color of burnt honey. Tony was excited just looking at the car parked in his driveway, but when Bill put the top down before they even took off, Tony thought he might have just died and gone to heaven.

The indoor stadium housing the car show wasn't far from where he lived, but it was the drive of a lifetime for Tony. He remembered it as if it were yesterday. His hair blew, his eyes watered, and he felt like a million bucks. He wished with all his might that some of the kids from his class would see him ride by, but that didn't happen.

He asked Bill many questions about the car. Surprised that Tony knew as much as he did about sports cars, Bill answered easily and knowledgeably. In about ten minutes they were comfortable with each other, and before the day was over, they had formed a friendship that twenty-five years later wasn't over.

Bill traveled for the investment company where he worked, so he didn't see Tony every weekend, but he saw Tony often. Sometimes they tinkered with one of Bill's three sports cars, which were always in varying degrees of running order—or not—and sometimes they went to a baseball game or a movie. But Tony liked it best when they went kayaking.

Gliding along in a kayak at Weedon Island Preserve, they talked. Tony told Bill about a teacher who was hassling him, a kid in school who was in trouble, his mother and her latest temper tantrum, his frustration at never being able to bring his classmates to his house, and finally, the subject that embarrassed him slightly to talk to even Bill about: Luca's knitting.

Tony adored his father, but frankly, it embarrassed him greatly that his father knitted. About a year before, he had worked up the courage to ask his father about it. Tony and Luca had been sitting in Luca's study, Luca knitting a cardigan for Tony's mother in her favorite ice blue angora. The sweater was soft and pretty, Tony had to admit. "Where did you learn to knit?" he asked his father casually.

Luca had been expecting the subject to come up. After all, he'd been a teenager when he first learned to knit, and he could still remember that for years, he had felt uneasy about what would happen if any of his friends found out.

"My mother taught me when I was just about your age," Luca answered easily. Then, already guessing what the answer would be, Luca asked, "Want me to teach you, Tony?"

"No!" said Tony, his answer firm and sharp. It wasn't that he didn't appreciate the sweaters his father knit for him. Actually, Tony thought they were cool. It was just that, in his mind, men weren't supposed to knit. What if, heaven forbid, any of his friends saw his father knitting? It wasn't likely, because so far, at least, Luca had knit only at home in his own study. Even so, the thought of discovery made Tony shudder.

Somewhat amused, Luca responded with his usual calm acceptance. "I can tell you have kind of strong feelings about my knitting, Tone." Without looking at Tony, he went right on knitting. "Wanna talk about it?"

"I thought men didn't knit, that's all." Tony hung his head a little, caught between feeling ashamed of being critical of his father and feeling justified for it.

"Lots of men knit, son. Let's see…" Luca set down his knitting, stood up, and walked over to his bookshelf. After searching a moment, he found the book he wanted and casually handed it to Tony. The cover of *The Manly Art of Knitting* by Dave Fougner showed a picture of a cowboy sitting in his saddle and knitting.

"Read this," Luca suggested. "It may make you feel better about my knitting. But son, with or without your approval, I'm going to keep right on."

"What does it do for you? To knit, I mean. Sure, the stuff you knit is great, but you can buy great stuff for a lot less trouble. Why knit?" Tony asked, looking straight into Luca's eyes. "I guess I just kinda need to know, Dad."

Luca leaned back and closed his eyes. Tony was fourteen. This was an age, Luca remembered, when male teenagers were half boy and half man, and adults sometimes expected them to be one and sometimes the other. Not being a mind reader, whatever a teenager did was apt to be wrong. Tony's asking about Luca's knitting was part of a boy's need to know something about what it meant to be a man, and Luca knew his answer could be important to Tony's image of himself. His heart ached a little over Tony's discomfort, and he gave the kid credit for braving a conversation about a subject that could be a bit touchy.

"Well, first, son, I knit because I like to knit," Luca began slowly. "I like to take these strings of yarn and turn them into little works of art. For me, it is as good a way to express myself as painting a picture, or playing a piano, or writing a book. But that's not the only reason. I'm also very good at knitting, and it matters to everyone to be good at something.

"But beyond that, it's calming. I like the simple orderliness of knitting. The yarn does what I tell it to do and goes where I want it to go. It doesn't give me any grief, you know? And frankly, Tone, I can't say that about much else in my life these days." Then, realizing he might be getting a little too philosophical for a fourteen-year-old, Luca cuffed Tony gently on the chin. "Including you," he said teasingly.

Tony relayed the gist of that old conversation to Bill as they drifted in the kayak around some thick clumps of cattails. Then he admitted, "I kinda understand what it means to my father to knit, but it'd still embarrass me if any of my friends found out about it."

Bill guided the kayak into a little cove where it could drift safely, and then turned so he could look directly at Tony. "Did you read the book he gave you?"

"Yeah, I did, and it was pretty cool. If the guy who wrote the book ain't lying, a lot of guys do knit. Truck drivers, football players, businessmen, even one Congressman. They all gave different reasons for doing it, but mostly, it was to keep from being bored. Knitting uses up their extra energy better than reading or playing cards or other stuff does."

"Do you think your father has a boring life, Tony?"

"Well, my mother keeps it pretty interesting, and he has me to see to, too. But yeah, I guess he doesn't get to do much that he would like to do. He hasn't got any friends. He's probably kind of bored sometimes."

Reaching into the cooler for a couple of cold Cokes and handing them to Tony to pop the tops, Bill prodded. "Why do you think he doesn't have any friends?"

"He doesn't have time, I guess."

"And if he did have friends, do you think he'd be any more willing to invite them to your house than you are to invite yours?" Bill was careful to keep his tone gentle so Tony could think more about his answers than about Bill's questions.

"I suppose not."

"You really love your father, don't you, Tony?"

"I feel bad for him, Bill. I really do. And yes, I love him. I love him a lot. I wish there was something I could do to make his life easier."

"How about letting him knit without worrying about your disapproval?"

Tony sat still for a long while.

Bill didn't say a word.

"I guess that's what caring about someone is all about, isn't it?" Tony finally said. "Letting them do what they want to do just because they like to do it, instead of thinking about how you feel about it. He does that for me. He doesn't try to talk me out of doing new stuff, even if it isn't stuff he would probably like to do."

"We're all different, Tony," Bill said kindly. "We can do anything we want with our lives if we believe we can. But if we want to be free to do what we like, we don't have a lot of right to decide what other people should do with their lives, do we?"

"He asked me if I wanted to learn to knit and I said no," Tony offered, hanging his head a little as he remembered how he hadn't just said no; he had spit out a strong, "No!"

Bill reached over and put his hand companionably on Tony's shoulder, letting him know that whatever his answer was, it would be okay. "Do you want to learn to knit, Tony?"

"Well, it would be actually pretty cool to knit one of those big, heavy ski sweaters. Maybe I could learn and make you one for Christmas." Tony grinned at Bill and then clapped him on the back—his way of saying thanks for letting him talk about his concern without making him feel stupid.

"Now, that would be cool," Bill said, signaling Tony to turn the kayak around and head back for the dock.

Tony did knit that sweater, he remembered, although it took him almost a year to finish it. It was his first sweater, and it had a few slipped stitches. But if the weather was cool enough, Bill wore that sweater proudly almost every time they went somewhere together.

Yeah, Bill is cool, and knitting has turned out to be even cooler, Tony thought, getting up to refill his coffee cup. *It's kept me from being bored, too, a few thousand times. And think of the bundle I've saved by not buying presents!*

It continued to amuse Tony that after all these years and dozens of great knitted presents, it still freaked out his best friend Frankie to see Tony knit.

Tough, Bro, knitting is just my thing, Tony thought.

When Tony came back to the balcony, Frankie was still on his mind, and Tony began to think about their first meeting.

GO TO ELF!

It all began, Tony remembered, on an otherwise uneventful school night when he was seventeen, just before summer vacation started.

Luca came home from work that day as usual. He and Tony cooked dinner and cleaned up the kitchen, and while Tony was doing his homework, Luca went through his usual routine to settle Tony's mother down for the night. When he thought she was asleep and he had checked to be sure Tony was okay, Luca went into his study and closed the door, as he did every night.

But that night, Tony's mother wasn't asleep. She got out of bed, and when she couldn't find Luca to scream at, she ferreted out Tony in the living room where he was watching TV. He listened to her for a while before trying to calm her down the way he had seen his father do. It didn't work.

She wasn't stupid. She wanted to hurt someone else, anyone else, to try to ease her own pain. And she knew just how to do it. She didn't hit Tony with things, but she hit him with words—painful words, horrible words—shouted over and over and over again.

Because he resembled his father in looks and mannerisms, she used one of her favorite verbal tirades to insult Tony's Italian heritage. "You're just like your father, nothing but a dumb guinea. You'll never amount to anything any more than he has. You're too stupid to go to college and too full of your own good looks to see what a loser you really are."

Tony could see she was warming up for more to come, and not knowing what else to do, he bolted. He grabbed his jacket and ran up the back alley as fast as he could. Crossing a couple of busy streets, he cut through some vacant lots and kept running until he was completely out of breath.

Bent over at the waist, panting and gasping, he slowly raised his head. He was standing by a patch of woods he guessed to be about the size of a basketball court, right in the middle of town.

Dusk was deepening, but there was still enough light for Tony to check out the woods. As soon as he could breathe normally again, he pushed his way into an area where the trees grew close together and the underbrush was thick. The farther he went the darker it grew, but he didn't slow down. He kept plowing through until he found himself in a clearing in what he thought must be about the center of the woods.

It was only a small patch of forested ground covered with a thick layer of pine needles, but to Tony, it seemed like the most secret, private, safe place in the world.

Until that moment, he had no idea how much he wanted a secret, private, safe place of his own.

Sitting on the ground with his back against a tree, he breathed deeply, unable to prevent the replay of his mother's angry words in his mind. The bleakness of all their lives was overwhelming. *It's all hopeless, absolutely hopeless*, he thought, as the tears he had held back for years began to stream down his face. Faster and faster the tears came until deep, wracking sobs shuddered throughout his body. He cried for his mother, he cried for his father, he cried for the loss of Denny and Lazy, he cried for the loss of their whole happy family, and he cried for his own helplessness to do anything to change things.

Bawling uncontrollably, he beat his fists on the ground until he was so spent he could hardly move. Then, drained and unaware of his own movements, he curled into a fetal position and sank into the oblivion of sleep.

The birds woke him at dawn. Gradually becoming aware of his surroundings, he was amazed to find himself in the woods and stunned by the relief he felt from having released the raging emotion he had held inside far too long. He lay on the ground a long while without moving. Then he sat up and carefully looked around, delighted with the new secret place he had stumbled upon the night before.

Heading out of the woods for home, he spoke to the birds. “I’m calling this place Sherwood Forest. You can stay here because you were here first, but otherwise, from now on it’s all mine!”

CHAPTER TWO

Tony could hardly stay away from Sherwood Forest. Nothing in his personal experience had exposed him to churches or cathedrals, mosques or temples, or even grottoes or shrines, except for what he had read. But he had no need to know about them. He got the same awesome feeling of wonder when he sat in that little grove of trees that some people get in the finest edifices ever built to worship the gods.

He didn't make it to the woods every day, but he went there when he could, sometimes right after school, and sometimes at night after everyone in his house was asleep. Occasionally, when he needed to work out a sulk or a "mad," he sought the sanctuary of Sherwood Forest. But more often than not, Tony went there simply to think, plan, and dream the way any typical seventeen-year-old boy would.

Lately, he'd been thinking about what he might do after he got out of high school next year, and now he had something new to think about. He had been doodling on his notebook before class started when his new art teacher, Mr. Barnes, walked down the aisle to look at his student's work.

"Do you do much drawing outside of class?" asked the teacher.

"Yeah," Tony told him, "I draw things sometimes like you see in newspaper advertisements. I like to see if I can make my stuff look like their stuff."

Leafing through Tony's notebook, the teacher saw other doodles, too. "And can you?"

"I can most of the time. I like that kind of drawing. It's cool."

"Is it something you might like to do when you get out of school, like work for an advertising agency?"

"I think I'd like that a lot," Tony replied, "but I don't know if I'm good enough for that."

"You could go to Vo-Tech," his teacher suggested. "They have classes in graphic arts. Let me see what I've got," he said, handing back Tony's notebook. "I think you've got some talent there, Tony. It ought to be explored."

Mr. Barnes went to a cupboard at the rear of the classroom, came back, and handed Tony a brochure describing the graphic arts department at Vo-Tech.

That afternoon, the brochure in his pocket, Tony headed for Sherwood Forest. About twenty feet into the woods, he stopped cold. Someone else was there!

Tony listened as deep, wracking sobs broke the silence.

Tony felt the frustration and helplessness in those sobs. He had felt the same way, too, and not very long before. So for a moment, his empathy clouded his distress that somebody else was in "his" place and was using Sherwood Forest as the same safe spot that Tony had believed was his alone.

He waited for the crying to stop, and then quietly approached the center clearing. Sitting under Tony's favorite tree was an emotionally spent teenage boy about his own age, a picture of misery with his long blond hair falling onto his tear-streaked face.

As the sight of Tony from the corner of his eye, the boy sprang to his feet, a myriad of emotions crossing his face in rapid succession: surprise, fear, embarrassment, anger.

Tony stood perfectly still for a moment, quietly sizing up the kid and wondering who could take whom in a fight. They were very well matched, both boys well-muscled and about the same age and height. They could fight, of course, but Tony had a serious question about whether he could win. He didn't like to lose, so he decided he'd try to avoid a physical confrontation.

"What are you doing here?" Tony said, snarling.

"No, what are you doing here?" the other boy shouted. "You got no right walking in on me. This is my place."

"In your dreams!" Tony shouted back. "This is my place, and I think it's about time you got the hell out of here."

"Unless you own these woods, fella, I ain't going nowhere," the blond boy said, taking a defiant stance and holding it. "How long have you been standing there?"

"Long enough." Then, remembering the sound of the boy's sobs, Tony lowered the fist he hadn't realized he'd raised. "Look, I don't own this place, and I don't suppose you do, either. And don't worry about me hearing you bawling. I come here sometimes to do that myself when I'm seriously bummed out. That's why, I guess, I've been letting myself believe this place was all mine."

The boys locked eyes, each boy seeing in the other's eyes an odd kind of mirror image, each set of eyes holding a degree of understanding and acceptance that neither had ever seen from anyone else.

"I'm Frankie Doerrer," the blond boy said, extending his open palm toward Tony.

"Tony Celentano," Tony answered, accepting the handshake.

"You live around here?"

"A few blocks east of here," Tony answered. "You?"

"A few blocks west of here. We must be about the same age, but I've never seen you in school. I'm a junior at St. Pete High. You?"

"I'm a junior at Northeast," Tony said. "I guess a few city blocks make a difference in your school assignment. Why were you bawling? Girl trouble?"

"I wish," Frankie said. "No, my old man drinks, and then he comes home and beats on my mother. I can live with that. What I can't live with is that she lets him. This morning we had to go to the emergency room, but she wouldn't press charges. She just takes it and takes it, and maybe she can, but sometimes I can't." Frankie released a long slow sigh, wondering why he had confessed all this to a perfect stranger in the middle of a patch of woods. He must really be losing it.

"I know how you feel," Tony said. "I've got the opposite problem. My mother beats on my father every night. If she isn't yelling swear words at him at the top of her lungs, she's punching him or throwing things at him, and the sicker she gets, the stronger she seems to get. Last night I had to patch up a big cut on his eyebrow from a plate she threw at him. He probably should have gone to the emergency room, but he wouldn't go."

Frankie was surprised by the response. They fell into silence for a moment, each thinking that as weird as his own life was, maybe it wasn't quite as weird as the other guy's.

"How did you find this place?" Frankie asked.

"I just ran out of the house one night until I couldn't run any farther, and here it was. I fought my way into the center here and thought I'd found the most private place in the world. I've been coming here ever since, especially when I want to think about something serious."

"I've been coming here for the same reason for the last three months," Frankie said.

"I wonder why we haven't bumped into each other before."

"I guess it just wasn't time," Frankie answered philosophically.

"Yeah, so now we share it?"

Frankie was surprised again, this time because he was less upset to hear Tony ask that than he would have thought. "I guess we do. I have a name for it," he said, suddenly feeling a little self-conscious again, but somehow compelled to explain. "You'll probably laugh your head off, but I call it Sherwood Forest, because it seems like the place where Robin Hood picked to be safe."

"No kidding!" Tony answered in amazement. "That's what I call it, too—Sherwood Forest!"

And somehow, from that moment on, Tony and Frankie weren't just friends, they were brothers.

Speaking of which, Tony thought on his balcony, *I'd better get showered and dressed and go meet Frankie.*

He and Frankie had a standing Saturday morning breakfast date at nine o'clock at the Dome Grill on Central Avenue, and they hadn't missed a single Saturday in twenty years.

As Tony went inside from the balcony, Trainwreck, his big orange and white cat, rushed toward him, winding himself enthusiastically between Tony's legs. To avoid tripping, Tony bent down and lifted the cat to his chest. With a soft purr, Trainwreck nestled his head into the bend of Tony's neck, content now that breakfast was on the way.

About a year before, Tony had been coming out of a downtown office building after visiting a client when he turned a corner and saw a terrified cat stranded about four feet up a telephone pole, a snarling little dog nipping at the cat's tail. Feeling sorry for the cat, Tony had chased the bad-tempered dog away and peeled the cat off the pole, wondering if he would be clawed in exchange for his good deed. Instead, the cat had turned and nestled his head into Tony's neck the way he was doing now, obviously grateful to be rescued.

Tony had carried the cat to his car and set him down on the front seat, thinking he would take him to a veterinarian. But when he examined the purring cat, he discovered that all his wounds were old ones—a scarred bald patch on his back where fur no longer grew, a notch bitten out of his tail, and one of his ears chewed half off.

"You look like a train wreck," Tony told him, and without further thought, took the cat back to his condominium. He poured Trainwreck a bowl of water and opened a can of tuna, and the two had been very compatible roommates ever since. By now, Trainwreck weighed nineteen pounds and was a fine, healthy specimen of pure tomcat, complete with battle scars and a surprisingly happy disposition.

Now in the kitchen, Tony gathered up Trainwreck's dish—one made for a small dog—and rinsed it under the faucet. Then he opened two small cans of cat food and emptied them into the dish. Putting it down in front of Trainwreck, Tony said with a grin, "Better beef up, Buddy. You just never know when Darth Vader may come by."

Tony chuckled as he thought he saw Trainwreck shudder. Darth Vader was the six-pound Chihuahua who lived in an apartment down the hall, and he scared Trainwreck right down to his marrow. If the cat even heard the tiny dog in the hallway, he scrambled hell-bent-for-leather to the top of the armoire in Tony's office and didn't come down until the condo was quiet for at least two hours.

Half an hour later, freshly showered and wearing slim-fitting jeans and a white t-shirt tucked in at his trim waist, Tony stepped into the hallway. Checking his watch one more time, he decided to drive to the restaurant. He usually loved the walk up Central Avenue, but today he didn't want to be late. It was too important a day.

Finding a parking space about half a block from the restaurant, he got out and was striding easily down the sidewalk when a paradoxical thought caught him: Although part of life sometimes changes dramatically in what seems like an instant, other parts stay remarkably the same.

For twenty years, he and Frankie had kept their Saturday morning breakfast date without fail. Week after week, they had come to each other with good news and bad, sniffles and sneezes, broken hearts and broken bones. But always, they had come to each other.

Since that day in the woods when they had taken joint ownership of Sherwood Forest, they had each other's back one hundred percent.

In those same twenty years, the Dome Grill had changed little. The décor was the same. The menu was the same. The owner was the same. Solid, Tony thought as he pushed open the glass door.

The owner stood at the counter smiling, thinking pretty much what Tony had been thinking: As much as things change, that's how much they stay the same. Business had been alarmingly slow for the past six months, but Pete knew that good economy or bad, he could depend on having two regular customers every Saturday morning: Tony and Frankie. Somehow, that helped keep Pete grounded. But Tony and Frankie weren't just his customers anymore, they were his buddies. They had seen him through good times and bad before, and they would see him through this time.

"Hi ya, Pete," Tony said cheerfully. "How's it goin'?"

"Good, good. Good to see ya, Tony. The usual?" Pete asked with a grin.

"What else? Frankie here yet?"

"At your table," Pete answered as he called the order over his shoulder. "Two over easy, corned beef hash crisp, Dome fries, whole wheat toast and butter it hot." He hit the sale button on the old-fashioned cash register, collected Tony's money, and handed him a thick, mud-colored pottery coffee mug. "Cream, no sugar," he added with a wink.

"Yeah, yeah, so I'm in a rut," Tony said, smiling and shrugging.

Carrying his coffee and a few extra napkins, Tony rounded the corner into the dining room and spotted Frankie reading a magazine at what they really did think of as "their table." In all the twenty years they had been coming here, they'd had to sit somewhere else only half a dozen times.

Ruts are not bad things, Tony thought. *They are pretty comforting to slip into when all the rest of your world is going through its spin cycle.*

The restaurant may not have changed much in twenty years, but he and Frankie certainly had. Even though they had been built much alike as teenagers, they were different now. Maybe it was Frankie's German heritage, or maybe it was the manual labor he did that had thickened his body, but he was a big bear of a man now. About six feet two, Frankie was 250 pounds of solid muscle without an ounce of excess fat. His light blond hair had turned sandy, and he wore it in a long crew cut. His eyes were still piercing blue, his somewhat round face was clean-shaven, and his overall look was wholesome.

Tony also was six feet two, but slim—lanky by some standards. He, too, was muscled and toned. He worked out in the gym at least four days a week and did curls with twenty-pound weights every day. Most nights, he also swam laps in the condo pool. His almost black hair was well styled, his features were quite fine, his skin was a bit on the olive side, and his oval face wore a close-cropped beard.

The two men didn't dwell on it, but they knew they were good to look at, especially when they were together.

"Hey, Bro," Tony said as he set his coffee mug on the table.

Frankie looked up expectantly into Tony's smiling eyes. "Hey, yourself!" Frankie said, rising quickly to give Tony one of those handshake-one-armed-hug combinations that men give when they're genuinely glad to see each other.

"Am I late?"

"Hell, no, I'm early," Frankie answered. "I had to take my sister to work this morning. Her car broke down, and if Mike had taken her, they would have had to wake Andy up to go with them, so I volunteered to be Julie's driver. Then I picked up a magazine and came here for an extra cup of coffee. I told Pete to put my order in when he put yours in so we can eat together."

Tony reached over and picked up Frankie's magazine. Not surprisingly, a picture of Mickey Mouse standing at the front gate of Disney World was on the cover.

"Anything new happening in Fantasy Land?" Tony teased,

grinning widely as he passed the magazine back to Frankie.

Frankie loved— in fact, adored—Disney World in Orlando. It was one of his passions. He went there as often as he could spare the time, just because he liked being there.

"Not much," Frankie answered seriously, ignoring Tony's smirk. "They're talking about building a new section called the Land of Horrors, but so far, I don't see anything about them starting up yet."

"Well, won't that just float your boat?" Tony's eyes continued to twinkle. "You can do *The Rocky Horror Picture Show* and the Magic Kingdom all at the same time. Your dream come true."

"If you don't stop trash-talking my special interests this morning, Bro," Frankie said with an edge in his voice, "I'll stand on the table and announce to the whole restaurant that you knit."

"You can do that if you want to, but I'd rather call a truce," Tony said, still having difficulty covering up his amusement. "Just for getting you riled up so early in the morning, I'll go up and get our breakfast. Give me your ticket so I get the right number in case you ordered something different today."

"Yeah, yeah, I will the day you do," Frankie growled. "When you come back, you can tell me what's got you so full of piss and vinegar this morning."

Tony brought back the food in two short trips and then fiddled with ketchup, salt, and napkins before deciding he wasn't quite ready to share his news yet.

They talked about this and that, mostly about Frankie's work and the soap-opera style lives of his various crew members. Then Tony asked. "So how is Julie?"

Frankie grew a little misty-eyed when he thought about his sister. "It just makes me so damn happy to see her so happy. She really loves Mike, and I think he's perfect for her. And that baby girl, she sure is somethin' else! She wrapped herself around my heart when she was only minutes old, but she's growing up so fast! She can actually play with me now. And you should see that kid eat!"

Noticing that Tony was again grinning widely, Frankie stopped abruptly. “Well, you asked,” he said.

“It makes me happy, too, Bro, to see you so happy about Julie,” Tony said, chuckling and genuinely glad for Frankie. “You worried about her for a long time.”

“Yeah, I did. I wasn’t sure she would ever get married. She was so afraid she might marry someone like Dad and wind up like Mom. But thank God,” he let out a sigh of relief, “that ain’t happenin’. Now, tell me what has you so feisty this morning.”

Tony looked at the clock on the wall. *It’s eleven-thirty already, and we’ve talked about everything but me so far.. Well, I guess it’s now or never.* “What have you got going on today, Frankie, when we finish here?”

“Are you trying to change the subject again?”

“No, I just thought if you weren’t busy, I’d rather tell you what I have to tell you back at the condo. If you’ve got time, I’ll give you a beer and tell you about my whole . . .” Tony stopped in search of the right word and didn’t find it. “I guess you could say ‘interesting’ week.”

A short time later, they waved goodbye to Pete and took off in separate vehicles, each heading for Tony’s condominium.

Back in his car, Tony’s thoughts picked up where his morning tour down memory lane had ended.

When his graduation from high school was just a few weeks away, Tony had initiated a conversation with his father that Tony had put off as long as he felt he could. He wanted to study graphic arts, but couldn’t see how he could do that without continued help from Luca. He told Luca what he wanted to do, and then asked if he could get a part-time job and go to school at Vo-Tech for eighteen months while still living at home.

"I think, Tony," Luca answered calmly, "that you should be setting out on your own once you turn eighteen."

Tony was astonished. Apparently his father, too, had given Tony's future some thought.

"Well, Dad, I hadn't thought about moving out quite so soon. Can I ask a few questions? I mean, do you think, without some additional training, I can find a job that pays me enough to live on my own right away? And why do you think I want to move out and leave you alone with Mom just because I'm turning eighteen?"

Before Luca could respond, Tony rushed on. "How come you don't seem at all surprised that I want to be a graphic artist when I just figured it out for myself? And just so I can understand what you just said, how long have you been thinking about all this?"

Then, taking a deep breath, Tony tried to settle down a little so he could hear Luca's answers.

"Okay, let's take those one at a time," Luca said seriously. "A nice little efficiency apartment on the north side, not too far from downtown so you can walk to work and Vo-Tech, will probably cost you about two hundred and fifty dollars a month, maybe a little more, plus utilities and telephone. Then you'll have food and some entertainment, though you probably won't have too much time for that until you graduate from Vo-Tech. I'd say you'll need about eight hundred dollars a month, maybe a little more, to live pretty decently. You can work at least thirty hours and still go to Vo-Tech. You can probably earn two hundred dollars a week, even unskilled, especially if I pull some strings for you at the Times. And you could probably eke by on that. But here's what you don't know, Tony.

"I've been putting money in a savings account for you since you were born, twenty dollars a week taken out of my pay. I know that doesn't seem like much now, but eighteen years ago, it was a sizeable chunk out of the money I brought home to feed the family. Since it came out of my pay automatically, I didn't ever seem to miss it, and your mother never even knew about it.

"On your eighteenth birthday, I will change the account from my name to yours. It will have almost twenty thousand dollars in it, and I'll add enough to make sure it's an even twenty. With that money, plus what you earn while you are in school, you should be well able to make it on your own, Tony—not only until you get out of school, but until your career really takes off."

"Dad," Tony said, emotion filling his voice, "I don't know what to say."

"Well, don't say anything yet, son, because since I'm on a roll here and you asked all the right questions, I'd like to finish giving you the answers. To answer question two, the reason I want you to move out when you're eighteen is because you really aren't going to have any other choice. I've been talking with your mother's doctors and her sisters back in Connecticut. They have found a really nice place up there near them that will take her in and take care of her."

"Take care of her?"

"This may be hard for you to accept, Tony, but your mother isn't happy and I'm not happy. I don't know about you Tone, but I'm tired of not being happy. I loved Denny as much as a father could love a little boy, and I love you even more, because I've loved you longer. And believe it or not, I still love your mother, but she doesn't even know who I am some of the time," Luca explained patiently.

"Her rage is so blind that she is living with a stranger, and so am I. The doctors say there is always a chance she could snap out of it, but there's nothing they can do to make that happen. I can't live like this forever, Tony, any more than you can. And beyond that, I have to be practical and ask what would happen to your mother if something happened to me. Did you think I wouldn't fix things so you wouldn't be left with that responsibility?"

"I never even thought of it, Dad. I'm sorry, but I just never did."

"It's not your job to think of things like that, Tony, but it is mine. And believe me, I've thought about every part of this a lot." Luca absently reached for his knitting, but changed his mind and kept talking.

"I'm only forty-seven years old, and because I started at the Times when I was eighteen, I can retire next year after thirty years and get a pretty good pension. Your aunts assure me that the place where they want to put your mother is very nice, and it looks beautiful in the pictures they sent. They have a very competent staff to help her there, and to tell you the truth; I think they secretly suspect that if they could get her away from us and out of this house where Denny died, maybe she would get better. And for all I know, Tony, they're right. Anyway, that's the plan."

Tony felt as if the breath had been knocked out of him. "When?"

"Next month, probably, after you graduate. Serenity House, which is what this place is called, will have two openings then, and they've agreed to put your mother in one of them on a six-month trial basis. I have to pay for the first six months, but after that, the state of Connecticut will pay for her care if she stays. I plan to take her up there as soon as Serenity House says they can take her. Her doctor here will sedate her before the plane trip, and their doctors will meet us at the other end.

"It's perfectly okay for you to stay here alone for a few days while I'm gone, Tony, but you can have Frankie come and stay with you if you want the company."

"Then you'll be coming back here?"

"Until I retire, sell the house, and you find your own digs, yeah. I thought you and I could stand a few peaceful months together before we go our separate ways. You'll be starting a new job, starting school, starting life as a man, Tony. And you'll be okay. You've always been okay. You've been mostly taking care of yourself, and even your mother and me, since you were ten years old. You can cook and clean and do laundry and even hold a part-time job. The only difference between living here and living on your own," Luca said with a smile," is that I won't be in the next room knitting."

"That will hardly be the only difference, Dad. You've never not been here for me, not even for one day since I was born."

"I've been here physically, Tony, but sometimes I've checked out emotionally. It was either that or go crazy myself."

"So when I'm living in my own apartment working and going to school and becoming a man, what will your separate way be like, Dad?"

"When the house sells—and by the way, you can have anything you want from here for furniture to get yourself started—I'm going to New York and share my brother's apartment for a while. Your Uncle Fred is alone and I'm alone, and we're still relatively young bucks. We both have pensions. He's got a part-time job, and I'll get one. We won't be eligible for Social Security for a while, but eventually, that will kick in. We figure we can try getting into some trouble together as two bachelors for a while. I'll be near enough to Connecticut to visit your mother if the doctors think I should, but…"

"But?" asked Tony after a fairly long pause.

"But you might as well know I'm going to get a divorce, Tony." Luca watched an array of emotions pass across Tony's face—relief mostly, he thought, but some sadness, some regret, and maybe some panic.

"You okay, son?"

"Yeah," Tony answered automatically. "I'm okay. I guess it will all sink in after a while. Mostly, I'm sort of stunned that you did all this planning right here in the same house with me, and I had absolutely no idea you were thinking of leaving."

Luca had never been a demonstrative man. He had loved Tony's mother, and still did, in some ways. In the early years of his marriage, he'd felt comfortable enough touching her in front of other people, but he knew he'd never transferred that physical affection to Tony, even though he loved him dearly. *It's a bit awkward to start now*, he thought, *but now is when he needs it.* So Luca put his hand securely on Tony's shoulder and drew him into a hard, manly hug.

"Do you want me to answer your third and fourth questions, Tony?" Luca asked as he drew apart from the son he loved so much.

"I don't even remember what they were," Tony answered,

feeling as though at least a month instead of just twenty minutes had passed since he had asked those questions.

CHAPTER THREE

"You asked me, Tony, why I'm not surprised you want to be a graphic artist," Luca said, continuing the discussion of the changes soon to take place in their individual and collective lives. "It's because you've been fascinated with advertisements and commercials since you were a baby."

Luca paused, letting his mind wander back a few years.

"I remember when you weren't much more than two, your mother and I took you with us to a restaurant. You couldn't read yet, of course, but when the waitress put a bottle of A1 sauce on the table, you recognized the bottle from an ad you'd seen on television and calmly announced, 'Ah, the touch that adds so much!' The waitress looked at you in amazement, and your mother and I burst out laughing.

"Then right after we moved into this house—I guess you were eight then—you and your mother were getting ready to dye Easter eggs. She realized after she read the directions on the box of dye that she needed vinegar. I offered to run down to the store to get some, and you reached up, gave me a big hug and sang, 'Oh, thank heaven for 7-11!'

"You copied and colored grocery ads and furniture ads from the Sunday paper all the time as you were growing up. I used to find your drawings all over the house," Luca said, chuckling, "and I had a hard time throwing some of them away, because sometimes they were pretty good."

Luca got up, went to his desk, and pulled a file from the bottom drawer. "In fact, I didn't throw all of them away," he said, handing the file to Tony. "I just couldn't."

Not only was Tony surprised to find himself looking at drawings he had long since forgotten, he was amazed to hear Luca tell stories about when Tony was a little boy. *Why have I never heard these stories before? I guess it was just too painful for Dad to talk about the time when we were still a pretty happy family.* Then Tony tuned back into what his father was saying.

"So I'm sure learning to create ads is the right thing for you, Tony, and that you will be good at it. When you knit, you show me that you understand design. You've taught me things I never would have known to do with the yarn without your coaching. I taught you to knit, but you taught me how to use my knitting to make more beautiful things. You have a keen imagination and a quick wit, too, and they're both important qualities for work in advertising. I've known some great graphic designers at the Times, Tony. They like what they do and they make good money at it. I think it's just about a perfect calling for you."

"That means an awful lot to me, Dad," Tony said. "I'm pretty grateful to Mr. Barnes for looking at my doodles and encouraging me to consider designing for a living. Since you think it's a good idea, too, that's about all I could ask for."

"I'll have to drop by and thank Barnes, myself," Luca said. "You know, I had him as an Art Appreciation teacher in high school at Boca. He was a good guy, and I enjoyed all of his classes. I think he'll be glad to hear that I still appreciate him, but this time, because of what he's done for you."

Realizing that this was turning into the best and longest conversation he'd ever had with Luca, Tony was surprised when his normally quiet father went right on talking.

"Now for your last question," Luca said as Tony drew a blank.

"You asked me how long I have been thinking about this, making these plans, and I guess I would have to say since shortly after you met Frankie Doerrer last year. He was the first boy you ever brought home. And when I heard you guys in your room playing records, and talking about sports and girls and all the things teenagers should be talking about, I realized how abnormal your growing up had been.

"But you and Frankie weren't allowing the strangeness of your lives to keep you from having a sense of normalcy, some good times, and a really close friendship. Again, you became my teacher, Tony, because I realized I wanted some of that normalcy, too," Luca confessed. "So I let myself think beyond what I had always just accepted as my duty, to see if there might be other solutions for me, too. And then your aunt called and proposed this new idea. At first, I thought, 'I can't put Helen in some kind of home in Connecticut. How do I know she'd be happy?' Then I thought, 'Well, she's certainly not happy here, and neither are the rest of us.'

"So I read the material your aunt sent me, and I talked to your mother's doctors here about how they thought she would be cared for in a group home like that. And since they fully approved, the whole plan seemed to make more and more sense the more I thought about it."

Luca walked over to his desk again and pulled a brochure for Serenity House out of his file. "So as long as I know that I'm living close enough to check in on her, at least for the first year, I feel all right about it. I will be less than an hour and a half away by train from Serenity House when I'm living in Brooklyn with Fred, and Helen's sisters will live only a few miles from her," he said, handing the brochure to Tony.

Tony put it in his pocket for later. "I'm really going to miss you when you go to New York, Dad," he said, his voice a little shaky. "Having you so far away all the time will take some getting used to."

"Well, don't think I'm not going to be keeping my eye on you, too, Tone," Luca said, cuffing Tony lightly on the arm the way he often did. "Your Uncle Fred hates winters in New York, so we've already decided I will use the money from the sale of this house to buy a little condo here, and we'll both come down for at least three months every winter. When we get a little older, maybe we'll even stay down here for good."

And every January for twenty years since, just as Luca had promised Tony, he and Fred had driven from New York to St. Petersburg and, depending on the weather in New York, had driven back in either April or May. The rest of the year, a steady stream of their New York friends had come down to enjoy the condo for short periods.

As Tony pulled into his space in the parking garage of his condo, Frankie angled into a visitor's space on the same floor. They got into the elevator together, and when the door opened on Tony's floor, there stood his neighbor ready for a walk with her dog, Darth Vader. Tony wished her good morning, ruffled Darth's tiny ears, and then headed toward his apartment with Frankie.

"Who was that?" Frankie asked.

"That was the only other resident on my floor, and frankly, one of the few left in the building," Tony said. "And believe it or not, Trainwreck is scared to death of that dog."

"Can't say I think much of the dog, either," Frankie commented. "But the owner? Now, that's not a bad little package."

As soon as they were inside the condo, Tony headed to the kitchen for a couple of beers and to check his phone messages while Frankie sat in the living room waiting patiently for him to come back and tell his story.

The couch, strategically angled toward the sliding glass doors to the balcony, faced an ever-changing panoramic view of Tampa Bay. The deep blue sky dotted with snowy white clouds, and the smooth-as-glass water of the bay just a slightly deeper shade of blue than the sky, combined to showcase the pristine sails of dozens of large and small boats whose fortunate owners were out for a Saturday sail.

Looking southwest along the coastline of Tampa Bay, Frankie saw the St. Petersburg Pier, and farther south, Al Lang Field and Albert Whitted Airport. He even saw the stack of a cargo ship docked at Bayboro Harbor.

A bit of local color was associated with these landmarks. The first scheduled commercial airline flight had taken off from Albert Whitted in 1914, carrying the United States mail to Tampa in just twenty-three minutes. As teenagers, Frankie and Tony had gone to Bayboro Harbor to watch the *Calypso*, Jacques Cousteau's famous ship, being refitted for its next great exploration. Just last year, Tony and his father, and Frankie and his sister had toured the tall ship *Bounty* when it docked for a winter at the Pier. The vessel had been used in the filming of both the *Mutiny on the Bounty* with Marlon Brando, one of Luca's favorite movies, and *Pirates of the Caribbean: Dead Man's Chest* with Johnny Depp, one of Tony's favorites.

After just a few moments gazing at this scene of peace and tranquility, Frankie felt fully relaxed. Shifting his attention back inside, he was struck, as always, by how good looking Tony's apartment was. In Frankie's opinion, Tony's natural instinct for good design was always amazing, whether he was creating an advertisement, designing a sweater, or decorating a room. Frankie readily admitted to having no such talent, but he appreciated simplicity and style when he saw it.

The room Frankie was admiring hadn't happened by accident. When Tony had first moved into the condominium, he had lived for more than a month with nothing in the living room but the canvas deck chairs and glass-topped table now on the balcony. Once he developed a real feel for the way he wanted the room to look, he had carefully selected the furniture and artwork to create a design he knew he would love to live with.

A dark brown leather sofa, faced by an oblong autumn-brown granite coffee table, anchored the room. On the table sat an exquisitely designed Steuben glass dolphin about eighteen inches tall. Facing one another across either end of the coffee table were a modern version of a large wing chair covered in a teal blue silk, and a three-foot square ottoman covered in chocolate-brown suede. Banking the sofa on each end was an identical pair of bamboo Chinese chests, each holding a sturdy bronze lamp topped by a raw silk shade the color of heavy cream. Tossed casually on the back of the sofa was the beautiful hand-knit throw Tony had made in that same rich shade of cream. The combination signaled a warm invitation to lie down for a long, peaceful nap.

Tony hadn't seen a need for window treatments on the opposite wall, considering that he lived on the eleventh floor and no other buildings faced his condo. Instead, he had a magnificent deep teakwood frame built around the extra-wide sliding glass doors. As a result, the panoramic view of Tampa Bay appeared to be a moving work of art.

For a bit of whimsy, Tony had selected a three-foot-tall tooled leather hippopotamus with an engaging smile to greet guests at the front door. Other artwork placed attractively around the room consisted of the framed original drawings of some of the ads Tony had designed.

At that thought, Frankie frowned. The ad agency where Tony had worked for more than fifteen years had closed its St. Petersburg office. *Wow, it must be eighteen months ago now,* Frankie thought.

Tony had struggled to find work, but he had complained little. *Well, maybe that's what his big news is going to be today*, Frankie considered. *Maybe Tony has landed his dream job.*

Tony came back into the room carrying two bottles of cold beer and a bag of pretzels. Sitting down on the end of the couch opposite

Frankie, Tony glanced out the window and wondered if they should sit on the balcony. *No, this will be better*, he decided to himself as he flipped up the lid of the ottoman and took out his knitting.

Uh-oh, Frankie thought. *This is serious, because he doesn't knit in front of me unless he has to really think before he talks*. Tony had never quite convinced Frankie that it was normal for a grown man to knit.

"What are you working on?" Frankie asked, thinking it might be easier for Tony to warm up to a more serious subject if he talked about something else first.

"A throw for the new couch in Dad and Uncle Fred's apartment," Tony answered, spreading out his work. Using textured yarns, he had created a tone-on-tone checkerboard-patterned throw in navy blue. To Frankie, it looked good enough to be featured on the cover of a decorator magazine.

"I told you they redecorated their apartment, didn't I?" Tony asked.

"Yeah, you said they got a wild hair, sold all their old stuff, and called in a decorator. Did they ever tell you why?"

"No, but I think the furniture they had was mostly hand-me-downs from Fred's old house, and they probably decided they didn't want to bother replacing one piece at a time. Dad always was one for calling in an expert rather than trying to do something he didn't know much about.

"Here, look at the pictures," Tony said, reaching into the ottoman again and removing a small picture album. "Dad sent these last week."

Frankie looked at the first picture and raised an eyebrow. "Wow, this is pretty classy, Tony! It must have cost a mint."

"Yeah, well, my old man's a classy guy," Tony said in a half-amused, half-amazed tone.

"Must have inherited those genes from his son," Frankie said, still thinking about how much he liked the way this apartment looked.

Tony took a deep breath. "Okay, Frankie, I'm gonna just tell this story exactly the way it happened, and if you have any questions, just interrupt me, okay?" With that, he began to knit vigorously.

"Last Tuesday morning, I transferred five thousand dollars from my savings account to my checking account to pay my monthly bills, just the way I've done every month since my severance pay and unemployment benefits ran out eight months ago. Of course, I knew I was using up my savings while I looked for a job, but I didn't realize how much I had spent until my account showed a balance of only two thousand dollars after Tuesday's withdrawal. Not enough for even one more month's expenses.

"I felt pretty depressed about it all day, but that night, I bit the bullet and made the mortgage payment, my car payment, and the minimum payment on my credit cards. And then it really hit me. This is it. I could lose everything now.

"I tell you, Frankie, I've never felt like that before. We didn't have much money when I was a kid, but I was always warm and fed and had a roof over my head. And I've worked since I was sixteen years old. I never had any trouble supporting myself. I lived well and I saved for a rainy day, but who ever knew it was gonna pour for eighteen months?"

"Geeze, you could always come to me, Tony," Frankie said, interrupting.

"I know that, Bro, but for how long? I didn't have any long-term solutions in sight. I probably wouldn't admit this to anyone else on the planet, not even Dad, but I was scared to death. I mean petrified. And I panicked. If I could have gone back to Sherwood Forest and bawled it out there, I would have, but I couldn't. So instead, I did it right here. I sat right here on this couch and cried my eyes out like I did when we were kids. And once I got started, I thought I'd never stop. Poor Trainwreck went mad. He even licked my tears, for God's sake, and all I could do was rock him in my arms and cry some more."

GO TO ELF!

Tony set his knitting aside, visibly shaken by the memory of the episode. He took a swig of beer, got up, and looked out the window briefly until his emotions settled down.

"Now brace yourself, Frankie. The rest of this is gonna be a little hard to swallow, but it's true. I swear it's true," Tony said, sitting back down on the couch.

"In the middle of rocking Trainwreck and sobbing and trying to stop bawling, I started to get mad. I began screaming and hollering at myself for being so stupid, because I had put myself in this place—or rather, I spent myself into this place—and I knew it. That dolphin alone cost two thousand dollars," he said, gesturing toward the glass sculpture in front of them. "But I should be able to get myself out of this mess, too, shouldn't I? It just seemed like the whole world had conspired against me. No one would hire me and I just didn't know what else to do.

"As my temper began to cool off, though, I suddenly remembered how some of those crying and screaming jags used to end in Sherwood Forest. And Bro," Tony turned and put his hand on Frankie's shoulder, "this is about the only thing that ever happened to me that I've never told you about, but I guess you'll see why when I tell you now."

"I'd get mad at myself back then, too, for whatever stupid thing I'd done. And all by myself in the woods, I'd scream and holler and swear and beat my fists on the ground. But sometimes, when my temper began to cool off, I would look up and see a happy little guy who looked like an elf peeking out at me from behind a tree. Of course, I thought I had finally gone nuts, but it didn't seem to matter at the time. He would slowly come out from behind the tree and climb up on my knee. He never said a word, but his eyes were full of understanding, and then he would smile at me and I would just know that everything would be all right. All that temper and all that sadness would suddenly be gone and I would feel very peaceful. Then I'd turn my head or something and he would just be gone.

"I hadn't thought of that elf for years. In fact, I didn't let myself think of it even then, except for a few minutes after he was gone. I knew a hallucination when I saw it, and I wasn't admitting, even to myself, that I had just had one.

"But when I was sitting here bawling, that elf came back to mind, and I wished with all my heart that he would come again and take away the terrible pain I was feeling—worse at this age, I can tell you, than it was when we were kids, Frankie. At the time, we didn't think everything was our fault. But now, there's no one else to blame," Tony said, shaking his head.

"So I laid my head back, and just the thought of him calmed me down a little. So I said to Trainwreck, 'Where is that elf now when I really need him?'

"Trainwreck put his paw on my face and began to pat it, as if he was trying to get my attention, and I opened my eyes. And I swear to you, Frankie, there was the elf! He was sitting right here on the edge of this coffee table swinging his legs and smiling that same kind smile, just waiting for me to discover him."

Frankie got up and walked to the window, his back toward Tony. Why does this not sound as crazy as it should? Frankie wondered, gazing at the view. Something about an elf rang a bell in his mind from way back somewhere, but he couldn't bring it forward. Maybe if he just kept listening he would remember why the things Tony was saying actually made some kind of very weird sense.

He turned back toward Tony. "How about another beer?"

Tony relaxed visibly. At least Frankie wasn't going to bolt. "Sure, I'll get it. Want anything else?"

"Yeah, I do," Frankie said. "I want to hear the rest of this story."

When they settled down on the couch again, Tony began to describe the elf. "He was somewhere between two and three feet tall. Since he was sitting down, I couldn't tell exactly. He had a very kind face and a little white beard. His eyes were green and soft. He was wearing a purple, pointed hat, just like I would expect an elf to wear. His head was solid, human-like, but his body was made up of colored bands of pulsating lights. I could see his body, but it was also sort of transparent, like those holograms we used to see in the Star Wars movies. Remember?"

Frankie nodded, "Yeah, I remember."

"Anyway, I asked him, 'Who are you?'" Tony then repeated the conversation to Frankie.

"I am the ELF," he said, "which is short for the Eternal Life Force. I am the life force that created you, and I have been inside you since before you were born, Tony. I've also been with you all the time you have been here on planet earth, and I will be with you after you die. I am you and you are me, everywhere and always. But normally, I am invisible to you. Generally, you can't see me like you are seeing me now, nor do I usually speak to you in words."

"How come I've never known about you before if, as you say, you are me?"

"Oh, you have known me before, Tony. You know, as all human beings do, that something you can't see operates your body when you aren't paying attention, and heals it when it is hurt. You are also in constant communication with me, and I with you. You talk to me with thoughts and I answer you with feelings."

"How come I can see you now?"

"You are, just at this moment, in such a state of distress that I knew I couldn't get through to you any other way. The power to solve your problem has always been available to you, Tony, but you need my help to discover what you already know. So here I am in a somewhat physical form so you can see and hear me. This isn't the first time you've seen me like this, is it?"

"Was it you who came to me in Sherwood Forest?"

"It was."

"How come you didn't talk to me then?"

"I didn't talk to you, but I did communicate with you. Before you saw me, your mind was filled with thoughts of things you didn't want, and it was your thoughts that were making you feel so sad, and then mad. But when you were still a boy, just the sight of me startled you out of your bad thoughts, and when I would climb onto your knee and smile at you, it made you feel better immediately. You began to think hopeful thoughts, like 'Everything will be all right now,' and as soon as you started thinking that way, good things began to happen to you."

"They did?"

"Yes, they did. Whenever you think hopeful thoughts, good things start to happen. If you remember, not long after I came to you as the ELF the first time, you met Frankie."

"I sure didn't put that together," Tony admitted.

"That wasn't your job, certainly not as a teenage boy, anyway. But the information I am giving you now will help you for the rest of your life on earth, Tony. You're old enough to understand it and remember it now. Whenever you are thinking about something you don't want to happen, you will begin to feel some sort of bad feeling. For example, when you thought about possibly losing everything you'd ever worked for, you felt really, really bad, didn't you?"

"You could say that. I don't remember ever feeling worse."

"Those really bad feelings could have served as a signal to you that you were thinking about things you didn't want to happen, like foreclosure, repossession, loss of credit, and even homelessness. It is very important that you turn your attention away from what you don't want so you can begin to experience what you do want.

"Even Trainwreck tried to distract you from thinking about those things, but you were so deep into those thoughts that it took something pretty drastic to bring you out of it. So that's why I'm here, Tony," the ELF explained. "To help you think the thoughts that will solve your problem instead of continuing to make it worse."

"Why isn't Trainwreck afraid of you?" Tony asked. "He's scared to death of Darth Vader, and that dog is a quarter the size of you, and he doesn't vibrate."

When he heard his name, Trainwreck jumped down from Tony's lap and lazily strolled toward his litter box.

"I know he is," said the ELF, chuckling. "Even I think that's funny. Trainwreck has had such bad experiences with dogs in the past that he avoids the whole species, no matter what the size. He and I will have to work on that. But to answer your question, he isn't afraid of me because all animals are very much in contact with their own spiritual nature."

"Were you communicating with Trainwreck when he was stuck up that telephone pole?"

"He called for help, yes, and not just to get away from the dog. He was also telling me he was tired of fighting for his life out on the streets. For a while it was fun, but he wanted to finish out his life in a cushier place.

"Now, you probably won't remember this part, Tony, but the night before you met Trainwreck, you and Frankie were visiting his sister, Julie, and you were petting her cat, Cat Ballou. You liked that cat and you sent out a strong vibration that told me you might like a cat of your own. So when Trainwreck called for help and you happened to be in the neighborhood, I made it possible for you to find each other.

"You know, it confounds me," the ELF said, "that human beings still believe their best relationships happen by coincidence. Isn't there enough evidence of such miracles to help you all 'get it' that there are invisible forces working on your behalf?"

"So you choose who we have relationships with?" Tony asked. "Are we just fooling ourselves that we have something to do with that?"

"No, I don't choose your relationships for you," the ELF answered firmly. "Part of the purpose of your human experience is for you to make your own choices about everything you have and do. But I do arrange for compatible life forms to be together in the same spaces sometimes. I made it possible for you and Trainwreck to meet, yes. But you decided to take him home and make him your roommate."

"Did you put me and Frankie together in Sherwood Forest?"

"I did, but I didn't decide that you would become friends; you did. You each wanted someone in your life who would understand what you were going through and who would like you anyway. When the two of you met, you weighed your choices to either beat each other up or take a chance and become friends. You chose to become friends."

Tony looked at Frankie. "You still all right with this story, Bro?" he asked cautiously.

"I'm listening," answered Frankie. It was about the only thing he could manage to say at the moment.

"Okay, so you say I already know how to solve my own problem," Tony said to the ELF, still suspicious. "I have to ask. Does this have anything to do with religion? Am I going to have to start going to church and doing stuff like that to get my life back?"

"Not unless you want to," the ELF said, smiling. "Religion is not a spiritual concept, it's a human creation. It works for some people but not for others. I don't think church is really your bag, Tony."

Tony snickered mildly. "You don't talk much like something as huge as an Eternal Life Force; you talk like a regular person."

"Well, as I said before, I don't usually talk at all, but I want to help you work through your problem. And more than that, I want to help you understand how to solve other challenges for yourself in the future. Are you ready to get started now?"

"I thought I was at the end of my rope before you showed up," Tony said simply. "I have never ever felt this helpless before, even when I was a kid. Am I going to be homeless?"

"There is no end to your rope, Tony. I will always give you all the rope you need. And you're going to be homeless only if you choose to be."

"I can't see any way out of this," Tony said. "I've looked at it from every angle, and I'm just trapped, that's all. Even though I swore when I left home that I'd never let myself get trapped again, by anything, I spent my way into this mess, thinking I would always be able to earn a living. I still can hardly believe I can't do that."

"You already know what the solution is to that problem, too, Tony," the ELF added. "But that is not what we need to talk about first. You never have a question in your heart without already knowing the answer. As a matter of fact, you also know how to get out of your financial crunch with relative ease. You're just not willing to see the solution right in front of you."

"What do you mean?"

"I mean there is a solution you are not allowing yourself to see or to take advantage of."

"It's pretty difficult to see any kind of solution when you aren't bringing in any money and all your savings are gone," Tony said, frustration returning to his voice again. "At least it seems that way to me."

"And when you think about all your savings being gone and having no job, how do you feel?" the ELF asked.

"I feel just awful."

"And you will keep feeling awful as long as you continue to think about those things, Tony, because you are thinking about what you don't want."

"Well, what the h...—oops, sorry. What should I think about, then?"

"What do you have that is valuable, Tony?"

"What I have," Tony answered with real irritation, "is an almost empty bank account, a mortgage that will soon be overdue, a car payment that will soon be overdue, and credit cards I won't even be able to make the minimum payments on.

"What I *don't* have is an income that will provide the money to change that. I don't see anything of particular value in any of that," Tony said, immediately thinking. *Exactly why am I talking to this imaginary toy? I must be almost as crazy as my mother was. Maybe it's hereditary.*

"You're not crazy, and you're talking to me because you don't have any better solution in mind at the moment, Tony," the ELF answered kindly.

"You heard that?"

"I hear what you are thinking all the time, Tony. I am you, remember?"

The ELF looked deeply into Tony's eyes and smiled the same smile Tony remembered from his childhood. "Just relax, Tony. There is a very simple way for you to solve your own problem, and you're going to like it. I promise."

"And immediately, Frankie, I knew he was right," Tony said. "And I did feel better.

CONCEPT II

Realizing . . .

You are the cause of your own problem

CHAPTER FOUR

Tony checked in with Frankie again. “I appreciate you hanging in here with me, Bro. The rest of the story is just as interesting, even though I know the whole thing sounds a little on the fantastic side. Do you want to hear more?”

“If you stop now, I may have to hurt you, Tony. You started this and I hope you’re going to finish it. I’m waiting to hear that you lived happily ever after.”

“Just stay tuned, Bro, just stay tuned. After the ELF told me to relax a little and that he would see me through to a solution, I did relax, and he seemed pleased.”

“Now that you have your thoughts focused away from your problem and toward a solution, Tony,” the ELF continued, “I’m going to ask you again. What do you have that is valuable?”

“Well, I have this condominium, and I have my car, and I have my personal stuff like clothes and furniture, you know. But I owe money on all of those things, so what good is their value to me now? I can’t sell any of them for what they’re worth.”

“Well, let’s see if we can figure that out together. How much would your car be worth if you sold it?”

“Ha! A lot less than I paid for it, but I could probably get fifteen thousand dollars for it, if I’m lucky,” Tony said, shaking his head in disgust.

"How much do you owe on it?"

"Right around eighteen thousand."

"Okay. No help there, right? Now, just so you really understand how your thinking is related to the way you feel, let yourself feel how it would be to sell your car and still owe three thousand dollars on it. Plus, you would have no wheels. How does that feel?"

"Hopeless."

"Then let those hopeless feelings signal you that thinking about selling your car at a loss isn't your answer. Get it?"

"I've got that part. I'll stop thinking that I might have to sell my car."

"Okay. Now what else do you own that is valuable?"

"I own this condo, but there is no market to sell it now, even if I wanted to. There are no buyers for downtown condos at a price anywhere close to what they're worth. Mike Palmieri, an investor, offered me an insulting price for it about a month ago, but I told him to get lost."

"Was his insulting offer for more than you owe on the mortgage?"

"Yes, he offered me four hundred fifty thousand in cash, but I told him absolutely no. It would be a crime to let this property go for that. I wouldn't accept one penny less than six hundred thousand for this place, and even that would be a bargain. He's just a crook looking to take advantage of people like me who are in trouble. He's a vulture, and I'm not going to help him be a better one."

"Let's change the subject for just a minute, Tony. How would you feel if I waved a magic wand and made you free of all debt, plus gave you sixty thousand dollars to spend any way you wanted to? Don't think about anything else, Tony; just answer my question."

"I would feel relieved and I would feel grateful. That would certainly solve my problem."

"And the thought of that makes you feel good or bad?"

"It makes me feel great!"

"Well, so just for fun, run by me what would happen if you changed your mind and accepted Mike Palmieri's offer of four hundred fifty thousand dollars."

Grimacing, Tony said, "Well, if he paid cash and covered the closing costs, which he said he would, I would walk away with about a hundred and fifty thousand dollars in cash."

"And how much would you have left out of that hundred-fifty grand after you paid off your car and your credit cards completely?"

"About sixty thousand," Tony said, a glimmer of realization beginning to creep into his mind.

"And how does that make you feel?"

"Better than I thought it would," Tony answered. "I see what you're trying to show me. If I was willing to take four hundred and fifty thousand for my condo and give up my idea that it's worth at least six hundred thousand, I could get myself out of my mess with sixty thousand dollars to spare."

"I happen to know it isn't the idea of selling this condo that upsets you, Tony, because you planned to sell it in another year, anyway. It's the idea that you shouldn't sell it for less than six hundred thousand that has you boxed into what appears to be, at least to you, a no-win situation. You told me you looked for a solution to your financial crunch from every possible angle, but never once did you look at that six-hundred-thousand-dollar sale price for this condo that you were holding in your mind. You built a mental box around that figure and decided it was not negotiable, even if it cost you everything you own."

"Did you send Mike Palmieri to offer me the four hundred fifty thousand dollars?" Tony asked.

"I made it possible for you and Mike to meet. He wants to buy condos in this building, and you have one that could be sold. But again, let me make this perfectly clear. The choice is always yours, Tony. You can accept his offer or refuse it. Either way, you will have a life experience, and that's what you came to earth to do: to have various life experiences. Choice, or as some of you call it, 'free will,' is one of the great perks of being part of the human experience. No one but you can take away your right to choose."

Tony now knew he would be interested in selling if Palmieri were still interested in buying. "What causes people to build boxes, like I apparently built around how much this condo should sell for?" Tony asked.

"It is always ego that causes human beings to build boxes," the ELF explained. "Here is how your ego got in your way this time, Tony. If you sell your condo to Mike Palmieri, you will walk away with a hundred and fifty thousand dollars, and you will have made a real profit of seventy-five thousand dollars on your original investment.

"But you didn't have in mind doubling your money, Tony. When you bought this property, you had in mind making a killing, which to you meant selling for no less than six hundred thousand dollars. When the market went down and no one was willing to pay that kind of money for this property, you couldn't seem to accept that. You built yourself a very strong mental box around that price. If you break that box open, Tony, your financial problems will be solved. But remember, it's always your choice whether to keep your boxes or get rid of them."

"And again, how can I tell which is the right choice?"

"By the way you feel, Tony. Here, test it for yourself. Think about holding out for the six-hundred-thousand-dollar price and possibly facing foreclosure, maybe even bankruptcy. How do you feel when you think about that?"

"Awful."

"Now think about a quick closing on this condominium, having the mortgage cleared, owning your car free and clear, and having your other bills all paid off, plus a bank account with sixty thousand dollars in it. How does that feel?"

"Amazingly sweet, I'm surprised to say," Tony answered. "I'd have to move, of course, but I certainly could afford to. And I could stop being in a total panic about not yet having a job."

"So, based on the information that if you are feeling good you are thinking about what you really want, then what is your best choice?"

"Selling the condo to Palmieri. And if I do that, I will have broken open that stupid box I let myself get trapped in, right?"

"That particular box, yes. You may have others relating to other issues, but that box will disappear when you accept anything less than six hundred thousand dollars for your property."

The ELF shimmered and bands of light pulsated throughout his body. "Hold on now, Tony, because I can feel you start to feel bad again about building that box in the first place. So don't go there. Stay in your good place. If it's any comfort to you, everyone who is in physical form puts himself or herself into a box at some time or other about something. Let me give you another example. Your father is a very good man, Tony, by anyone's standards. Wouldn't you agree?"

"I would. And a smart one, too."

"Your father was raised to believe that good men, especially good Italian men, take care of their families at any cost, and his ego held him strictly to that standard. He built himself a very strong mental box that said only he could care for your mother. So for eight years after Denny died, your dad didn't allow himself to consider any possibility other than keeping your mother in her own home under his personal care.

"It wasn't until she became more and more unhappy at home that he allowed himself to consider that she might be better off living somewhere else. When he finally got control of his ego and broke open that very limiting box, a much better solution appeared for him, and for her, as well.

"I know you have more questions, Tony," the ELF said, holding up his hand to stop Tony from asking more. "I can hear your heart expressing them already. But I can't help you find all the answers you need in just one visit, especially since you now have important choices to make about the challenge you called me here to help you with today. Whatever choice you make is going to require you to take some action. So do what you have to do now, Tony, and do it soon."

"Wait, will you come back again?" Tony asked, feeling a little panicky at being left alone.

"I'll come back out where you can see me again, yes, Tony, but I'm not leaving you now or ever. You can, and you will, learn to talk with me when you can't see me just as well as you talk to me when you can see me. I promise you that. Before I leave," the ELF added, "let's review what we talked about today, so you can use these tools any time.

"When you are feeling any sort of bad feeling—hopelessness, helplessness, exhaustion, depression, anger, sadness, jealousy, greediness, or fear—understand that right in that moment, you are focusing your thoughts on something you don't want.

"That's the time to get hold of yourself and consciously start to think about something else, something that makes you feel at least a little bit better. As soon as you allow yourself to feel better, the circumstances of your life will get better.

"And on those rare occasions when you simply can't think of anything that will make you feel better, look to see if you have let your ego box you into some decision that could change if you would allow it to change. Release whatever is in that mental box, and the answer already in your heart will be revealed to you.

"Don't wait so long to call on me the next time you're stuck, Tony," the ELF said gently. "Stuff happens, but you never need to suffer because of it. When you need help the next time, just remind yourself to 'Go to ELF!'"

"And then he was simply gone, Frankie. As quickly as he appeared, he disappeared."

"So did you call Palmieri?" Frankie asked.

"I called him right then, even though it was eleven o'clock at night."

"Did he agree to buy the condo?"

"Yeah, I closed on it yesterday afternoon. I don't own this condominium any more, Frankie. I'm still trying to take that in."

"Well, don't worry, Bro," Frankie said kindly. "Just tell me when you need to be out of here and I'll help you move."

"That's just one more part of this unbelievable story, Frankie. I don't have to move. He leased this condo right back to me, and he charged me less than the going rate because he doesn't have to do any renovation or advertise for a new tenant.

"Plus, I'm ashamed to say, it turns out that he's really a pretty good guy. He played it square with me. We went out for a couple of drinks last night after the closing, and I actually like him.

"He told me a little bit of his story, you know, like how he was able to hand over four hundred fifty thousand dollars cash to buy my place. He inherited some money from his grandparents about ten years ago. Not much really, but he used it to buy and flip little houses on the south side when the market was good. And one property at a time, he worked his way up to buying high-rise condos.

"But he's not going to turn these until the market gets better, so mine is the last one he'll buy for a while. It's the sixth unit he owns in this building, and I have to give him credit. I think he's gonna sail through this recession, or depression, or whatever it is, with flying colors."

Tony got up and picked up the empty pretzel bag. Then he finished his beer and carried his and Frankie's bottles to the recycling bag in the kitchen. As he came back into the living room, he went right on talking about Mike Palmieri.

"He's being paid by the developer to manage this building, which isn't so hard to do right now because there are only three owners. That way, he can make sure the building is well maintained, which will keep his tenants happy.

"And get this. He just made a sweet deal with a Tampa investment company that rotates its executives every three years. The company includes housing as part of its employment package, so Mike will lease them four units for their employees to live in while they work at the Tampa office. Every three years, as a wave of tenants moves out, he will have each unit painted and cleaned, and will replace anything that isn't in good condition. Then a new set of tenants will move right in. Everybody's happy. The employees get to live in top-of-the-line condominiums with waterfront views and all kinds of amenities, the company doesn't have to waste time finding housing each time the rotations change, and Palmieri gets guaranteed tenants he knows will pay the rent."

"That's a pretty smooth deal, all right," Frankie said, getting up to again look at the sailboats on the bay. "I hope it works out for him." Then, feeling a nudging grip in his stomach, he turned to Tony. "What time is it, anyway?"

"It's two-thirty," Tony said looking at his watch. "Oh, yeah, I forgot you gave up wearing a watch. Why was that again?"

"So I wouldn't always feel like I'm going to be late for something. It really cuts down on the pressure," Frankie said. "But my stomach has its own time clock, and those eggs I ate at nine o'clock this morning are long gone, so I'm starving. Got anything to eat?"

"No, I've been too caught up in my stuff to do any shopping. But I'll buy you lunch at the hotel across the street if you still have time, because I'm not quite through with my story yet."

"Oh, good," Frankie said as he rolled his eyes and bent down to give Trainwreck a good tummy scratch. "Because the last two minutes when I thought you were through have been really boring. Let's go."

The two long-legged men strode with purpose through Straub Park to a café located in an old residental hotel called The Fillmore.

At one time, the city of St. Petersburg boasted a couple of dozen grand hotels like this one, but by now, most of them had been torn down and replaced by high-rise office buildings or city parking lots.

The Fillmore, built in the roaring twenties, still stood proudly, its lovely elegance boasting a grand entrance where automobiles pulled up in front of carved and gilded front doors. In earlier days, a doorman would have been standing there to help guests out of their vehicles. But that was then and this is now.

The ground floor of the hotel featured an elegant, high-ceilinged lobby with a wide, mahogany front desk, a stately marble fireplace, and very attractive furnishings. A thickly carpeted staircase rose to the second floor, as did a small elevator. A larger elevator, the kind that had once required an operator, carried residents to the upper floors.

The second floor was devoted to rooms for overnight or temporary guests, but the remaining six floors were comprised of efficiency apartments called "bed-sitters," each rented to guests who live in the hotel year round. The hallways were elegantly carpeted, the door to each room set back in its own little alcove. Most residents personalized the entry to their bed-sitter with small pieces of furniture, statues, or floral arrangements according to their individual tastes.

The bed-sitters were larger than ordinary hotel rooms. Each room included a double bed, a dresser (or two upon request), a desk and chair, two comfortable reading chairs, a television set, a small refrigerator, and a microwave oven, even though guests were encouraged to take their meals in the restaurant when possible.

Seafoam-green raw silk draperies hung at the windows of every unit, and beds were covered in matching quilted spreads. A local artist's watercolor paintings of the gulf beaches brought additional muted color to the décor. Each bath had both a tub and a shower, and each room had a walk-in clothes closet and a shelved storage closet.

Careful not to violate any federal laws, the management discreetly screened all applicants for residency to avoid, as much as possible, anyone whose habits might be loud or unruly or who might otherwise disturb the current residents, most of whom were elderly women living on their Social Security incomes plus whatever money they had inherited or saved. For the most part, they made good neighbors for one another, and they had a mutual appreciation for the gracious sanctuary that was the Fillmore.

Tony and Frankie walked into the hotel restaurant, which was open to the public as well as to residents. Sitting on ice cream parlor chairs at a small, round, marble-topped table, the men surveyed the menu.

"Why are there so many things crossed off the menu, I wonder," Frankie said.

"That's part of my story. I'll tell you in a minute, but let's order first," Tony suggested. "Let me make it easy for you. You can have meatloaf, a hot turkey sandwich, or corned beef and cabbage. And save room for dessert, because the pies are delicious."

"Okay, I can live with those choices," Frankie said, highly amused. "How come you know so much about this place? You dating one of the little old ladies upstairs?"

"No, just this beautiful thing," Tony answered, smiling lustily as the sixtyish server approached them. Five-feet-one and 150 pounds, her hair was strawberry red, and she wore too much make-up and a too-bright lipstick. Her face reddened at Tony's flirting.

"Hello, beautiful," he said. "Norma, this is Frankie. And Frankie, if you're really nice to her, she'll serve you the second biggest piece of pie for dessert."

"I'm much nicer than he is, Norma," Frankie said, "and if you ever get tired of this bozo, just give me a call. How's your meatloaf today?"

"Our meatloaf is the best you ever ate, isn't it Tony?" Norma asked with enthusiasm. "Would you like mashed potatoes or French fries with it?"

"Mashed."

"Green beans or corn?"

"Beans."

"Gravy on your potato?"

"Absolutely."

"Somethin' to drink?"

"Iced tea, sweet."

Turning to Tony she asked, "Hot turkey again, Tony?"

"Yep, haven't had my fill yet, Norma. I'll take mashed potatoes and string beans, extra cranberry sauce, and a Diet Coke."

As Norma shuffled off toward the kitchen, Frankie looked directly into Tony's eyes. "She's perfect for you, Bro. I know the two of you will be very happy together."

"Thanks. As long as she keeps the hot turkey coming, I'll do my best to make her happy."

"Okay, I've braced myself again," Frankie said, stretching his legs and making himself as comfortable as possible on a chair several sizes too small for him. "Now lay the rest of it on me."

"Well, I was pretty antsy between the ELF's visit on Wednesday and the closing on Friday," Tony explained. "Thursday morning I couldn't seem to sit or stand still. I checked the Internet for job openings and came up blank. I went to the gym and worked out until I was beat. I swam in the pool until I cooled down. I took a walk out onto the pier and fed the pelicans. Then I walked back to this place to get something to eat. It was an odd time of day, like this, and I was the only one here.

"After I tried to order several things they didn't have, Norma let me know about the big three: meatloaf, hot turkey, and corned beef. So I ordered the hot turkey, which is delicious, by the way. And after she took my order, I went up to sit at the counter to jaw with the owner. Sam's his name, Sam Casey. He's owned this restaurant ten years. It used to be a little gold mine, but lately, the people who live downtown here have been saving money by either eating in or doing without, and his business has dropped off to less than half. That's why they cut the selection of food on their menu. If they have to prepare only three entrees, it saves them a bundle.

"Sam told me," Tony went on, "that if it wasn't for the hotel residents, who used to make up only a small portion of his clientele, he'd be out of business by now."

"Too bad," said Frankie, shaking his head. "Small businesses are closing up fast, and a few big ones, too, especially downtown."

"Yeah, but it turns out there is something on the bright side happening for Sam. There's a new bank going into the building across the street, and this is the nearest eating place for over a hundred and fifty employees to catch lunch. The problem is, Sam doesn't know how to get them in here the first time, or whether he can hold them even if he gets them. While he was telling me all that, Frankie, it occurred to me that I know someone who knows how to get those people in here."

"Yeah? Do I know him, too?"

"It's me, Frankie. I'm the big, successful advertising executive, aren't I? Shouldn't I know how to steer people toward any business?"

"I guess, but this is no Tyrone Mall or Home Shopping Network," Frankie noted. "And you've never had a customer smaller than that, have you? Were you able to convince Sam to hire you?"

"In a manner of speaking," Tony answered, frowning at how really bad the old menu looked. "And he's also going to hire you."

"Now I'm fascinated," Frankie said, leaning toward Tony. "I'm going to help this guy save his business?"

"Yup."

"Are you going to explain what you are talking about anytime soon?" Frankie said, sounding slightly annoyed. He remembered having been drawn into some of Tony's schemes that he should have avoided. "Or are you and I going outside so I can knock the details out of you before lunch?"

"I'll give you all the details right after Norma finishes serving us," Tony said sweetly, smiling up at Norma as she set their plates down.

Taking a long, slow drink of his Diet Coke, Tony turned his attention back to Frankie. "Okay, so I said to Sam, 'If you want new customers who go to work in suits every day, you're going to have to spruce this place up and then advertise as professionally as possible what you've got to offer.'

"And he says to me, 'To tell you the truth, Tony, I'm just too tired and too broke to do that. I know the place needs cleaning, and I know I need marketing. But it exhausts me just to think about cleaning all the nooks and crannies of this old place. I can't do it myself, and I don't know anyone else who can, either.'

"He kind of got to me with that, ya know, Bro? Then he said, 'When I found out the bank was opening up across the street, I called a couple of ad agencies to see what they could do for me to get some people in here. Frankly, what they told me is just out of the question right now. The kind of advertising campaign they suggested would cost five thousand dollars just to start. You know—ads in the Times, direct mail, coupon books, that sort of stuff—and they couldn't tell me where it would end. I can't risk using that much of my capital, even if it is to bring in more business.'

"I felt really sorry for him," Tony said, "especially when he said, 'I guess I've finally let this place run me instead of me running it.'

"Then it hit me like a ton of bricks, Frankie. There must be hundreds of small business owners who are hanging on by their fingernails like Sam is. They need only a little help to promote their businesses, and they would pay a reasonable price for it. But there isn't an advertising agency in town that offers what they need at a price they can afford. And you know what?" Tony asked, his voice full of excitement. "I could fill that gap. I could help small business owners promote their businesses every bit as well as larger competitors can, and in my humble opinion, even better. I can give them Cadillac service at Chevrolet prices. So before I knew what I was doing, I heard myself saying, 'Maybe I can help you, Sam.'"

"And Sam said?"

"Sam said, 'Talk to me.' So we sat there together for two hours, without a single customer coming in to interrupt us, and I told him I could create a menu card for him that would look high-end but still feature only his three main entrees. And I could help him figure out at least three ways he could afford to let the new bank employees know about his menu, his hours, and his prices. The rest would be up to him, of course. I can bring the customers in, but it's up to him to bring them back.

"But I also told him, Bro, that I wouldn't do it unless he hired you to deep clean the restaurant and make it look as good as it can look."

Pointing to the ceiling, Tony said, "I mean, look at those chandeliers, Frankie. They're exquisite. This place could be pretty classy, like it used to be, but those lights are so dirty you can hardly see them now."

"And Sam went for it?" Frankie asked, beginning really to look at the place for the first time.

"He made up his mind pretty quick," Tony answered. "He hired me and he agreed to hire you, too. After we eat, I'll take you over and introduce you, and you and he can decide when you and your crews can start getting this place cleaned up."

Frankie looked up at the tall, intricately carved columns stretching from floor to ceiling. Then he looked down at the dingy marble floor, which needed serious cleaning and polishing.

"It's not going to be cheap," Frankie said. "It will require scaffolding and experts in cleaning old plaster. All those crystals will have to be polished individually and the dead bulbs replaced, and the floors will take a lot of work. But we can do the job, all right.

"But before we talk to Sam about me, I want to hear more about you working for Sam. Will it be worth your while to create the ads and flyers and menus for him and work up the promotions? Can you make a living doing that kind of stuff, or would it just be a sideline?"

Tony signaled Norma that they were ready for their pie. "That's the part I'd like to run by you. I've got some ideas, and I want to know what you think of them."

"I'm all ears, Bro," Frankie said, looking at the plate Norma was putting down in front of him. "And you're right," he said grinning at Tony. "Norma apparently didn't find me charming enough, because you definitely got the bigger slice of pie."

CHAPTER FIVE

"You were asking me if I could live on the kind of money Sam would pay me," Tony said, licking the blueberry pie filling off his fork. ''And the answer is no, I couldn't live on it if Sam was my only client. But I figure there are tons of guys like him with a big need and little money. I can give them what they need: flyers, brochures, business cards, menus, e-mail ads, blogs, and stuff like that at good prices, because at the moment, at least, I have a very low overhead. If I should get swamped at any one time, I know a few freelancers who could help me out.

"See, these small businesses don't need the services of an ad agency all the time, but all of them need one some of the time. They won't have to sign an annual contract with me or pay a retainer. They can just hire me when they need me and pay as they go. The trick for me will be making sure I always have enough customers to keep me busy all the time. The reason I think that's possible is because my specialty for the ad agency was coming up with promotions. You know, the stuff that brings customers in the doors. I won't charge for those suggestions, they'll just be kind of a bonus for working with me. Once I have a few successes, word will get around, I just know it.

"So, here's the bottom line, Bro. I'm very seriously thinking about going into business for myself."

"Really? That's great, Tony," Frankie said, raising his eyebrows. "And if you do, how about if I become one of your first customers? I'm thinking that I'm the kind of small businessman you're talking about, actually."

"Yeah?" Tony was surprised. "What do you need an ad man for?"

"I've still got enough going to keep my crews working regular," Frankie said. "But when I lost the contract for the Parker Building because they decided to do maintenance in-house, and then McKenzie's folded, it put a dent in my income stream. I don't want to let any of my guys go, especially now, so if you can drum me up a few more big buildings to clean, I'll be happy to pay you for it."

"You know what, Frankie? That makes you my fifth client, and I've only been in business informally for two days."

"No kidding. Me and Sam and who else?"

"Well, Sam took me to meet the hotel manager, because Sam needed his permission to hire you. His name is Ed Ferguson. And after we finished with Sam's business, Ferguson asked if he could talk with me privately. He told me that the Fillmore had to give up its ad agency contract over a year ago because the hotel just couldn't afford to renew it, but he still needs a way to keep the hotel visible. Mr. Ferguson likes to keep a waiting list of potential residents so when one of his tenants dies, or becomes ill and goes to live with a relative, he can fill the vacancy pretty fast.

"So I worked him up some small ads to go into the programs for the Florida Orchestra and the Tampa Bay Ballet Company, and in the magazines for the Dali Museum and the Museum of Fine Arts—places like that. He thinks those are the venues most likely to attract people who fit his tenant profile."

"And you can do that?"

"Ad design is ad design, whether it's for a big company or a small one. And in time, when I'm placing ads with those kinds of publications for more than one of my clients, I'll be able to negotiate better prices for all of them. So, to make a long story short—"

"As if that day will ever come," Frankie interjected. "But don't let me interrupt you."

"I won't," Tony said, taking no offense. "Then Ferguson sent me to the walking stick guy, Clive Mason."

"The walking stick guy?"

"He has a shop right here in this hotel and sells canes and walking sticks. Some of his customers are off the street, but he also does a pretty good mail order and e-mail business. I didn't even know what walking sticks were, at least not up close and personal. But they're very interesting, Frankie."

"Oh, I'll bet," Frankie said with a little grin. He hadn't seen Tony this fired up in years, and he was really enjoying listening to him.

"They are. They're gorgeous big sticks, five feet tall or more, made out of beautiful woods. He wants me to create a direct mail piece, probably a color postcard he can send to the members of some hiking clubs he belongs to, and he also wants an ad for some of his canes to send to his e-mail customers. So yesterday, I took some pictures of Clive with one of his walking sticks at Boyd Hill Nature Park, and I'll design the postcard using one of those pictures.

"So, since you asked, here's my client list. I'll make you number one," Tony said, counting on the fingers of his right hand. "Sam makes two, Ferguson three, Clive four, and Mike Palmieri makes five. After we talked last night, Mike hired me to create a general brochure for his real estate company. Are you impressed, Frankie? I'm telling you, I'm really into something here. I'm feelin' it."

"Feel anything else?"

"Yeah, I feel the sides of another mental box splintering. Here's what I've figured out for myself since I talked to the ELF.

"I've been looking for a job for a year and a half, but I had set very rigid parameters for the job I would be willing to accept. It had to be with a well-known ad agency. After working fifteen years for ADPRO, my pride wouldn't let me work for a company without at least as good a reputation as that. It had to be in Tampa Bay, because I have no intention of moving. The job had to pay a minimum of sixty-five thousand dollars a year to start, salary plus commission, and I was determined to get a benefit package at least as good as the one I lost. What I did to myself was to take an already limited field of opportunity and narrow it down to a footpath. No wonder I wasn't having any luck finding a job."

"Do you think that's what the ELF meant when he said you already knew the solution to finding the right job?" Frankie asked, holding up his empty glass and signaling Norma that he'd like some more iced tea.

"Yes, and remember, he said it wasn't time to talk about it then. I think he meant until after I got myself out of debt, which I did yesterday afternoon. The mortgage was paid off at the closing, of course, but then I immediately paid off the car and all the credit cards, and I feel about a hundred pounds lighter. I actually have sixty-five thousand dollars left in the bank, and I didn't even have to move, Frankie. I still can't get over that, can you?"

"No. And you know, I find it hard to believe it was only this morning that we met at Pete's. It seems like at least a week ago, and I have a feeling you're not quite done yet."

"Well, almost," Tony said, suddenly feeling some of the energy he had been pumping start to slack off. "But I would like to know for sure what you think about my going into business for myself."

"It sounds perfect for you, Tony. Honest," Frankie answered, getting serious again. "You can either let your business grow by word of mouth, which seems to be working for you so far, or you can give it a boost. Who could possibly be better at promoting his own business than you?"

Tony felt a little twist in his stomach. Rubbing his hand lightly over it for a few seconds, he wondered. *Why does the thought of promoting my own business always make me feel uneasy?* It wasn't the first time he'd had that feeling. When he thought about starting his own business he felt fine, but when he thought about creating a campaign to promote himself and his talents, he felt jittery. *I'll have to check that out with the ELF*, he thought.

But to Frankie, he said, "I hoped that would be what you would say, because Monday I plan to go over to the Court House to see what kind of license I need to start up my own freelance advertising and promotion firm."

"Thought of a name for your agency yet?"

"You bet. I'll incorporate as Tony Celentano, Inc., but I'm going to do business as E.L.F. Promotions. I want to be constantly reminded that the ELF is always with me, and with my clients, too."

"And did you 'Go to ELF!' about that?"

"Actually, I 'Go to ELF!' all the time now. I talk to him out loud in the shower and in the car sometimes. It sounds like I'm talking to myself. And of course, I suppose I am, in a way. But I really feel I'm connecting with the little guy, or Big Guy, or whatever."

"Did you ask him if going into business for yourself was what he meant when he said you already had the answer you needed about finding a job? I'd like to hear more about that, if you know any more."

"I felt pretty foolish when I realized what I had been doing—you know, looking for a job in all the wrong places. But I wasn't sure that going into business on my own was right either, so I asked him about it."

"What did he say, exactly?"

"He didn't say anything in words, but when I started to think about how I could rework my resume and broaden my search for available jobs with other agencies, I began to feel really bad again. Yucky, ya know? But when I began to think of all the ways I could help to promote independent businesses, I felt great. Excited. Good to go. He made it pretty clear before he left me last Tuesday that I should pay attention to my feelings, so I guess he answered me in his own way.

"So I really let myself begin to think about starting my own business, and I realized I already have all I need to start right up. My office in the condo will work for a while, until I can afford to rent an office. I can even meet clients there if I need to.

"I own a state-of-the-art computer and printer, a scanner, a copy machine, and I also have a top-of-the-line drafting table and plenty of supplies. Plus, I have a whole computer file of local support services—artists, photographers, videographers, editors, proofreaders, printers, engravers—I know personally from my work with the agency. The more I thought about all those things, I just felt better and better and better."

"Do you think the ELF would help you get clients?"

"He said he sometimes may put me in the same space with people I can help if I decide I want to. I'll try to be alert to that, in case it happens. For all I know, maybe it already has. So far, I've said yes to everyone who has asked me."

Tony stood up and took out his wallet. "Lunch is on me. So come on, Bro, and I'll introduce you to Sam. You and he can talk about getting this place cleaned up." He scooped up the two checks, left a generous tip for Norma on the table, and headed for the cash register.

Handing Sam the check and a twenty dollar bill, Tony said, "As soon as you ring that up, I've got something to show you, Sam."

Sam dropped the change into Tony's hand. "Step into my office, guys," he said, moving his ample body a few feet to his left so he could lean across the long granite counter.

Tony opened the manila envelope he was carrying and pulled out the sample menu he had created for Sam. On one side, in a very subtle sepia ink, Tony had sketched the inside of the restaurant with all of its elegant lines and features. A well-dressed man and woman clad in the fashion of the 1920s were seated at one of the marble-topped tables, obviously enjoying their meal. The place looked like a million bucks.

Sam caught his breath. “I sure hope the customers won’t be disappointed when they actually get here.”

“Well, this is the menu, Sam, so they’ll already be here. And this picture shows the way this place looked when it was brand new. Now take a look at the other side.”

When Sam turned the menu over, he found himself looking at four beautiful color pictures of his three menu specials as well as luscious-looking slices of pie and steaming cups of coffee. In the background, Tony again had sketched the same dreamy-eyed couple sitting at a table, this time dressed in contemporary clothing and enjoying a piece of pie heaped with ice cream.

“Mary will eat this up,” Sam said, referring to his wife, who ran the kitchen. Then he read carefully every word describing Mary’s meatloaf, hot turkey, and corned beef. “This is terrific, Tony. It looks like it was done by a real advertising agency. I absolutely love it!”

“It was done by a real advertising agency, Sam. Mine,” Tony said wryly.

“Well, you’re the real deal, Tony, no doubt about it. How much is this puppy gonna run me?”

Taking the last piece of paper out of the envelope, Tony handed Sam the bill. “My fee for the design and overseeing the first printing is two hundred and fifty dollars. Printing and laminating fifty copies will run you another seventy-five. You can seat only thirty-five people at a time, so fifty copies should be plenty. This will get you started, and then I’ll design you some table cards to sell your pies, too.”

“Well, I can handle that, Tony. No problem. You want a check now?”

“No, on delivery will be fine.”

Looking longingly at the sepia drawing, Sam said, “I wish I could get the place looking like that again.”

“Well, here’s the guy to help you get started, Sam. This is my friend, Frankie Doerrer, of Executive Cleaning Services. Remember we talked about how I knew someone who could give this place a topnotch clean and polish?"

Sam smiled as he shook Frankie's hand. "I sure hope you can help me, Frankie," Sam said. "But to clean and polish this place will take an army of hardworking elves, it seems to me."

Tony and Frankie exchanged an amused glance.

"Do you see how high these ceilings are and how ornate the columns are all the way up to the ceiling?" Sam asked, looking up and pointing to the columns. "There are six of these and fifteen hanging light fixtures, all of which are dusty and need new bulbs. The floors are this black and white marble, the tables are marble, and the counter is granite. And they all need to be seriously polished. Even the windows, which I try to have washed once a year, are over twelve feet high, and they are mean to keep clean.

"Of course, we're under inspection by the health department all the time," Sam explained, "so we keep our kitchen spotless and the counter, table tops, and floors very clean. But the whole place hasn't really had a deep cleaning since I opened ten years ago—probably even longer than that—mostly because I've no idea how to clean it."

Frankie handed Sam his business card. "My company cleans high-rise office buildings, shopping centers, and educational complexes like Eckerd College and USF," Frankie explained. "We have equipment and chemicals designed to clean every kind of surface there is, and experts who know how to use them. We also have the ladders and scaffolding to reach very high places. We can't paint this place for you, Sam, but we can make it shine."

Sam was wary. "Any idea how much it will cost?"

"I assume you want it cleaned at night, right?"

"Yeah. I'm open seven days a week because the ladies upstairs have to eat."

"Well, it looks like it will take two crews two nights, and a boatload of cleaning supplies. Even if I give you a twenty percent discount because you're a friend of Tony's, it will still cost close to fifteen hundred dollars."

"I couldn't do it myself for that," Sam said, "even if I knew how. Will you take five hundred now and a grand when you're finished?"

"Absolutely," Frankie said, "and if it doesn't take as long as I think it will, I'll adjust the second payment."

"When can you start?"

"How about next Tuesday and Wednesday nights?"

"Do I have to do anything to prepare the place?"

"Just chase all your customers out by seven o'clock and clear off the tables and counters. Then go home and relax. We'll take care of the rest."

Turning to Tony, Sam asked, "Any idea when I'll get my new menus, Tony?"

"I'm going to push to have them ready by Wednesday, too, Sam. Can't promise, but I'll do my best."

"Well, looks like there are going to be some changes around here. And it's about time," Sam said, shaking hands with both young men. "Have a good day, fellas, and thanks for everything," he called as they went out the door.

Frankie took out his cell phone and checked the time. "Geeze, it's four-thirty already. I've got to go home and shower and change, drive by and check to see if my night crews need anything, and then pick up the Lovely Anna by seven o'clock."

They started to walk back across the park. "Where are you going tonight?" Tony asked.

"To dinner at Ted Peters, and to see a regular movie at the Beach Theater. Then we're staying for *Rocky Horror*."

"Aren't you ever going to outgrow that stupid cult movie thing?" Tony asked, shaking his head as he always did when Frankie mentioned *The Rocky Horror Picture Show*.

"Not as long as it pays off for me, Bro."

"What do you mean, pays off for you?"

"That," he said, punching Tony on the arm, "is where I met the

Lovely Anna."

As they approached Frankie's van in the condo parking garage, Tony put his hand on Frankie's shoulder. "Thanks for giving me your whole day today. There isn't anyone else on the planet I could share all this with, and it would be a drag not to be able to tell you about it."

"Yeah, well, I don't know how to explain it, Tony, but I feel somehow involved in this thing with the ELF. Your story should be harder for me to swallow, ya know? But it seems like I already knew about it before you told it. I can't exactly explain what I mean by that, but as soon as I understand it myself, you'll be the first to know."

"Okay. Oh, by the way," Tony said as Frankie got into his van. "You've been dating this girl for quite a while now. Just when am I going to meet the Lovely Anna?"

"Soon. Very soon," Frankie called out the window of the van as he drove away.

Frankie's mind was full of thought as he drove to his little house in Woodlawn. He had inherited the house from his mother, and not long afterward, had given up his apartment and moved into the house. He wasn't crazy about it, but he didn't want to invest the time and energy it would take to sell it and buy another.

His thoughts drifted from his mother, whom he seldom thought of anymore, to his graduation from high school, and then to his first job at Executive Cleaning Services, the company he now owned. When he was right out of high school, he had been happy to get that job because physical labor was the kind of work he enjoyed most, and because he could work nights, which really mattered to him then.

Night time was the safest time for Frankie to be away from the house, because even though his father often came home very late at night roaring drunk, his pattern was to fall into bed without speaking to anyone. If his father were to abuse his mother, Frankie knew it probably would be early in the morning when his dad was hung over and feeling mean. So Frankie made it a point to be back home by five-thirty in the morning. At nineteen, Frankie was several inches taller than his father and much stronger, and he could hold his father off his mother if he had to. But somehow, his father still slipped past him every now and then and clobbered his mother.

Frankie's sister, Julie, had moved out two years before, and Frankie was more than ready to do the same. He determined that when he turned twenty-one, he would give his mother a simple choice. She could come with him when he left home, or she could stay and deal with his father on her own.

But he never had that conversation with his mother.

One morning when he came home at about five o'clock, he found a police car parked in the driveway. His heart in his mouth, Frankie rushed inside to find his mother sitting on the couch weeping softly as a female police officer attempted to comfort her.

"Oh, Frankie," his mother wailed when she saw him. "Your father is dead."

Frankie was stunned. "What happened?" he asked, turning to the other police officer standing nearby.

The officer explained. As Frankie's father had tried to unlock his car outside his favorite bar the night before, he had lost his balance and fallen backward directly into the stream of fast-moving traffic. He had been rushed to the trauma center at Bayfront Hospital, but doctors couldn't save him.

"He had no ID on him, son," the officer told him. "We didn't know who he was until we impounded his car and traced the registration. Then Officer Miller and I came to tell your mother. We've been here only a few minutes."

Frankie and his mother and sister, still in shock at the abruptness of his father's death, struggled their way through the funeral. His father's parents, whom Frankie had never met, still lived in Germany, so they didn't come to the funeral, but his father's brother, Uncle Lawrence, came from Connecticut to represent the Doerrer family. Frankie knew that his uncle was aware of his father's addiction, but Lawrence never spoke about it, at least not to Frankie.

It had always amazed Frankie that despite his father's excessive drinking, he had managed to hold down a job as an insurance salesman, and to do reasonably well at it. August Doerrer performed his custodial duties for his family without fail. Their house was well kept; the family car was always clean, tuned, and never more than three years old; and they all wore good-quality clothes and ate good food. And they also had a ridiculously dysfunctional lifestyle.

So Frankie wasn't surprised that in the good, stalwart German tradition, his father had financially provided for his family as well in death as he had in life. He left a $200,000 life insurance policy payable to Frankie's mother, and the house on 14th Avenue North was free and clear. There must have been other money as well, Frankie realized, because his mother paid cash for the funeral.

For a short while, Frankie allowed himself simply to feel relieved that the biggest drama in his life had ended, glad that he no longer had to sleep with one ear cocked for disaster the way he always had.

His mother grieved for a while, but Frankie could do nothing about it, so he let her be.

One morning when he came home from work, she met him at the door, her hair combed and her dress fresh. She had decided to sell the house and buy a new one, she told him as he sat eating the breakfast she had made for him. He was welcome to live with her if he wanted, or to get his own place. She also had decided to pass on to Frankie and his sister half of the money his father had left her, she said, handing him a check for fifty thousand dollars. Her plan was to fulfill her lifelong dream of going back to college to become a nurse.

And that's exactly what she did; she saw her dream fulfilled, Frankie thought as he pulled his van into the driveway of his house.

He was at her graduation ceremony when she was awarded her RN, and he knew she loved her work in the critical care unit of All Children's Hospital, where she worked tirelessly for ten years. Then with what seemed no warning at all, she was diagnosed with cancer and died less than three months later.

Although it bothered him a little to admit it, even to himself, Frankie had never been close enough to either of his parents to miss them much after they died. He felt some pride that his father had supported his family in spite of his addiction, and that his mother had finally found her ground and accomplished something that made her life meaningful to her. But beyond that, he preferred not to think of them at all.

The only person on the planet Frankie had ever really loved, besides his sister Julie, was Tony. Sometimes he thought he would have died if he hadn't met Tony when he did.

Frankie's thoughts continued to tumble as he stepped into the shower. He couldn't seem to slow them down, so he went along with them.

Not surprisingly, he and Tony both had relationship issues. Tony had managed to have two long-term relationships, if a couple of years could be called long-term, but so far, he had avoided any permanent commitment. Frankie had never maintained even one long term relationship, until he met the woman he called the Lovely Anna. They had been dating for about a year, and had been sleeping together almost since the beginning. The big question for Frankie was whether he wanted to take this relationship any further. Lately, Anna had been hinting that it was time they talked, and he was almost certain he knew what she wanted to talk about.

The raw truth was that, even though he was thirty-nine years old, Frankie was far from sure that he was ready to be married. He suspected, at some level, that he might never be ready, and he knew he was commitment shy because of his childhood exposure to what a really bad marriage can look and feel like.

It wasn't that he couldn't afford to get married. He'd worked hard, planned well, and was in a very secure financial position for a man of his age. When his mother had given him the money from his father's insurance policy, he couldn't deal with deciding what to do with it at that point, so he banked it and went right on working for the same company.

Frankie liked his boss and had earned his trust, and by the time he was twenty-five, Frankie was overseeing three commercial cleaning crews that worked in a half dozen of the largest office complexes in Pinellas County. He knew how to operate every piece of equipment, assemble interior and exterior scaffolding, order supplies, pack the trucks, and estimate a job. And he knew how to hire, fire, and train employees.

Commercial cleaning was exacting work and sometimes dangerous. His crews were bonded and insured, and they had agreed-upon standards to meet with every contract. Frankie made it his business to see that those standards were well met every time.

He had been with the company about ten years when his boss called him into the office and said he intended to retire. To do that, he had to sell the business. Was Frankie interested in buying it—contracts, equipment, vehicles, office furnishings—the whole thing? The price was $250,000, with $50,000 down and $50,000 a year for the next four years.

Frankie didn't hesitate. He took his inheritance out of his savings account, and six weeks later, he was the owner-operator of Executive Cleaning Services. He worked his tail off shoulder to shoulder with his crews every night those first four years, and drummed up new business during the day. He kept his personal expenses, and therefore his salary, to a minimum. In only one of the four years did he have to borrow part of the annual payment to his former boss. Now, six years later, Frankie owned the business free and clear, and he paid himself a respectable annual salary.

He made other investments, too, and he owned his house.

Frankie could easily afford a wife, but did he want one? Did he love Anna? He felt sure he did, because he'd tried to imagine his life without her and had a hard time doing that. But Frankie wondered if he even understood what love was when it applied to a woman. He loved Tony and would live or die for him, but could he—or would he—ever be able to make that same commitment to Anna?

I guess maybe I'd better make some decisions about that pretty soon, Frankie thought. But later. I'll do it later. Right now, I'm just going to enjoy Anna.

CHAPTER SIX

Showered, shaved and back in his van, Frankie was dressed in black jeans and a black turtleneck sweater. His plans were for a casual evening with Anna. He would take her to one of their favorite haunts for dinner, and then to a movie. Later, at the same theater, they would see a second movie that they both loved: *The Rocky Horror Picture Show.*

This 1975 English cult-classic film is a strange phenomenon in the history of movie making. A low-budget musical spoof on horror films of the day, the movie has attracted super loyal fans since its release. In most good-sized cities, even all these years later, an art cinema somewhere replays the film weekly. Sometimes Rocky Horror fans dress in costumes to mimic their favorite roles and, knowing almost all the lyrics to the songs, the audience often sings along with the actors.

Frankie had attended his first performance of *Rocky Horror* when he was in his late teens, and he was hooked from the start. The movie was so strange that it lifted him out of his own weird life and transported him to a place where weird was not only acceptable, but cherished.

Some twenty-two years later, it was still Frankie's habit about once or twice a month to drop in on a showing of *Rocky Horror*, the movie that never goes away.

About a year ago on a cool December night, he had first met Anna there. Sitting in the row behind her, he had heard her singing along with *Over at the Frankenstein Place*, one of his favorite pieces.

Sweet voice, Frankie thought. *I'll have to make it a point to see what she looks like.* So a few minutes before the show was over, he got up and went outside to stand and watch for her. His breath caught in his throat at the first sight of her face. She was tiny, certainly not over five feet tall, and she was absolutely beautiful.

The fans of *Rocky Horror* customarily stand around to chat after the movie ends, and it's a safe place to meet new people who share an interest. Frankie knew several married couples who had first met at *Rocky Horror.*

Walking up to the little group that included Anna, he was sure he would be welcomed. He listened quietly to the conversation for a few minutes before catching her eye and motioning for her to step away from the group.

"I heard you singing," he said. "You have a really nice voice, and you obviously know the lyrics by heart. How long have you been a *Rocky Horror* fan?"

"Since I was a teenager. But this is the first time I've seen it in Florida. You?"

"I started coming here right after I got out of high school," he admitted, "and I still drop in every once in awhile. Are you visiting here?"

"No, I live and work here now," she said, surprising him by reaching out and running her fingers lightly over his sweater. "That is a beautiful, hand-knit cashmere sweater you're wearing. Whoever made it has a real talent," she said, lightly patting the soft yarn before quickly withdrawing her hand.

Tony's head would be swelling if he could overhear this conversation, thought Frankie. "Do you knit?" he asked, making easy conversation.

"No, but my mother does. I guess there aren't too many nights here cool enough to wear a sweater like that. But where I grew up, it's practically year-round attire. I like it. It reminds me of home."

"Which is where?"

"Colorado. Where are you from?"

"I'm a Florida native, and you must know that makes me a very rare species," Frankie bragged. "It's possible you might not meet another one for years. For that reason alone, I'm hoping you'll let me take you to dinner before next week's show."

And that was how it started. Now, Frankie wondered, where, exactly, is it going to end?

They went to *Rocky Horror* only occasionally now, and they didn't always go in costume. But this night, they had agreed to have a little extra fun playing their favorite parts. Frankie had enjoyed the day they went shopping together for the costumes of Riff Raff, a handyman, and Magenta, a maid, a couple in the film who have a love affair.

He and Anna had never admitted it to each other, but they both knew that acting these parts turned them on in a way that made going home together after the movie a delightful continuation of the playful plot.

Now when he pulled up in front of Anna's house and saw her standing on the front porch, he knew he was ready for a night of fun. She looked amazing in a full black skirt and black turtleneck sweater that matched Frankie's. Her deep chestnut hair curled sassily around her face, and Frankie knew the shopping bag on her arm held the pieces of her very sexy Magenta costume.

My God, how can I ever forget how beautiful she is? Walking around the car to open the door for her, Frankie wanted nothing more than to spend this night—all night—with her.

Ted Peters is something of a St. Petersburg landmark restaurant and a great favorite of the locals. As Frankie and Anna drove into the parking lot, he was glad to see a few outdoor tables available. Sometimes in the months when tourists swelled the population of the city, an outdoor table at Ted Peters was at a premium. But now that the weather was getting a little cooler, fewer people were choosing an outdoor venue.

This restaurant was another happy coincidence in the Frankie-Anna discovery package, along with other mutual interests that included Disney World and *Rocky Horror*. They both loved to eat at this restaurant, but for different reasons. Anna's favorite menu item was smoked mullet, a Florida delicacy for which Ted Peters was known, but Frankie preferred the restaurant's other specialty: a juicy hamburger with a side of authentic German potato salad.

Most of the tables scattered around the perimeter of the restaurant were picnic tables. An inside dining room was open on cool nights, but Frankie had never been inside. As far as he was concerned, if it was too cold to eat outside, it was too cold to go to Ted Peters.

They sat next to each other on the same side of a picnic table big enough to seat six. After they ordered, Frankie wrapped his arm around Anna's shoulders and she snuggled into him.

"Cold?" he asked.

"No, not cold," she answered hesitantly, "but there is something I need to tell you."

Frankie felt himself involuntarily stiffen. *Why does a simple statement like that tend to make a man's blood run cold?* What he wanted most was a night with no drama. But in all fairness, Frankie knew that Anna had very few issues. She had listened to him enough times as he griped about customers and the economy and government regulations and his sister—and the list went on—and he owed her his time and attention when she had an issue.

"Shoot," he said, turning to look directly at her.

Taking a deep breath, Anna plunged in. "I have a new job

offer," she began slowly, afraid of what she was about to say. "I guess you could say it would be my dream job. I'd be the assistant to the top pediatric surgeon at one of the best children's hospitals in the country."

Anna had started her career as a nurse in Denver, and after doing all the additional training necessary to be certified as a nurse practitioner, she had come to St. Petersburg to work with the most severely ill children at All Children's Hospital, the same hospital where Frankie's mother had worked. Anna loved giving very personal care to her patients, and bringing hope and comfort to their families, as well.

"And why, exactly, is being offered your dream job a problem?" Frankie asked warily.

"Because the job is in Orlando at the Florida Hospital for Children, Frankie. Not only is it a prestigious place to work, but my salary would almost double. I know it's only two and a half hours away and we could still see each other," she went on. "But at least at first, I would be working all the hours the doctor doesn't want to work, which means I would be on call weekends and holidays. It wouldn't be easy for you and me to find time to spend together.

"I should be ecstatic about this opportunity, but frankly, I feel torn between two things that both matter to me very much. I just can't decide what to do about it, Frankie. And in all fairness, you need to be part of my decision."

"When do you have to decide?"

"He's given me a week from today to decide. If I don't accept by next Saturday, he will offer the job to someone else," she said, looking fairly miserable.

Frankie lowered his forehead to touch hers and closed his eyes as the impact of Anna's news played in his mind. Then he drew back and they looked intently into each other's eyes.

If the little scene had been drawn into a cartoon panel, the balloon over her head would have read, "I won't go if he asks me to stay," and the balloon over his head would have read, "She won't go if I ask her to stay."

But he didn't ask her to stay, because just at that moment, the waitress delivered their food. By unspoken agreement, they put aside any further talk about Anna's possible move until they could give it more thought, together and separately.

They fell into easy conversation. Frankie told Anna about Sam and what it would take to make the Fillmore Café sparkle, and about Tony's new business. She told him about her mother's latest boyfriend and about a stoic little girl she called Patty-Cake, Anna's favorite patient, who had graduated that day from the first grade at the hospital's special school for chronically ill children.

Frankie then opened his wallet and showed Anna the latest picture of his little niece, Andy, who was hugging the leg of a teddy bear. The bear, much larger than she, was a gift from Frankie, of course.

The theater was less than five minutes away from the restaurant, so Frankie and Anna lingered, slowly nursing their mugs of beer and enjoying each other and the beautiful night until it was almost time for the movie to start.

The Beach Theater, a tacky little theater in the heart of St. Pete Beach, is a favorite of locals and tourists alike. A classy place at one time, it had been showing films day and night nonstop for more than seventy years, and it showed signs of considerable wear and tear.

If a first-run movie were missed on its original rounds, it probably could be caught a month or two later at the Beach Theater. Tonight's feature was *The Secret Life of Bees*, which neither Frankie nor Anna had seen. It was followed, of course, by The *Rocky Horror* Picture Show.

Anna quickly got into the story of *The Secret Life of Bees,* but

Frankie barely saw or heard it. He played and replayed his day in his mind, ending with the urgency Anna's new job offer was putting on his need to decide what to do about their relationship. He didn't appear stressed on the outside, but inside, he was a jumble of churning confusion.

When the first movie ended, he and Anna mingled with the other *Rocky Horror* fans who had gathered outside the theater, some dressed in costume.

"I'm going to the van for our costumes so we can go to the restroom and change," Frankie whispered to Anna.

"I'll go with you," she said. But as they walked toward the van, she took his arm to slow him down. "How much would you mind if we just went home instead?"

"I wouldn't mind at all. You tired?"

"Yes, and I have to be at work at eight tomorrow morning. The hospital is running a disaster drill and we're actually going to move all the patients."

"You want me to take you home, then?"

"Yes, your home," she said, still a little shy about making arrangements for them to sleep together. "That is, if you're willing to take me back to mine in the morning early enough to change before work."

"No problem, gorgeous," he said, taking her in his arms right there on the sidewalk. She was gorgeous, and somehow it always stopped him cold when he realized it. He couldn't imagine living without her.

We'll think of something, he thought, opening the door of the van and lifting her up onto the passenger seat. *I don't know what, but we'll think of something.*

Frankie unlocked the door to his house and went straight to the wet bar next to the fireplace. He took down two glasses and poured them each a glass of wine. Then he turned on his iPod and set it to play an album by Yo Yo Ma, a Frankie-Anna favorite performer. Turning down the volume low enough to allow for easy conversation, he carried the wine to the couch where Anna was sitting.

Anna slipped off her shoes, curled her legs underneath her, and prepared to talk about anything Frankie wanted to talk about. But when he pulled her comfortably onto his lap, she put down her wine and let all the tension from a very confusing day slip away. Cuddling into his chest, she simply enjoyed the moment. "If I knew how to purr, I would," she said, closing her eyes to savor the feeling of complete contentment.

Although Frankie wouldn't have looked any less content to someone peering in from the outside, he wasn't purring inside; he was growling. He had Anna, for the moment, exactly where he wanted her. But what would he do without her if she moved to Orlando? She might as well have punched him in the gut with both fists when she told him her good news at Ted Peters. Frankie wanted her to stay right here with him. God, how he wanted her to stay! But how could she know that? He had tried to show her in thousands of little ways that he cared, but he just couldn't say the words he knew she wanted to hear.

Why not? he thought. *I'm absolutely crazy about her, and what fool wouldn't be? Why can't I tell her that just the sight of her when I pulled up to get her tonight made my heart thump like a bass drum in my chest? Why can't I bring myself to say, 'I love you'? I'm not scared of much, but I'm scared of those three little words.*

Beginning to feel physically sick, he closed his eyes and laid his head back on the couch to let the feeling pass.

Suddenly, a violent scene sprang to life in his mind. He was about ten years old, and he and his parents were in the living room of the house where he had grown up. Frankie was crouched in a corner watching helplessly as his father, drunk and slobbering, tried to kiss his mother. When she turned her head away, his anger flashed.

"I love you, you fuckin' bitch," his father screamed. "Don't you understand how much I love you? You're my wife. Act like it!" Then he crushed his mouth down on hers, squeezing her shoulders so hard that Frankie could see his mother's flesh turn red. Frankie's stomach turned upside down. Watching his father beat his mother mercilessly, Frankie silently began to vomit and thought he'd never stop.

Where the hell did that come from? Frankie thought, feeling hot tears forming behind his eyelids. Without thinking, he lifted Anna unceremoniously off his lap and dropped her on the couch. Jolting up, he walked to the middle of the room and just stood there, as if in some sort of trance.

He heard them. He heard them loud enough to make him shake his head. If thoughts could scream, his thoughts were screaming at him violently from some place inside where he'd never been. *You are not your damn father and Anna is not your mother! Their life was theirs and yours is yours! You are nothing like them! Nothing!*

He recognized that those words, or ones very much like them, had come out of his mouth about a year ago when his sister Julie told him how scared she was to marry Mike, even though she loved him. Frankie had been incensed that Julie would think she was anything like their mother and Mike anything like their father, and he had told her so. He could see clearly that she was about to make a huge mistake if she let the memory of their parents' marriage keep her from having a perfectly good marriage of her own.

But he hadn't realized that he was doing exactly what she had been doing: letting his own memory of his parents' marriage keep him from daring to be married to Anna.

I've built myself a fuckin' box! Frankie thought, remembering what Tony said the ELF had told him. *I've been scared of the words 'I love you' ever since I heard my father ram then down my Mother's throat when I was just a kid!*

All of a sudden, a vision appeared to Frankie. He saw a wooden box about a foot square. Inside the box were the words 'I love you' written in the middle of a circle with a diagonal red line running through it to symbolize danger. You're crazy, he yelled at the box.

The box disintegrated and the vision faded.

Frankie was surprised at how much better he felt. It took him a moment to fully focus, and when he did, the first thing he saw was Anna. Sitting motionless on the couch where he had dropped her, she looked lost and bewildered as tears silently streamed down her ashen cheeks.

Good God, he thought, *have I been talking out loud?*

Walking back to Anna, he knelt in front of her. "Everything is all right now, Anna. It's more all right than it has ever been before. I love you, I love you, I love you more than I love breathing, and I just couldn't say it to you before."

He held her tightly until she stopped shaking. "I'll explain, sweetheart. I promise I'll explain," he said gently. "But first, tell me you don't think I'm a lunatic. Tell me you're not afraid of me. Because I would never, ever do anything to hurt you. Oh, God, you have to know I'd never hurt you."

Pulling back, he looked directly into her eyes. "Anna, I want you to marry me. I want to love you and take care of you for the rest of my life."

Anna didn't even blink. "I love you too, Frankie," she said, her voice still a little shaky. "And yes, I'll marry you. And as long as whatever just happened made you able to tell me that you love me, you don't even have to explain it to me. Just keep loving me, Frankie. Please, just keep loving me." Winding her arms around his neck, she drew him into a deep, emotion-packed kiss.

Frankie stood and lifted her gently into his arms. Carrying her into the bedroom, he whispered softly in her ear. "Forever, Anna, I promise. I promise I'll keep on loving you forever. And I'll tell you so, every day."

GO TO ELF!

Frankie lay awake most of the night holding a sleeping Anna in his arms. The next morning as he drove her home to change her clothes for work, he knew there was one more thing he had to say to her. Because he loved her, he couldn't—or wouldn't—do anything to stand in the way of her dream job. If she wanted to work in Orlando, no matter what they had to do to have time together, they would find a way.

He told her and her response was simple. "I really appreciate you saying that, Frankie. It makes me know that you understand how important my work is to me. But you see, last night I got a job offer I like even better."

Laying her tiny hand on his huge one, she added, "Being your wife and making a home with you here is more than a dream come true. So as long as that's what you want, too, I'm not planning to go anywhere that you are not."

Frankie breathed a long, deep sigh of relief.

On the way back home from Anna's house, Frankie stopped at the Café Mozart Bakery on 4th Street for his favorite: a couple of almond paste German coffeecakes. They were his very best comfort food, and after the extremely emotional day the day before, Frankie wanted to be comforted.

On Sunday mornings, he usually did the routine chores of a bachelor living an orderly life. But this was the first week of the month, and the irreplaceable Mrs. Krause had been there on Friday to scrub his house from top to bottom, do his laundry, and fill his freezer with homemade casseroles, so he had a free morning.

He made a pot of coffee, sliced and buttered a healthy portion of coffee cake, and carried them to the back patio. From the other side of the hedge, he could hear his neighbors piling into their van to go to church.

One of Frankie's former girlfriends had called him a heathen because he didn't go to church. He told her he felt more in communion with God in his own back yard than he did in the pews of her church. And just to irritate her, he said he preferred to attend services at Our Lady of the Patio every Sunday.

And here I am, really doing it. Frankie chuckled to himself as he looking appreciatively at his trim back yard complete with cherry red bougainvillea blossoms tumbling riotously over the back wall—another little legacy from his mother.

It's really nice out here at Our Lady of the Patio, he thought, realizing that he felt a deep, almost overwhelming gratitude.

"I'm madly in love with the most beautiful woman in the world," he announced to the noisy mockingbird scolding him from a nearby oak tree. "And guess what? She loves me back!"

Once again, Frankie felt tears forming behind his eyelids, but this time, they were joyful tears. His mind and his heart lay wide open, and for a while sitting contentedly on his own patio, he felt safe enough to leave them that way.

Sometime during the previous night while lying with Anna's little body nestled into the curve of his big body, he had figured out why Tony's ELF had felt so familiar to him. Frankie had thought he was dreaming at first, but then he realized it was another very vivid memory rather than a dream. He had also seen and felt a little elf climbing up on his knee in Sherwood Forest, magically lifting his misery away. Tony had said he had thought of his boyhood visits from the ELF as hallucinations, and because of that, he had been able to put them out of his mind. But Frankie hadn't made even that much sense out of it, so his way of dealing with it back then had been simply to pretend it had never happened.

He now knew it had happened, and he wondered if the time would ever come when the ELF would come out and talk to him, too, the way he talked to Tony.

I sure have a few questions of my own I'd like to ask him, Frankie thought. *I'll just do what he told Tony to do. I'll 'Go to ELF!''*

He closed his eyes and did his best to remember exactly what the elf in Sherwood Forest had looked like. Then, prepared to "talk" about his problem in his mind and wait for some kind of answer, he opened his eyes. And right there on the table in front of him, a little pulsating light began to flicker and the ELF slowly materialized, exactly as Frankie remembered.

"Hi, Frankie," the ELF said kindly. "You have some questions you want to ask me?"

"Are you Tony's ELF?" Frankie heard himself ask.

"No, I'm your ELF, Frankie. Everyone has an ELF of his or her own. Think of me as the ELF in yoursELF."

"Is that what I should call you?"

The ELF shifted his energy a bit, brilliant colors pulsating throughout his little body in rapid succession and creating an effect like the lights on the columns of an old-fashioned juke box.

"Most of you who are currently on earth in physical form trust that I exist. Some people call me God. Others call me Holy Spirit, Source, or The One. There are lots of different names for me.

"Many modern scientists who say they don't believe in me at all are comfortable describing me as the Matrix or the Field or the Grid. Although they don't acknowledge me as a divine being, they do accept that an all-knowing intelligence is spread throughout the universe and can be accessed when needed.

"Because there is really nothing in your three-dimensional world that can help you understand completely who and what I am, all of you try to figure me out in different ways. However, of all the ways human beings perceive me or the names they call me, Frankie, the Eternal Life Force comes closest to what I truly am. I am the life force that both creates and sustains all life, and I am eternal.

"You are welcome to call me ELF, though. It has a friendly sound, don't you think? And of all the many relationships you and I have, Frankie, I am above all, always and ever, your best and closest friend. Do you have any questions about that?" the ELF asked.

"No, I think I get it. You are the sustaining force within everything that lives. Is that right?"

"Actually, that is very accurate and very succinct. I am the sustaining force within everything that lives," said the ELF, looking uncommonly pleased with Frankie.

"So you created me and you sustain me. I get that part," Frankie said. "But I'm not sure exactly how we relate to each other now. Can you help me understand that better?"

"I can," the ELF said, another ripple of energy pulsating through his body. "But first, would you mind getting me a glass of water with ice cubes in it? And if you don't mind, I'd prefer it in a clear glass."

"Sure thing. Just don't go anywhere, okay?" Frankie said, heading for the kitchen.

"I can't go anywhere, Frankie, because I am everywhere. George Lucas was right about that part. The Force is always with you."

CONCEPT III

Realizing . . .
You came here primarily to have fun

CHAPTER SEVEN

Frankie brought two glasses of ice water and set them on the table next to the ELF.

"Are you going to drink this?" Frankie asked as he looked at the ELF's little, transparent, pulsating body and wondered where the water would go.

"No," the ELF said, laughing. "There is no need for food and drink in my realm. I'm going to use it to help answer your question. Are you ready?"

"I'm ready," Frankie answered, his curiosity high.

"Where did the water in the glass come from?" the ELF asked.

"From the faucet."

"And where did the water in the faucet come from?"

"Through the pipes, I guess from a water tower somewhere."

"And where did the water in the tower come from?"

"From a reservoir, I believe. But if you're going to ask me where that water comes from, I don't know," Frankie said.

"What you have been describing is a very clever method that physical beings, who live together in communities, have devised to deliver water directly to their own homes, businesses, and public meeting places," the ELF explained. "All people on the earth don't enjoy such sophisticated water delivery systems, of course. Many still draw water from underground wells, or take it out of the rivers and lakes in buckets, or catch rainwater in vessels. But ultimately, everyone somehow gathers water from a never-ending supply of water.

"And here is what makes that water supply never-ending, Frankie. The cycle begins when water falls to the earth from the sky in the form of rain or various other types of precipitation. Some of that rainwater is stored underground, some of it fills the rivers and streams, and some of it collects at surface points such as lakes and ponds, bays and bayous.

"Water evaporates from those surface points and rises to form clouds, which eventually drop rain back onto the earth again. The cycle is never-ending, and although human beings have managed to disrupt some of the process some of the time, nothing will ever seriously disrupt the cycle, because water is the sustainer of all life. In other words, I'm bigger than they are. Are you following me so far, Frankie?"

"Yes, I think I am."

"A few minutes ago, you siphoned off an individual portion of the earth's water supply into a single glass, and then you added ice cubes. What are the ice cubes made of, Frankie?"

"Frozen water."

"And if you leave that glass sitting out here on the patio for a couple of hours, what will happen to the ice cubes?"

"They'll melt, of course."

"And when they melt, they become water again. So here's the big picture, Frankie. Although sometimes water takes different forms, ultimately there is absolutely no difference in the content of those forms. The water in the ice cubes, the water in the glass, and the water supply for your entire planet are all the same perfect mix of hydrogen and oxygen you call water."

"I can follow that."

"Then let's translate it to the relationship between you and me, Frankie. Together, we are a single expression of the creator and sustainer of all life called the Eternal Life Force, but we are expressed in different forms. I, the ELF, am expressed as our spiritual or non-physical nature. You, Frankie Doerrer, are expressed as our human or physical nature. We are one single entity that is simultaneously visible and invisible, both made up of the same stuff as each other and as the Eternal Life Force. That's why I say that I am you and you are me, everywhere and always. Get it?"

Frankie blinked. "Well, let me try to explain it in my own words and see if I've got it or not. The water in the glass is invisible like you, and the ice in the glass is visible like me, but actually, they are made up of the same substance as each other and as the never-ending water supply. And they are all being expressed simultaneously in different forms.

"You, the ELF, are invisible, and I, Frankie Doerrer, am visible. But we are made up of the same stuff as each other and as the Eternal Life Force, and we are all being expressed simultaneously in different forms. Is that anywhere close to what you meant?"

"That's exactly what I meant, Frankie!" said the ELF, excitedly shimmering brilliant colors so rapidly and so vigorously that Frankie had to turn his eyes away because the vibrating energy was making him a bit dizzy.

"Okay, then, I guess I've got it," Frankie said. "But I'd hate to try to explain it to anyone else."

"You can share with other people what you have learned about me, but some won't be ready to hear you at the time you tell them about it, Frankie. Don't worry about that. They'll either figure it out for themselves or they won't. Of course, if they ask me for help, I will help them."

"How did I get to be human?" Frankie asked.

"You asked to be human."

"But why did I ask? What do I get in physical form that I didn't have in non-physical form?"

"Oh, far more goodies than you can contemplate, Frankie," the ELF said. "Before you were born, when we were both non-physical, we looked on the earth and saw how spectacular this planet is. You saw oceans to cross and mountains to climb, and you saw grand openings and The Grand Prix. You saw sunrises and sunsets, and *Rocky Horror* and Disney World, and pizza and beer. You decided you wanted to experience all those things, and other things not available to you when you were in non-physical form. You chose to be human for the fun of it, Frankie. And believe me, being human can be great fun."

"Oh, come on. Are you really saying the human experience exists just for fun?" Frankie asked, an incredulous tone edging into his voice.

"Exactly. It isn't the only reason you chose to be born, but it certainly is one of the main reasons. Maybe this will help you to understand better. To use one of your favorite places as an example, being born into human form is just like buying a ticket to Disney World. You, of all people, should be able to understand that. And while you are here, you get to decide whether to do fun things, or scary things, or things that are just plain interesting, or all of the above.

"When you go to Disney World, you go there to enjoy it all, don't you? You ride both Space Mountain and It's A Small World with equal glee. You find Frontierland just as interesting as Tomorrowland. And nobody enjoys a parade more than you do.

"But other people go through Disney World and don't enjoy it at all. They see only long lines of people in their way. All they experience is the heat, the crowds, the high prices, and a bunch of grown-up people behaving like children. Whether or not you enjoy the human experience is a personal choice, Frankie, just as whether or not you enjoy Disney World is a personal choice. Everything you do here is a personal choice."

"I know. I wish Tony enjoyed Disney World. He can't seem to find the fun in it," Frankie said. "I wish he'd just let loose and enjoy it, but he never has."

"True, but the real beauty of the human experience is that no two people have to enjoy the same things. For instance, Tony loves a good basketball game, but you couldn't care less about it. In fact, in the final minutes of the Final Four, I can assure you that he is every bit as excited as you are at the top of Space Mountain. The fact that you enjoy different things has never affected your friendship negatively, though, has it?"

"No, it never has."

"And that's the way it should be between all individual human beings.. Each of you came here for different reasons, and there is never any need to convince anyone else that he or she should enjoy what you enjoy."

"So I should be concentrating more on having fun than on anything else while I'm here?"

"Pretty much. And you do that well already, Frankie. Better than most," the ELF said. "Basically, you allow for both work time and play time. You know that something has to pay for your toys, so work matters, too, but you kid around with your employees and your customers. You keep it light when you can, so you even make work time as pleasant as possible.

"Still, I'd encourage you to go a little heavier on the play time. You might want to hire Mrs. Krause to clean your house more often so you can spend more of your Sunday mornings like this, especially now that you'll be spending them with Anna."

"Any other suggestions for increasing my fun time?" Frankie asked, warming up to the way this conversation was going.

"Yes, you could become more creative about the way you use your five senses. I know you don't appreciate how big a part they play in having fun."

"Non-physical beings don't have senses?"

"No, because we don't have bodies. I can feel your emotions, but I can't experience anything physical that might create those emotions. When you eat that almond paste coffee cake, for example, I can feel your pleasure, but I can't taste the coffee cake. I can feel your relief when you drink a cold beer on a hot day, but I can't taste the beer or feel the way it slides down your throat. I can feel the peace, even the awe that you feel when you watch a sunset, but I can't see the colors you describe. Do you see the difference?"

"Wow, no pistachio ice cream or German potato salad? No wonder I wanted to be human!"

"And no sex, either, Frankie."

"Oh, God!"

"Yes?" the ELF replied with a smile.

"Let's change the subject, if you don't mind," Frankie said, suddenly feeling very exposed. "What happens when we die?"

"What happens to the ice cubes, Frankie?"

"They melt and become water. Are you saying that we will all just dissolve into non-physical beings again?"

"Exactly."

"So in effect, I will never really die, then? I will just change form?"

"Because all that many human beings recognize about themselves is their physical bodies, they think their life ends when their body stops functioning. But that simply isn't true, Frankie. Your trip here to earth is a very small segment of your eternal lifetime. There is really no such thing as death; there is only transformation from one form of life to another. Eternal life is cyclical, Frankie, the same way the never-ending water supply is cyclical. Sometimes you are having an earthly experience and sometimes you are not."

"That is wild," Frankie exclaimed. "But we are still accountable for everything we do while we're human, aren't we?"

"Accountable to whom for what? Because if I am you, what could you possibly have done in human form that I wasn't already part of?"

"Well, you know. What about Judgment Day? Won't I go to either heaven or hell, depending on what I did when I was here?"

"When you die, you return to non-physical form and your

human experience ends, Frankie, just as when you walk out of Disney World and drive home, your Disney experience ends—at least for that visit. There is no Judgment Day. You see, there are no opposites in spirit, Frankie. There is no right and wrong, good and bad, tall and short, black and white, hot and cold, in and out, up and down, high and low, or any other such contrasts. Those opposites, along with heaven and hell, belong only to the human experience."

Frankie was incredulous. "There are no paybacks when you die? Not even for terrorists or serial killers or despots like Adolph Hitler? My father was never punished for beating my mother?"

"No, Frankie, he wasn't. There are no paybacks in spirit. Paybacks are a human experience. You, as a human race, have set up a system of rewards and punishments and standards of behavior, which most of you uphold because the majority of you believe they are necessary. You live with those for a while, and then you change them and live with the changes for a while. Then you change them again. Whatever the majority of you here on earth agree on becomes your standard of conduct.

"But in your personal life experience, Frankie, you can create the kind of life you want according to your own rules. You can even change any experience you are having but don't like by simply asking me to help you change it. You've always had access to all my wisdom and power, just as I have instant access to all of the wisdom and power of the Eternal Life Force. The only difference between today and yesterday, and all the rest of the days of your earthly life, is that now you remember that you are connected to me, and that through me, you are connected to all that power and wisdom, twenty-four/seven/three-sixty-five."

The ELF let that sink in a minute, smiling fondly at Frankie.

"That would make me superhuman, wouldn't it? Something like a superhero," Frankie said.

"All human beings are superheroes, and you all have superpower when you are consciously connected to me. Nothing brings me greater joy than to see a human being claim his or her own power by consciously accessing mine."

"You don't mean that I have no limits, though?" Frankie asked.

"Accepting the concept of limitation is a choice, Frankie, and many human beings don't accept that concept. Keep in mind that someone in human form learned to fly, someone else discovered how to span the space between earth and the moon, another believed that people could talk to each other across oceans, dozens collaborated to create the Internet, and Walt Disney decided that human beings could increase their level of joy by watching the antics of a cartoon mouse. Currently, some human beings are trading internal organs from body to body. Limitations are a myth, Frankie, so go find something fantastic to do, if you want to, and I will help you do it."

The ELF began to shimmer again, shifting his brilliant lights. "I know there are lots of other things you would like to talk about, Frankie, but I suspect you've remembered enough for one day," he advised. "Why don't you take a nap and let some of this new understanding really sink in? But before you do, let's look at the new ideas you and Tony are working with so far.

"Tony is figuring out that when he thinks about something that will make him happy, he feels good, and when he's thinking about something that will make him unhappy, he feels bad. He's beginning to understand that he can use his feelings to steer himself in the direction he really wants to go. He's also discovering that if he can't get himself to feel good no matter what he does, he has boxed himself in somehow, and he's slowly learning how to break away the old boxes that have kept him feeling limited.

"Today you discovered that you are superhuman as long as you are in communication with me, that human beings never really die, and that one of the main reasons you chose to be human is to have fun. Speaking of which, don't you have some shopping to do later this afternoon?"

"I do."

"You'd better get some practice saying those words, Frankie," the ELF teased.

"Tell me about it," Frankie said, grinning. "So you will be with me today when I buy the ring, and you will be with me tonight when I officially ask Anna to marry me. And—oh, God!—will you be with me when we're having sex, too?" he almost wailed.

"I won't have the same physical experience that you have," the ELF said, his eyes shining in amusement as he felt Frankie's emotions start to spike, "but I will feel the way the sex makes you feel emotionally. So to put it in your language, Frankie, I guess you could say that if it's good for you, it will be good for me, too."

With a deep chuckle, the ELF began to fade away. "Always remember, Frankie. I am you and you are me, everywhere and always."

And with one last shimmer, he gave one more reminder. "When you need help, just 'Go to ELF!'"

When she got home from work, Anna called Frankie.

"It's a beautiful night," he said after they greeted each other. "You game for a sunset?"

"I'd like to take a shower. Do I have time?"

"I think so. Sunset is just after seven. I'll pick you up in an hour, and we'll go right to the beach. We can catch a bite afterward, okay?

"I'll be ready. Gotta run. Bye," Anna said, kicking off her shoes and unbuttoning her uniform as she hung up the phone.

Sitting on a bench near the shore, they held hands and watched the sun sink slowly toward the horizon. As the edge of the hot sun appeared to touch the cool waters of the Gulf, Frankie made a low sizzling sound. Anna giggled, laid her head on his shoulder, and they drank in the wonder of the brilliant colors sweeping across the sky.

It's too bad you can't see this, too, Frankie said silently to the ELF. *But I want to thank you, because I suspect you made the sky extra beautiful tonight just for Anna and me.*

"That was lovely," Anna said, sighing and turning to look at Frankie as the sunset-streaked sky began to fade into darkness. "Were the colors really that brilliant, or am I just so happy that everything looks twice as beautiful as usual?"

"A little of both, probably," Frankie said. "And by the way, I have it on good authority that you're supposed to be happy."

Frankie reached into his back pocket and pulled out the tiny velvet box he'd been carrying around since early afternoon. "I just can't wait any longer to make this official," he said as he took Anna's hand, "and I thought a sunset would be a perfect backdrop for it."

Sliding the diamond solitaire out of its box, he slipped it onto Anna's finger and dropped to one knee in the sand. "I want to hear you answer me again, Anna. Will you marry me?"

"Yes, I'll marry you, Frankie," she said, her eyes brimming with happy tears.

"I love you, Anna."

"I love you too, Frankie," she said, lowering herself to kneel in the sand facing him. Framing his face with her small hands, she kissed him with such tenderness that he felt his heart melt.

"Forever, Anna, forever," he said, returning her kiss.

They sat together on the bench in happy silence for a long while listening to the waves break gently against the shore. As a full moon bathed them in soft light, Frankie took off his jacket and put it around Anna's shoulders. Then drawing his cell phone out of his pocket, he whispered in her ear, "Okay, now who shall we tell first?"

GO TO ELF!

The first person they called was Anna's mother; the second, of course, was Tony. To say that he was surprised didn't cover the emotion Tony felt at the thought of Frankie getting married, especially since they'd had breakfast together just the day before and Frankie hadn't even mentioned it.

When they were in their twenties, they had talked a lot about getting married. But in the last eight or ten years, the subject had never come up. So when Frankie arrived with his crew on Tuesday night to begin cleaning the Fillmore Café, Tony was there waiting for him. Knowing that Tony had questions, Frankie asked him to wait a few minutes until he got his crew started. Then the two men went into the hotel lobby and found a quiet place to talk.

"I've loved her all along, Tony," Frankie said simply, "but I was scared out of my mind to admit it, even to myself. When you and I had breakfast last Saturday, I had no intention of asking her to marry me. In fact, it was probably about the farthest thing from my mind. But when she told me she had an offer to go to work in Orlando, I figured out real fast that I didn't want her to go anywhere without me, ever.

"What happened to make me finally get up the courage to tell her I loved her is—uh, complicated. So if you can wait, I'd rather tell it to you on Saturday. But in the meantime, I think you will feel a lot better when you meet her.

"Have dinner with us Friday night, okay? I'll call you and tell you where to meet us." Cuffing Tony on the arm and grinning, he said, "Once you get to know her, you'll stop worrying about me. I can just about guarantee it."

On his walk back to his condo, Tony had a little talk with the ELF. As he began to think about Frankie marrying someone Tony had never met, he expected to start having bad feelings, but to his surprise, his feelings stayed neutral. He didn't feel wonderful about Frankie's news, but he didn't feel bad about it, either. He took that as a "wait and see" message from the ELF and decided not to think about it anymore until after he met Anna on Friday and had a good talk with Frankie on Saturday morning.

Instead, Tony channeled his considerable energy into thinking about an engagement present for Frankie. Quickly he decided. He would create a piece of art that would tell the story of how Frankie and Anna met.

Tony spent about an hour on the Internet researching *The Rocky Horror Picture Show*. He knew that Frankie had heard Anna singing and was drawn to her voice even before he saw what she looked like, so Tony focused on the music from the movie.

The lyrics from *Dream It*—"Can't you just see it? Don't dream it, be it!"—struck Tony as very appropriate for two people starting a new life together. So Tony used those words, a few simple scenes from the movie, and Frankie and Anna's names as inspiration for his work.

He started the sketch and touched it up that night, and worked on it again most of Wednesday night. Thursday, he slept until noon—sleeping late was one of the perks of owning his own business, he had discovered—and he finished coloring the piece on Thursday afternoon. Then Tony called in a favor from a custom framer he knew and picked up the finished product Friday night at five o'clock, just an hour before he was to meet Frankie and Anna at Carrabba's for dinner.

The framed piece was two-and-a-half-feet wide by almost four feet high. Tony knew that the perfect spot for it to hang was in the foyer of Frankie's house, which soon would be Anna's house, too. He usually didn't do large design work because it was easier for him to work on a small scale and have the drawing enlarged later, but this piece was special, so he made it an exception. He was more pleased than ever with the finished product when the framer offered him $750 for it, unframed, even though it had no personal meaning to him.

Tony spread a new white blanket on his bed and placed the framed graphic on it. Wrapping it like a box, he taped the ends of the blanket together to protect the frame before placing the package in the trunk of his car.

Tony pulled up in front of Carrabba's and stopped the car. He got out and carried in the package, stood it up against a wall in the lobby, and then went back outside and parked his car.

When he came back into the restaurant, the interest of the staff in the lobby was definitely piqued. Seeing Frankie and Anna sitting on the far side of the restaurant, Tony asked one of the busboys to help him, and they threaded their way through the narrow aisles carrying the graphic to Frankie and Anna's table. By the time Tony stood the package against a wall behind their table, everyone in the restaurant knew that he and his package had arrived.

Frankie then introduced his future wife and his best friend, each of them understanding that this was a huge moment for all of them. "Well, Bro, you didn't exaggerate," Tony said with delight, gallantly kissing her hand before pulling her into a bear hug. "Anna, you are more than lovely; you are exquisite."

Anna had expected this meeting might be awkward; after all, she was the new kid on the block. She had even pondered the possibility that she and Tony might be a little jealous of each other. They weren't. Since they each adored Frankie so much, how could they not fall in love with each other at first sight?

As Tony and Anna chatted easily, Frankie indulged in a little internal dialogue with the ELF. *Okay, now give me some credit here, too. You may have made it possible for me to meet these two absolutely amazing people, but I was smart enough to take advantage of it, wasn't I?*" He grinned as he felt an extra little burst of joy in his heart.

As they were enjoying their meal and conversation, the manager came to the table and asked if he could talk with Tony privately. Wondering if he might have parked his car in the wrong place, Tony followed the manager to an alcove a few feet away from the table.

"Sir," the manager began in a very stuffy tone, "about the package you brought into the restaurant."

"Yeah, what about it?"

"Do you plan to open it … uh, unveil it in the restaurant?"

"I suppose so. It's an art piece I made for the couple I'm with. They're getting married and this is their engagement present. Why?"

"Is there anything obscene or pornographic about it, sir?"

"Of course not," Tony said, aggravated. "Not that it's any of your business, of course."

"I don't mean to be offensive," the manager continued, "but it is hard to mistake it for anything but a work of art. And since you carried it all the way through the restaurant, many of our customers have asked the waiters if you plan to unveil it before they leave. You see my dilemma, I'm sure, sir. I have customers waiting in the lobby, but our current guests are, shall we say, lingering in hope of seeing what's under that blanket. Is there anything I can do to encourage you to unveil it soon? A bottle of champagne for your table, perhaps, compliments of the house? I would like all my customers to be satisfied."

Tony glanced around the room to see all eyes riveted on him.

"I think a bottle of champagne would be a great idea," Tony said. "As soon as you pop the cork, I'll unveil the picture."

The manager left, and a waiter soon appeared at the threesome's table with a bottle and a standing ice bucket. As soon as the waiter uncorked the bottle and placed it in the bucket, Tony loosened the tape and lifted the blanket with a flourish.

A roar of applause spread throughout the dining room.

Frankie, who couldn't imagine why it was happening again, felt tears well up in his eyes so swiftly that he could hardly see the picture. Wide-eyed, Anna simply stared.

The piece was stunning. Done in black and white, and highlighted in subtle touches of deep reds and golds, it would have held its own in any graphic arts exhibit at any major museum in the world. And it was all about Frankie and Anna.

All the stuffiness left the manager's demeanor as he stood admiring the work of art with true appreciation. Then, with Frankie and Anna's permission, he and his staff moved the picture to a place near the exit where other guests could admire it more closely as they left the restaurant.

Frankie sipped his champagne, his hand trembling. "It's beautiful, just beautiful, Bro. I don't remember ever telling you that those two characters, Riff and Magenta, are Anna's and my favorite characters," he said. "Did I?"

Tony looked at Frankie knowingly. "No," he said, "you never did. So I guess that particular direction must have come to me from somewhere else."

"I just don't know how much more good stuff I can handle this week," Frankie said, tears swimming in his eyes again as he reached for his handkerchief. "I never thought getting married would be such an emotional experience."

Tony, too, was close to tears as Anna, struck by the sweetness of the gentle giant she was about to marry, tenderly patted Frankie's hand.

CHAPTER EIGHT

Tony walked toward the Dome Grill the following morning with an extra spring in his step. He was genuinely relieved, after having met the Lovely Anna, to see how happy she and Frankie were together.

"Hey, Pete! What a gorgeous day!" Tony said, grinning widely as he bounded through the door.

"Well, you're in a good mood this morning," Pete said, automatically beginning to ring up Tony's order.

"I'm in such a good mood, Pete, I'm gonna add some orange juice to my regular order this morning."

"You're kidding," said Pete. Grabbing the cash register and holding on to it for dear life, he looked up at the ceiling.

"What's the matter?" Tony asked, casting a puzzled eye at the ceiling.

"I just thought the roof might cave in if you changed your order after twenty years."

"Very funny. And I didn't change my order, I just added to it. Frankie here yet?"

"No, you beat him this morning. Very unusual."

"Yeah, well get used to it. It's gonna get harder and harder for him to get out of bed in the morning. He's getting married. Can you believe it?"

"No kidding! Shall I congratulate him when he comes in, or wait for him to tell me?"

"I guess he should have the fun of telling you himself," Tony said, "unless he doesn't mention it for a couple of weeks. Then you can give him some grief about it. Hold my order 'til he gets here, will you? Thanks."

Tony paid his bill, picked up his coffee, and headed out the front door.

"Hey, where you goin'?" Pete called after him.

"Second change today, Pete," Tony said with a laugh. "It's such a beautiful day, I'm gonna eat outside and give all the girls going by something beautiful to look at this morning."

"Oh, get outta here," Pete said, laughing.

"I'm going, I'm going."

Thinking how lucky he was. Frankie pulled into a parking space directly in front of the door. To his surprise, Tony was sipping his coffee at an outside table.

"Hey, Bro," Frankie said, walking up to the sidewalk table. "What are you doing out here?"

"It's a beautiful day, Frankie. Why should we stuff ourselves inside on a day like this? Not too hot, not too cold. We're in Florida, aren't we?"

"Okay, okay. It's just that this is the one ritual that never changes," Frankie muttered. "And up until now, I've liked it that way. I'll get my breakfast and be back in a minute."

Is this another box?" Frankie silently asked the ELF. *I mean this Saturday morning ritual: same place, same food, same table for twenty years?*

He waited, but he didn't get a bad feeling; this morning it felt as good as ever to have breakfast with Tony. *Am I right, then, that it's not a box unless it feels bad? Unless it pinches or starts to feel confining?*

He smiled as he felt a surge of good energy inside his chest.

Bingo, he said silently as he waited to hear his ticket number called.

Frankie came back outside with his own breakfast, Pete following behind and carrying a tray holding Tony's order.

"Hey, thanks for the curbside service, pal," Tony said to Pete.

"It's my pleasure," Pete said, winking at Tony. "Frankie here tells me he's getting married and that he'll bring the Lovely Anna to breakfast here so I can meet her. She better be good enough for you, Frankie."

"You can see for yourself, Pete," Frankie said with a wry smile. "But no matter how much you like her, you can't have her. She's mine."

"She really is wonderful, Bro," Tony said when they were finally alone. "You weren't exaggerating or blinded by love." Then, just to eliminate one of the many little fears he had been harboring about how Frankie's marriage might affect their relationship, he asked, "Does the Lovely Anna always work on Saturdays?"

"Always. It's one of the days she covers for the doctor she works with. Isn't that handy?"

"Very," Tony answered, not realizing how relieved he sounded.

"By the way, you and I won't be having breakfast here next Saturday. We'd better tell Pete so he doesn't worry."

"We won't?" asked Tony, giving Frankie a serious look. "Where will we be having breakfast next Saturday?"

"In Mickey Mouse land."

"Me at Disney World? I don't think so, Bro."

"Well, that's where the wedding's gonna be, so if you're gonna be the best man, you're gonna have to be there."

"What? What's the hurry, Frankie? You just got engaged. Now you're getting married? Is she pregnant, for God's sake?"

"Only with possibilities," Frankie replied, laughing.

Then getting serious, he told Frankie his long story. First, he talked about the memory of his liquor-crazed father telling his mother he loved her, and how the memory had helped Frankie realize he'd built a box around the words, "I love you," promising himself at the age of ten that he would never say them to anyone. As soon as he dissolved the box, he knew he wanted to marry Anna.

Then he told Tony about his conversation with the ELF. He did his best to explain why Tony was an ice cube, but he was so excited about the wedding that the whole analogy between the Eternal Life Force and the earth's never-ending water supply didn't come through to Tony.

I'll just ask the ELF about that, myself, Tony thought.

Then Frankie told him that he and Anna had decided not to delay getting married when what they really wanted was to begin living the rest of their lives together. "It's my time to get married, Tony," Frankie said. "I'm not a kid, and I don't have to wait for anything anymore if I don't want to. And we're getting married at Disney World because it's one of the places where Anna and I just love to be. C'mon, you don't want to miss my wedding, do you?"

"Frankie, I wouldn't miss your wedding if you wanted to be married in Siberia—which, thank heaven, you don't. I guess I can stand a weekend in Never Never Land with the other Lost Boys if I have to. Who's gonna be there besides you and me and the Lovely Anna?"

"Julie and Mike and Andy will be there, of course. And that's all from my side, except for you. Anna's mother will be there, and Anna's best friend, Crissy, will fly in from Denver so she can be maid of honor. We've worked this all out with Disney World," Frankie went on seriously. "They will provide the minister. Mickey will walk Anna down the aisle, and Minnie will be a bridesmaid. After the ceremony, Anna and I will take a ride in Cinderella's coach to our favorite restaurant, Chef Mickey's, where Daisy and Donald will help us cut the wedding cake.

"The whole thing should take only about an hour and a half. As soon as we've all had cake and champagne, Anna and I will drive to Port Canaveral. We're going to take a four-day cruise to the Bahamas for our honeymoon, and the rest of you will be free to head home."

Tony's jaw had dropped when Frankie said Mickey would walk Anna down the aisle. Still unable to believe what he has just heard, Tony used the heel of his hand to push his jaw closed. "Frankie, have you completely lost your mind?" he asked with a note of real concern.

"No, Bro, I haven't lost my mind," Frankie answered, reaching over and laying his big hand on Tony's arm. "But I have definitely found my heart." And this time when Frankie teared up, he let it happen, because he didn't care whether anyone saw him or not.

Tony rested his hand on top of Frankie's and left it there for a moment until he regained his composure. Then Tony straightened up and took a sip of coffee. "Okay, Frankie. If this is what you and Anna want, then it's what I want, too. So what will my duties be as best man? And by the way, what will you and I and Mickey Mouse be wearing?"

"Anna and I decided to keep this all very fun and very casual," Frankie explained. "Slacks and an open-neck shirt will be fine for you and me. Anna and Crissy will be wearing sundresses. And your only duty is to hold me up and hand the minister the rings at the right time."

"That's it?"

"That's it, except we were wondering if on your way back to St. Petersburg after the wedding you could drop off Anna's mother and Crissy at the airport in Tampa so they can catch their plane back to Denver."

"Sure, I can do that," Tony said. "Just as a point of interest, what does Crissy look like?"

"I haven't the foggiest idea," Frankie said, "but she's married and has four-year-old twins."

"Oh, bummer," Tony said. Then, pausing slightly, he asked, "What does Anna's mother look like?"

Frankie choked on his coffee.

"Geeze, Frankie," Tony said, waiting for Frankie to steady

himself. “I didn’t say I was going to jump her bones, I just asked what she looks like.”

“Sorry. It was just the passing thought of your possibly becoming my father-in-law that I found … well, chilling.” They both burst out laughing.

“You know, Frankie, if I wasn’t so happy for you, I’d find all this joy you’re putting out kind of sickening.”

“Sorry,” Frankie said, chuckling. “I’ll try to tone it down.”

“So what’s on your agenda for the rest of today?”

“You know what? Nothing. I took the ELF’s advice and hired Mrs. Krause to come every Friday, so there’s nothing I have to do at home. I have no crews going out until tonight. Anna’s at work, and Julie and Mike and the baby are in Miami visiting his parents. I thought I might just go to Big Fellas and buy something new to wear for the wedding. Want to come with me?”

“Why don’t you ride with me instead?” Tony suggested. “I’ve got a few errands to run, and then I’ll go buy some new threads to wear to the wedding, too.”

“What kind of errands?”

“I want to go by and see Sam at the Fillmore. I haven’t seen the place since your crew cleaned it. Also, the print shop delivered his menus directly to him, and I want to see how they came out. Then I thought I’d go by Needles and Knobs. Christmas stockings are now my signature wedding gift, and I need to get started on yours and Anna’s. Now, don’t get that pained look on your German puss. There’s a hardware store right next door where you can poke around while I’m in the yarn shop.”

“Well, that would work out,” Frankie said, nodding, “because I need to buy a toggle bolt and some picture hooks to hang up our engagement present. I still can’t figure out how you did that so fast and got it so right without knowing much about *Rocky Horror*. When we got home last night, we looked at it for another hour, picking out all the little details.”

Then Frankie took a deep breath and added, "Since we're going yarn shopping, I guess I need to tell you about this, even though I'm afraid it will make your head swell out of proportion. But you know the sweater you gave me for Christmas last year?"

"Yeah, cashmere cream-colored, cable stitch, turtleneck, classy."

"Well, I was wearing it the night I met Anna. It was a big part of my good first impression."

"Good deal. But did you tell her I'm the one who knitted it for you?"

"Uh ... no. I wanted her to get to know you first and see that you're really normal. Oh, Lord, did I say that?"

"So when are you going to tell her?"

"Well, maybe… never?"

"Hmm ... you're going to have a hard time explaining the Christmas stockings then, aren't you?"

"Well, Christmas is still more than a month away. I'll see if I can work up my courage by then," Frankie said, faking a nervous shudder.

"So after we go to the yarn store, we'll go to Big Fellas and buy our wedding clothes. And if you haven't aggravated me too much by then, I'll buy you lunch at El Cap's. Deal?"

"Any time you mention El Cap's and you buying in the same breath, it's a good deal for me. Are you just trying to keep me busy so I won't get cold feet about getting married?" Frankie asked, throwing his arm around Tony's shoulder as they walked down the sidewalk to Tony's car.

"I looked it up in the dictionary, pal. That's what the definition of a best man is: keeping the groom from getting cold feet."

The next day was Sunday, and since he had run around like a mad man all week, Tony planned to make it a day of rest. He knew he would be very busy the first few days of the next week, and then he'd be off to Disney World for Frankie's wedding.

Frankie had already called him the night before and they had worked out the transportation arrangements for the wedding party. Tony had agreed to drive over to Orlando Thursday evening with Julie and the baby. Mike would follow on Friday after he picked up Crissy and Anna's mother at the airport. The wedding would be Saturday afternoon at one o'clock, all the guests would be free to leave by three, and the happy couple would sail away from Port Canaveral at nine on *Magic*, the Disney cruise ship.

Although he had planned to sleep late that morning, Tony had awakened early and spent some time in his office working on the prototypes for Clive's postcards. At about eleven, he made himself a second pot of coffee. It was a delightful day and he knew there would be a breeze on the balcony, so he carried his coffee outside hoping he could "Go to ELF!" to find out about ice cubes, or whatever he was supposed to have understood from Frankie the day before.

Sure enough, he was hardly settled in his deck chair before a shimmer of light appeared on the rail of the balcony. The ELF was back.

"Aren't you afraid you'll fall off and break your neck?" Tony asked with some concern.

"For starters, I don't have a neck," the ELF answered with gentle patience. "And beyond that, I'm not subject to gravity. So nothing to worry about."

"I guess you know that Frankie tried to tell me about the earth's water supply and how it related to you and me, but I didn't get it," Tony said. "Isn't he terrific though? He's so happy he's driving me nuts."

"You might want to get used to it," the ELF suggested. "Because I don't see Frankie's happiness ending any time soon, and that's a good thing."

"Okay, I'll brace myself," Tony said, laughing. "I have to tell you, though, that although I didn't really understand his explanation about water and ice cubes and whatever, Frankie seemed to understand it, and he was pretty stoked about it."

"So will you be when you get it the way he has," the ELF assured Tony. "But I think there's another way to explain it that will have more meaning for you. Do you remember the iceberg you drew for ADPRO's contract with that big air conditioning manufacturer?"

"Yeah, Cooltime. It took me forever to get that iceberg drawing right. What about it?"

"Do you still have that graphic on your computer?"

"Yeah, why?"

"Because I would like to use it to help you understand how you and I are related," the ELF explained. "Would you mind going in and printing off a copy?"

"No, hang on a minute," Tony said sliding open the glass doors. "I'll be right back."

"Don't worry. I'll be here, there, and everywhere while you're gone," the ELF answered.

Tony returned with the drawing of the iceberg.

"What is at the bottom of that drawing?" the ELF asked.

"The ocean."

"Then rising up out of the ocean is the iceberg, right?"

"Right."

"And what is the iceberg made of?"

"Frozen water."

"And in your drawing, part of the iceberg lies below the waterline and part rises above it, right?"

"Uh-huh."

"What is the difference between the ice above the waterline and the ice below it?"

"Nothing, except you can see the ice that's above the waterline and you can't see the ice below it."

TONY CELENTANO

THE ELF

THE ETERNAL LIFE FORCE

"Are they two separate pieces of ice, or are they all one piece—the part you can see and the part you can't see?"

"They're all one piece," Tony answered, thinking if this were the big secret of the universe, it seemed pretty elementary.

"It is elementary, Tony, in every sense of the word. But stay with me here. It's very important."

"I keep forgetting you can hear everything I think," Tony said. "I'm listening. Honest."

"One last question, Tony. What would happen if global warming got it and the iceberg melted?"

"It would turn into water and go back into the ocean, I guess."

"Exactly. Do you have a pen with you, Tony?"

"Yes."

"On your drawing, on the part of the iceberg visible above the waterline, please write your name, Tony Celentano. Then on the part of the iceberg that is invisible below the waterline, please write my name, the ELF. And on the ocean, write the words, the Eternal Life Force."

"What this drawing shows me," Tony summarized, "is that there is absolutely no separation between you and me and the Eternal Life Force. We are one contiguous energy that's invisible and visible at the same time."

"Exactly. This is why I say that you are me and I am you, everywhere and always."

"But even more than that, this drawing would indicate that there is absolutely no separation between you and me and the Eternal Life Force. If all of us are one contiguous energy, wouldn't that make us God?" Tony asked.

"I can feel your terror rising at that very thought, Tony," the ELF said, chuckling, "and your resistance. Relax. You and I aren't all of God, any more than the makings of one iceberg are all of the ocean. We're one small aspect of the Eternal Life Force, or if you prefer, God.

"But what is most important for you to understand, Tony," the ELF said, colors racing throughout his body as he became excited, "is that you have absolute access to me and I have absolute access to the Eternal Life Force, twenty-four/seven/three sixty-five. Once you thoroughly grasp the concept that each time you 'Go to ELF!' you access the infinite source of all supply, you will begin to create a very spectacular life for yourself.

"I like the way Frankie put it very much," the ELF added. "He said that whenever he consciously connects with me, he literally becomes superhuman."

"I don't have to do anything special to communicate with you?" Tony asked.

"No. I know everything you think, say, or do. But even so, you are a deliberate creator, Tony. It's your job to decide what you want to focus your thoughts on, and it's mine to see that you get it."

"And will you tell me again exactly how that process works?"

"Here it is in its simplest form," the ELF explained. "When you are thinking about, talking about, or taking an action toward what you want, you will experience good feelings, and those good feelings will draw you toward everything you ask for.

"In the same way, whenever you're thinking about, talking about, or taking an action in the direction of what you don't want, your feelings will be bad, and those bad feelings will draw you toward exactly what you don't want.

"Use the feelings that I send you, Tony, to alert yourself to whether you are moving toward what you want or toward what you don't want. This isn't complicated. Or as you would say, it's not rocket science. In fact, the process of communication between you and me is so simple that very small children do it all the time.

"Do you remember when you were in grammar school, on rainy days you and the other kids used to play a game called 'Hot and Cold'? The kid who was 'It' left the classroom so all the other kids could hide an object in some secret place in the room. Then the kid who was 'It' would be called back into the room to try to find the hidden object.

"If 'It' moved away from where the object was hidden, all the other players would yell 'cool' or even 'cold.' But as 'It' started to move toward the hidden object, the kids would yell 'warm' or 'warmer.' And when 'It' got really close to the hidden object, they would yell 'hot,' 'hotter,' 'hottest' until "It" found what had been hidden."

"I remember that game. We played it at Shore Acres Elementary School," Tony said. "When I was 'It,' I always found what they had hidden. Once, it was a kid's pet turtle they had hidden in the drinking fountain."

"Well, your good and bad feelings, Tony, act just like the directions those kids shouted to guide you, only now, I'm guiding you. When you are feeling good, think of it as if I were yelling 'warm.' And the better your feel, the more you will know that I am yelling 'hot,' 'hotter,' 'hottest!' Those good feelings mean you're moving closer to your goal. Anytime you're feeling bad, think of it as me yelling 'cold,' 'colder,' 'coldest,' to signal you that you're going the wrong way. Does that help make the process clearer, Tony?"

"What does it mean when I ask you for something and I don't get any particular feeling, good or bad? Like the other night, I asked you if I should be worried about Frankie marrying Anna, and I didn't feel anything. What does having no feeling mean?"

"It means you are asking the wrong question. You see, Tony, you didn't ask me if Frankie and Anna would be happy, even though that's what you really wanted to know. You asked if you should worry about whether Frankie and Anna would be happy. The answer to, 'Should I worry?' will always generate bad feelings, because worry never takes you toward what you want. In fact, it takes you in the other direction every time.

"But I knew you weren't consciously asking me for feedback on the good and bad aspects of worrying, at least not at that moment.

So I waited until you asked me for what you really wanted. The next time you feel like I'm not responding to something you need," the ELF suggested, "try rephrasing the question. A badly worded question isn't the only reason I don't answer right away, but it is the most common reason.

"Let me give you an example, though, of a recent time when you asked the right question and I gave you exactly the guidance you were looking for. I love when it works like that," the ELF explained, the colors in his body racing up and down exquisitely.

"Remember when you went on the Internet and looked at all the pictures of *The Rocky Horror Picture Show*, and you found out later you 'just happened' to pick a scene that depicted Frankie and Anna's two favorite characters?"

"Yeah, that was cool. Did you do that?"

"We did that. You had already sent a strong request to me to help you make Frankie and Anna's engagement gift absolutely perfect for them. So when you had to choose a movie scene, the perfect one for them felt better to you than any of the others felt, and that's the one you chose to draw. Can you see how well this system works when you let it?"

"Hmm…that will make me a superhuman designer then, won't it? As long as I want the best results for my clients, I will always know instinctively what will please them. How cool is that?"

"Very cool, actually," the ELF said. "It's an almost foolproof system, and I'm glad I thought of it. Did Frankie tell you anything else about our conversation?"

"He said I should concentrate on having more fun. He thinks I'm too serious and I don't play enough."

"You don't play enough, that's true, Tony. You've always been serious, even about choosing your toys. And when you do indulge yourself with some expensive toy like that beautiful Steuben dolphin in your living room, you never really let yourself enjoy it. For example, you've always thought the Steuben piece cost too much. But you're allowed to have nice toys, Tony. Everyone is.

"It's time you got over that, you know," the ELF said a little sternly. "You can have all the things you want. You just have to learn to believe you can. Practice, Tony. Practice. Why don't you start by having fun at Frankie's wedding? There is huge opportunity at Disney World for having fun.

"By the way, Tony," the ELF added. "If you happen to get scared when Frankie goads you into riding on Space Mountain, just relax, close your eyes, and 'Go to ELF.' I'll be right there with you flying down the mountain, and I'll be feeling everything you feel. Let's surprise Frankie and have some real fun!"

With a wave and a chuckle, the ELF faded away.

The yarn Tony had chosen on Saturday while running errands with Frankie came from the new boucle family of yarns that creates its own organic patterns: a rich emerald-green for Frankie's Christmas stocking and a deep wine red called Merlot for Anna's.

On the coffee table in front of him were the sketches he had drawn of the finished stockings. When he completed the knitting, he would take the stockings to his friend, Joanie, to be blocked, lined, and finished. Anna's stocking would have a two-and-a-half-inch cream-colored cuff made of dupioni silk. A silver ring would be sewn into the corner, and eight tiny silver bells would cascade from the ring on strands of silver ribbon. Frankie's stocking, which was half again as big as Anna's, would have a three-inch bronze leather cuff with a brass ring and one brass bell tethered by a leather thong.

Remembering that his father had taught him always to tackle the biggest job first, Tony started with Frankie's stocking. "Always eat the big frog first, Tone," Luca had said. "Then all the other little frogs will go down a lot easier."

Because he was dividing his attention equally between his knitting and the basketball game on TV, Tony almost didn't hear the timid knock on his front door. He looked at his watch. It was almost nine o'clock.

Tony checked the peephole. To his surprise, Darth Vader's owner was standing in the hall looking as if she might bolt at any second.

"Hi," he said, opening the door.

She cleared her throat several times before speaking. "I'm really sorry," she almost whispered. "This was a mistake." Backing away, she turned and started walking rapidly back down the hallway toward her apartment.

"Wait," Tony said, hitting the deadbolt to block the door so it wouldn't slam shut behind him. "Hold up a minute." Overtaking her about halfway down the hallway, he gently took hold of her arm and turned her toward him. "I don't bite," he said good-naturedly. "At least not often. You must have wanted something. A cup of sugar? The key to the exercise room?"

"I just need someone to talk to," she barely squeaked, looking down at the floor.

Oh, Lord, thought Tony. Is she suicidal? Pregnant? Diseased? She was definitely upset about something.

He teetered between getting involved and not getting involved before he heard himself saying, "Well, we hardly know each other, do we? And it's probably time we did. How about if I offer you a neighborly cup of tea and you take a few minutes to decide if I might be someone you can talk to about whatever you need to talk about."

"That would be nice," she said softly, without further hesitancy accompanying him back to his apartment.

As they walked toward his place, Tony realized he'd never really looked at her before. He'd been so absorbed with his gigantic cat's ridiculous reaction to his neighbor's little dog that he'd somehow missed how cute his neighbor was. Her small curvy body moved nicely in the black silk slacks she wore with a plain but well-cut white silk blouse. Her shoulder length hair, an auburn that Clairol had never exactly managed to achieve, was brushed into a casual pageboy. From where he was standing he couldn't see her face, but he certainly planned to look more closely in the next few minutes.

"Just have a seat while I make us some tea," Tony called over his shoulder as he headed for the kitchen. He took a teapot out of a cupboard, found his tea ball, and filled it with a fragrant blend of jasmine green tea. He set the water to boil, scalded the pot under the hot water faucet, and put the tea ball in the pot. When the water boiled, he poured it into the pot, put the steeping pot on the tray, and added honey, spoons, mugs, and napkins.

Sorry, sweetheart, he thought as he carried the tray in and set it on the granite coffee table. I'm fresh out of anything to serve you with this tea.

Then he noticed the white box on his coffee table.

"What's this?" he asked, clicking off the TV at the same time he began his visual tour of her facial features.

Eyes? Sort of sea green. Nose? Turned up a bit and showing a delightful spray of freckles. Skin? Creamy. Lips? Full and pink. Put the face together with the hair, and she could have been a poster child for the country of Ireland.

She froze under his intense gaze, and then looked at the white box as if she didn't know what it was, either. "Oh, I brought these for you," she said, recovering quickly. "But I suppose we could share them with our tea."

Tony lifted the lid of the box, and the look and the aroma of warm, dark chocolate blasted his senses. Reaching inside, he removed a plate of the most delicious looking brownies he'd ever seen.

"Terrrrrrrific!" he said delightedly. "I'll just get us some plates and more napkins." Tony loped back to the kitchen for supplies.

Tasting the brownies, Tony mumbled, "Umm, umm, umm!" his mouth full of culinary mastery. "Where did you get these?"

"I made them. That's what I do for a living."

"You make brownies for a living?"

"Well, desserts. At least that's what I'd like to do. That's what I have to talk to someone about," she said, sighing, leaning back on the couch, and closing her eyes. "I have to choose between two ways to make a living, and I'm having a hard time doing that all by myself."

"Well, with only this much evidence, I would vote yes, you should make desserts for a living," Tony told her. "No question about it. But maybe you'd better tell me the whole story."

"Okay, I'll try. My name is Molly Malone, by the way."

"'Cockles and mussels, alive, alive-o,' Molly Malone?"

"Of course. I've never heard that line before, though," Molly said with a look of resignation, obviously aware of the unofficial anthem of Dublin City.

"Sorry, it just sort of slipped out. I'm Tony Celentano. You absolutely look like a Molly Malone, don't you?"

"And you absolutely look like a Tony Celentano," she answered, a bit of amusement making its way to her mouth. "I suppose we're just a pair or stereotypes, then, aren't we?"

"I suppose we are," Tony conceded. I really like this woman, he thought. "But that's just fine with me. So why don't you tell me your whole story, Molly Malone?"

CHAPTER NINE

Trying to decide how much she needed to share for him to help with her decision, Molly gave him a very brief autobiography.

"I'm an only child," she began. "My parents are Pat and Mike Malone, and no, I'm not putting you on. My father is Mike and my mother is Pat, and we've all heard all the Pat and Mike jokes that have ever been written.

"But in spite of the comic aspect of their names, my parents are very serious people. They own a jewelry store in Utica, New York, and their main purpose for living, since the day I was born, was to send me to college. They worked hard and played little, and they still do.

"And I didn't disappoint them, at least not until now," she said. "I went to the Adirondack College for Women and majored in history. Then I got my master's degree in library science at Columbia University in New York City. For about fifteen years, I was the head librarian at Columbia University library. I was content, I thought. I enjoyed helping students find what they needed to complete their research projects, and based on what I learned from the students about their needs, I helped increase the library's inventory of research material until it is now one of the finest college libraries in the country.

"Then about four years ago, my gran, my father's mother, came to visit from Ireland. I invited her to stay with me in my apartment in New York, and she fell in love with the city and with me. Except she decided I was too serious and was missing out on the best part of my life.

"'You should be married, darlin',' she would say." Molly quoted her grandmother in a quite respectable Irish brogue. "'And you should be havin' fun and laughter and sex. You can't tell me you're happy stuck in that library all the time. You have to do more than read about life; you're supposed to live it!'"

Molly shifted, turning more toward Tony and noticing for the first time that he was knitting. Gran would have loved that, she thought. Then she began to talk again.

"After listening to Gran talk like that for a few weeks, I began to wonder if she might have a point. So one morning while we were having breakfast, I asked her how I might begin doing something that would be more fun.

"'Well, if you gave up your need to please that dull-witted son of mine and his very boring wife, and if money was no object, what would you do every day?' she asked me.

"'Oh, that's easy,' I said without even giving it a thought. 'I'd bake.'"

"'Well, you're a good baker, that's for sure,' Gran said as she bit into a blueberry muffin I'd just taken out of the oven. 'Tell me more about it.'"

"'When I was a little girl,' I told her, 'I used to dream I was the Queen's baker. I wore a long, white apron and a high chef's hat, and I baked beautiful desserts for all the people who came to visit the Queen.'"

"'Well, you know, Molly, a little girl's dreams have a way of coming true,' she said. 'Just never let go of that dream.'"

"Gran went back to Ireland in the spring. She never went north from New York City to visit my parents while she was here, and they never came down to see her. I guess she only came to get to know me."

Molly's eyes filled with tears and she stopped talking. Tony just kept knitting, waiting patiently until she was ready to go on.

"A cousin from Ireland called me a few months later to tell me Gran had died. Apparently Gran knew she was dying even before she came to America. She told my cousin that she had wanted to see what kind of child her son had raised, and she was very pleased with me.

"Then a lawyer from Dublin called and said my grandmother had left me over half a million dollars and a small cottage in Ireland, to which, the will said, she hoped I would at least pay a visit. So I took a leave of absence from the University and went to Ireland. I stayed in the little cottage for about six months. It was charming, and the people who knew Gran were very kind to me. But life in Ireland didn't really call for me to stay, so I put the cottage on the market and it sold in just a week. As I was packing up, I found a letter my grandmother had left for me. It said, 'Now you can do your baking, Molly. Don't let anything stop you, darlin', because I know in my heart that you will wind up baking for ambassadors and kings.'

"I thought about her letter during the whole flight back to New York and I made a decision. I resigned from my job at the library and entered the CIA."

Tony almost dropped a stitch. "The CIA?"

"Yes," she said, "I just wanted to see if you were still listening. People have a way of tuning me out sometimes, or at least my parents did. The CIA," she went on, "is the Culinary Institute of America in Hyde Park, New York. And when I graduated from the CIA as a certified pastry chef, I went to Paris and studied for a year learning to make French pastries in Montmartre, leaving there with the designation of executive pastry chef.

"Then, simply because I like the feel of this city between the Gulf and the Bay, I chose St. Petersburg, and Darth Vader and I settled into the condo down the hall."

"I'm just curious," Tony said, "about why you named your dog

Darth Vader."

"He may be little, but he's brave," she answered. "The first dog we encountered together on the streets of New York was a Newfoundland, friendly but huge. Tucked safely in my arms, Darth made his stand. He bared his teeth and began to breathe deeply, in and out, as if preparing to give the Newfoundland a piece of his mind. He sounded to me just like Darth Vader sounds before he is about to speak, so that's what I called him."

"He scares the bejeebers out of my cat," Tony said with a smile.

"I didn't know you had a cat," Molly said, looking around the room to see if she had missed it.

"You probably never will," Tony said, laughing. "He goes into hiding at the sound of your voice, just in case Darth Vader is hiding in your skirts."

"I'm sorry," she said. "I won't come back if I make your cat uncomfortable."

Setting his knitting aside, Tony looked Molly square in the eye. "I have a feeling, Molly, that you are just as sweet as your brownies." And probably as delicious, he thought as his eyes slipped down to the neckline of her silk blouse and then back up again. "But as much as I love him, Trainwreck doesn't choose my friends for me."

"Trainwreck? Why did you name him that?"

"He had a rough life before he found me," Tony said, remembering that before he met the ELF, he'd been under the impression that he had found the cat. "At the time, he was pretty messed up, and he looked like he'd been run over by a train. He doesn't look quite that bad now, but he still has battle scars. But let's get back to your story, Molly," Tony said, picking up his knitting again. "So far, I'm not hearing any problem."

"Well, I'm getting to that part. I now have to choose between two careers, and I just keep going over and over the same things, trying to decide. I thought maybe if I talked to someone else, I'd get a different perspective and maybe I could work my way into a decision. It's just that I don't know anyone here yet to talk to, and my parents aren't going to be any help, because to them, it's a non-problem. I do have a best friend in New York I normally would have called, but she's taking a cruise with her new husband. So on an impulse, I thought maybe you would talk to me, or at least listen to me talk."

"How am I doing?"

"You're doing just fine, and the fact that you keep knitting helps, because you aren't staring at me."

"Tell me more."

"Okay, here's my dilemma. I've spent quite a bit of Gran's money already. Going to school at the Culinary Institute for two years, and then in Paris for a year was pricey, plus the travel and housing in Paris. Then I paid cash for my condo since it was so cheap compared to housing in New York, and then I had to move my furniture down here. So I have less than seventy-five thousand dollars left. I could start my own business with that, but it would be a risk.

"If I open up my own commercial bakery, it will take most of what I have to rent a facility, buy the ovens and freezers and other equipment I need, buy a delivery van, and figure out how to sell my products. You know, all the costs of setting up a business like that. Going into business for myself is certainly my first choice, but once my money is gone, the business would have to support me. If it should fail, I will be in real trouble.

"Or I could apply for a job with one of the college libraries here at USF, Eckerd, St. Petersburg, or Tampa University. My credentials and recommendations are good enough I have no doubt I could get hired. But I would still have to spend a lot of Gran's money on additional education because, although colleges will probably always have buildings with stacks of books in them, the reality is that now most research is done online. Good college libraries are going to have to put the material that supports their major areas of study on the Internet and make it accessible by any number of kinds of electronic devices. I know all about the research needs and a little bit about the technology, but I still have a huge learning curve left, and it will keep on growing, because technology is almost obsolete by the time you learn to use it.

"I keep going back and forth, and back and forth, and back and forth again between those two choices, and it's driving me just plain crazy. My parents, of course, would like to see me go back to the library, and if Gran were alive, I know she would rather see me open my own business. I just don't know which to do."

"You didn't mention working as a baker for someone else as an alternative, like a hotel or a country club, for example," Tony said.

"I investigated that, but the trend now is for those places not to hire their own pastry chefs. They can buy very good pastry and have it delivered, fresh or frozen, even contracting for some signature desserts that aren't sold anywhere else. If I opened my own commercial bakery, that's the kind of service I would provide, and hotels, country clubs, and caterers would be my primary customers."

"Let me see if I have this straight," Tony said, opening the cover of the ottoman and putting his knitting away for the night.

"One, you could get a job doing what you've always done and use the rest of your money to increase your technological skills so you stay current with the needs of the college that hires you," Tony said. "Or two, you could use the rest of your grandmother's money to open your own business, making desserts you would sell primarily to restaurants, clubs, hotels, and more. Right?"

"Right."

"What kinds of desserts, beside killer brownies, do you make?"

"Well, all the standards, of course: tiramisu, all the mousses, carrot cake, pecan pie, key lime pie, crème brûlée, chocolate soufflé. But I'd really like to offer specialty desserts with an Irish flair, desserts that I have created personally."

"Such as?"

"Molly Malone's Irish Cream Compote, Molly Malone's Apple

Guinness Tart, assorted Irish tea cakes, Bailey's Irish Cream Cheese Pie, Irish Whisky Pudding. I've got about thirty that I've tested and re-tested, and I think they are now just about perfect."

"Hmm… well, if you need another opinion about any of those, I'd like to help you in every way I can," Tony said, adding playfully, "I've even been known to work for food, especially that kind of food."

"I'll keep that in mind," she said, laughing. "Any other questions?"

"Yes. What do you want to do?"

"Well, if money was no object and I wasn't afraid my parents would kill me, I would open the baking business in a flash. Just the thought of baking all the time and having my desserts make people happy is just about the best work I think I could ever do."

Tony decided to change the subject for just a minute. "Do you believe there is guidance available to you when you need to make a decision like this, not only from people outside of you, but from somewhere inside of you, too?"

Molly chuckled. "That's a silly question, considering that I'm Irish. Of course, I believe in the fairies. They are essential to my baking. They tell me everything I need to know about quantities and temperatures, and sometimes even set me thinking about ingredients I know I never would have thought of on my own. But they don't seem to be any help in making this decision, even though I've asked them for help."

"Perhaps they can't get through to you, Molly," Tony said gently. "Of course, all I know about this situation is what you just told me, but it seems to me you have an intense fear of disappointing people, and so you've built yourself a 'box' that says you'll never consciously do that. Now you're in a bad place because whichever of these choices you make, you're going to disappoint either your parents or your grandmother. Pretend for just a minute that there is no one to please but yourself. Which choice would you make? Don't think about it, just give me your first answer."

"I would follow the advice in Gran's letter," Molly said simply, her eyes filling with tears again. "'Don't let anything stop you, lass, because I know in my heart you will wind up baking for ambassadors and kings.'"

"What would be the worst thing that could happen if you tried running your own business, used up your seventy-five thousand dollars, and failed?"

"Well, I suppose there isn't a 'worst thing' that could happen. I could still find work as a college librarian somewhere, and if I had to have money to go back to school first, I could always sell my condominium and rent something."

"And how does that make you feel?"

"Starting my own business feels great. A little scary, but great. Failing doesn't feel so good, but at least I would have had a good time trying."

"Good girl," Tony said. "Let's keep thinking along the lines that make you feel good. What would you call your commercial bakery, Molly?"

"Molly Malone's Irish…I don't know. Confections? Creations?"

"Why not keep it simple?" Tony suggested. "Molly Malone's Irish Desserts."

"I like that," Molly said, "and I think Gran would, too."

"And what kind of symbol would you use to show people the kind of desserts you make? Have you ever thought about that?"

"Something did happen to make me think about it a little just the other day," Molly said, frowning and causing little lines to form between her eyebrows. "And again, it involved Gran. She used to say my desserts were as light as a feather. A few nights ago I had a dream about a fairy with a feather in her hand. But I'm always dreaming about crazy things like that."

"That's not crazy, Molly, it's wonderful. That vision could become what we call in the advertising business your 'brand.' If the name you choose is Molly Malone's Irish Desserts, the icon that went with the name could be a fairy with a feather. The words under the picture might say 'Irish desserts as light as a feather.'"

"I can almost see it," Molly said, her green eyes shining. "What do you know about such things?"

"That's what I do, Molly. I do advertising and promotions." He reached for his wallet and handed her his business card.

"E.L.F. Promotions. I suppose that means the fairies brought me to your door for help, then?"

"I suppose it does. I think I can help you find your first customers, Molly, if you would like me to help you get started."

"Well, I can bake in my kitchen here long enough to serve a few customers, but then I'll need a commercial kitchen and some more customers. So any ideas you might have about those things would be helpful, too. Have you lived here very long, Tony? Do you know your way around St. Petersburg?"

"I've lived here all my life, and I can help you find the kind of location you want. But first, you have to decide what you want to do, Molly. You have to decide if you are ready to start up Molly Malone's Irish Desserts as a working business."

"Well, one thing Gran always said was, 'Never make a big decision without sleeping on it. Don't think about anything child. Just sleep. The fairies will tell you everything you need to know when you wake up.'"

Molly got up and went to stand at the window. The Tampa Bay side of the shore was pitch black, except for a narrow sliver of silver moonlight reflecting on the water, but the lights of the city twinkled. *It looks like something of a fairy land*, she thought.

"You know, Tony, I haven't been able to sleep well for weeks, and my dreams have been very troubled. But I have a feeling I can sleep now that you've shown me that I've been keeping myself locked in a mental box that wouldn't allow me to make a decision either way. I guess the reality of life is that no matter what I do, I'm never going to please everyone else, so it might be wise for me to concentrate first on pleasing myself. How did you get so smart?"

"I'm not so smart all on my own, Molly," Tony said as he walked with her toward the door. "A few weeks ago, I was in my own box, and it was hell in there. But I met a friend, of sorts, and he taught me about the way we all build mental boxes at one time or another—boxes that imprison us until we consciously wake up and destroy them. And he also taught me to listen, first and always, to the desires of my own heart.

"Sleep well, Molly, and I know you'll make the right choice. And if you decide to start your own business, I'll do everything I can to help you."

He was at least a foot taller than she, which made her five-one or five-two. A head above her, he could smell her shampoo-scented hair and another light fragrance she obviously had applied elsewhere. Down boy, he thought. Still, he bent over and planted a light goodnight kiss on top of her head.

"Good night," she said, now outside the door. Then she turned back and called out softly, "Good night, Trainwreck, wherever you are. I think you would like Darth Vader if you ever got to know him."

Then she was gone.

What a fascinating little person, Tony thought as he turned out the lights, put down an extra treat for Trainwreck, and went upstairs to see where his dreams would take him.

Tony was booting up his computer the next morning when the energy shifted around him rapidly. First, he heard a knock on the door downstairs, and then Trainwreck bounced on the desk and sailed high to his perch on the armoire for the second time in less than twenty-four hours.

Well, I guess I know who has come calling, Tony thought as he jogged down the stairs. The door wasn't open more than inches when he picked up the aroma of fresh, hot cinnamon buns. He threw the door open the rest of the way, relieved Molly of the plate of pastry she was holding, and breathed deeply.

"Whatever you want you can have," he said, "as long as I can keep these."

"You can, but I'd love to have one with you, if you've time. I've come on business. I want to hire you to design my 'brand,' I think you called it."

"Okay, but there's no reason we can't talk business and eat cinnamon buns at the same time, is there? Why don't you go out and enjoy the view from the balcony? And take these with you. I'll make us some coffee."

A few minutes later, settling down in the chair beside her with his mug of hot coffee, Tony said, "It's a good thing you made this decision, because I woke up this morning thinking about fairies and feathers, and I was just booting up my computer to see what I could find."

"I'm going to do it, Tony," Molly said excitedly. "I had a dream last night that cinched it for me. My parents were sitting on one side of a table and their mouths were covered in duct tape. Gran sat on the other side, the roll of duct tape in her hand, grinning at me from ear to ear. I know what I have to do."

"I do have some ideas that may help you start your business more easily and less expensively than you think, but I don't want to tell you about them yet, because I have to check out a few things first," Tony said. "So here's what I'm going to suggest now. You spend today listing your product line. Write out as clear a description as you can of each dessert you plan to offer. Later, you'll probably have to make some samples we can take pictures of, but for now, the descriptions will do.

"And from your whole list, it would help me if you could select three that you think will be your best sellers. I'm going to make some calls this morning, go see a few people, and then I'll work up some logos for you to look at."

“How much will all this cost, Tony?”

“Some of it won’t cost anything, because if what I have in mind works out, I’ll just be introducing you to some people who can help you. For the artwork and the printing, though, I’ll work up an estimate. Give me your phone number, and I’ll call you around five o’clock. I may have something for you to look at by then.”

They talked a little longer, and she educated him about the kinds of desserts most popular in restaurants at the moment. He had never considered that desserts had trends, but he learned much about the dessert business in just a few minutes. He listened with great interest as she explained that today’s diners require their desserts to be lighter in texture and lower in calories than in the past, but desserts still had to have a certain “sin” factor to be tempting to most fine diners.

Now, that’s the kind of insider information that makes the advertising business really fun, Tony thought.

After about fifteen minutes, Molly reached for her purse and took out a little notebook. Writing down both her home number and her cell phone number, she tore the note out of the book and handed the paper to Tony. He put it in his pocket, picked up the plate that had held the cinnamon buns, ran a finger around the edge to gather the last bit of frosting, and licked the frosting off his finger.

“You surely are an appreciative food tester,” Molly said, laughing.

“Keep feeding me stuff like this and I may just become your love slave.”

She blushed, he noticed with amusement. *Better keep this strictly business, Tony, old boy*, he thought. *She’s way too innocent for you.*

“I’ll call you around five o’clock,” he reminded her.

“I’ll be ready,” she answered as she walked back down the hall, already forming in her mind the list Tony had requested.

After downloading several fairy drawings from the Internet for inspiration, Tony sat down at his drawing board and began to sketch his own fairy. He was both surprised and delighted when his sketch began to take on a life of its own. When he finished, he realized his little fairy looked remarkably like Molly, complete with wings, a feather, and a saucy expression on her face.

"Cool," he said, pronouncing his own creation good.

He carried the sketch to the scanner, transferred it to his computer, and began to illustrate the drawing. Then he selected a font he liked, played with the positioning of the text and the fairy until he was satisfied, and printed out a proof. *If Molly likes this as much as I like it,* Tony thought, *I'll do some finishing work on the fairy later.* His idea was to suggest that her cards be printed in green on a buff colored matte finish stock with a bit of silver embossing on the wings and the feather to give it a little flash. *I wonder if she would go for the idea of putting an Irish blessing on the back? It could give people a reason to hold onto her card longer.*

Tony consulted the Internet for some appropriate Irish blessings and printed off a few choices. Cutting a sample card to size to show to Molly later, he tucked it into his shirt pocket. Then he reached into his out-basket for the folder holding the postcards he had worked on for Clive, and headed to the Fillmore Café.

Without betraying any confidences, Tony told Sam and Mary about his new client, Molly Malone's Irish Desserts.

"She's a trained pastry chef and she's new in town," he explained. "She's going to have to rent a place and install a kitchen where she can do her baking. I thought I'd ask you what you might think of saving her some of that trouble. You close here at seven at night and don't open again until seven in the morning. I was wondering if she could rent your kitchen from eight at night to six in the morning. She might have to install a refrigerator and a freezer, and maybe build a counter in the back to roll pastry and hold her mixers, but that would be at her expense. You've got plenty of room for it. The only thing of yours she would use, besides the building, would be your ovens.

"She's neat as a little pin and very professional," he added, "so

I know she would be respectful of your space. The rent she would pay would help you, and working here would be less expensive for her than renting a whole building."

"And," said Mary, "maybe if her stuff is good, we could just buy our desserts from her. I could stop having to bake all those pies, which takes three hours a day and makes my back hurt."

"You'd be okay with that, Mary?" Sam asked. "The kitchen is entirely your territory, so whatever you think goes."

"More than okay," Mary said, "if she's all Tony says she is. As long as she doesn't create any more work for me and saves me from baking pies, having her work here at night would be like having three hours off a day and getting paid for it."

"Good pastries draw in good customers, especially the guys whose wives won't let them eat anything that tastes good at home anymore," Sam said, winking at Mary.

"How much rent would you want to charge, Sam?" Tony asked.

"Well, she'd pull some electricity baking all night, and there would probably be some extra insurance to run the place twenty-four hours, so I would have a few extra expenses. But otherwise, what she pays would be gravy. What do you think of six hundred and fifty dollars a month, Tony?"

"I'll ask her tonight, Sam. I think she'll jump at it. I'm going to see her around five o'clock. If she's interested, would it be okay if we came in at six so she could see the place? We'll eat here, and you can show her the kitchen after you close."

"You bet. If we can work a deal, she can start on the first of the month. And if she needs to install some equipment before that, I'll work with her."

"I like the fact that she's Irish," Mary said. "We should have a great St. Patrick's Day around here, that's for sure. Mary Casey's corned beef and cabbage and Molly Malone's Irish desserts. Who could possibly resist that, whether they're Irish or not?"

CONCEPT IV

Realizing . . .

You can choose to expect the unexpected

CHAPTER TEN

Satisfied that he was on the right track for Molly, Tony walked across the hotel lobby to Meanderings. For a moment, he thought the tiny shop was empty, but at his call, Clive emerged from a storeroom tucked behind a wall displaying walking sticks.

"Hey, Tony, old boy, I'm so pleased to see you," Clive said in his clipped English accent. "Got my postcard ready, have you?"

"I have, plus something else I thought you might like."

Opening the manila envelope he was carrying, Tony drew out a color proof of the postcard and handed it to him. "I've made sure it meets all postal requirements, Clive, and I also brought you the printer's estimate for either five hundred or a thousand postcards."

On the face of the card was the picture Tony had taken of Clive standing on a hiking trail in the middle of a beautiful wooded area at Boyd Hill Nature Park where a sun-dappled path wandered softly among the trees. Clive's hair just slightly windblown, his face wore a look of total contentment. Any outdoor lover receiving this postcard would be tempted to put a "Closed" sign on the door, take the rest of the day off, and join Clive on the trail.

In Clive's hand, exactly centered in the picture, was a handsome laminated birch walking staff with a leather strap. The caption at the bottom read, *Life just doesn't get much better than this!*

The opposite side of the card was divided down the middle.

The message on the left featured a close-up picture of the walking staff that showed off the carving and wood grain. Beside the picture were a verbal description; an invitation to visit Meanderings; its address and phone number; and this quotation: *The best thing about meandering is that you have time to admire Mother Nature's finest facial features.*

Clive was obviously touched. "I can't wait to send one of these to my mum in England," he said, uneasily clearing his throat. "She put up the money for my first year's rent on this place. I wasn't sure it would work, but it has. I sell mostly canes, of course—a good product for a retirement community—but my heart is in my staffs. Isn't that one a beauty?"

"It is, and you make a pretty impressive model, Clive. When I picked up the proof, even I thought about taking the day off and going hiking."

"Will you go walking with me one day, Tony? I fancy a good walk in the Ocala National Forest pretty soon. My God, it is beautiful up there, and the ground is a bit rolling, too. Flat-surface walking can get a little boring, and it isn't as good for you."

"I think I'd like that, Clive," Tony said, remembering what both Frankie and the ELF had said to him about loosening up and doing more fun things. "When will you be going again?"

"Well, December is the month most to my liking. It's starting to get cool and some of the trees are thinning out, so you can see more interesting things. Shall we plan a weekend meandering together next month, then?"

Tony checked the calendar on his iPhone. "I could leave around noon on the first Saturday in December, Clive. Is there someplace up there you like to stay overnight?"

Clive walked over to the calendar on his desk and made a note to go meandering with Tony the first weekend in December. "Yes, there's a wonderful little inn and pub just at the edge of the hiking trail. It reminds me a little of the pubs back home. I'll even see you to a game of darts on Saturday night if you like, Tony, but don't expect to win. The inn will pack us a nice lunch, too, for our Sunday walk in the woods."

"This is gonna be fun," Tony said, knowing that never in his life had he meandered, because he was always in a hurry to get from one place to another. Maybe it was time to get out of the box he had built for himself that said he must do something productive every minute. Even when he was relaxing, he was usually knitting or sketching.

"You're not going to get me lost in the woods up there, are you, Clive?" Tony asked, only half teasing. "I'm the quintessential city boy. I wasn't even a Boy Scout."

"Well," Clive said quite seriously, "I might get lost from time to time, but the wood sprites never do."

"Wood sprites?"

"Yes, my father taught me about them years ago. They're invisible, of course, but they travel with anyone who is in a woodsy place strange to him. I thought I would find them only in England, but I've discovered them here, too. If you have to choose between two paths in the woods, for example, and you don't know which one to take, the sprites will give you a sign if you ask them for help."

"What kind of sign?"

"Oh, one path will be dark and the other will have a sunbeam on it, or you will look down one path and see a patch of brightly colored flowers waiting for you to come investigate them. Once a butterfly brushed by and flew down one of the paths, almost beckoning me to follow it. The sprites are very clever, you know."

No, but I'm learning, Tony thought, somewhat amused. With Molly and her fairies, and Clive and his wood sprites, Tony really did need to have another talk with the ELF very soon.

"You say you've got something else in that envelope for me, Tony?" Clive asked, changing the subject.

"I do, Clive, and it's purely speculative. There's no obligation on your part to buy this. I just couldn't resist. I was in the hotel lobby talking to Mr. Ferguson about his hotel ad when I saw this really lovely woman picking up her mail. She was using a very unusual walking cane, and I asked her where she got it. She told me she bought it from you, and she was very grateful to you for finding her something that didn't make her feel dowdy when using it.

"So I asked her if she would mind having her picture taken with it, and she said no, she wouldn't mind a bit. She even offered to go upstairs and put on something that would look prettier in the picture than what she had on. When I took her picture, she signed a photo release saying you could use it to advertise in any way you want. But she asked me to tell you that she would really love to see what you do with it."

He handed Clive the second postcard. The picture of Jane Roberts was striking. An ageless woman, she could be sixty or eighty or anywhere in between. She was wearing a magenta-colored silk suit with silver buttons that played off her perfectly-coiffed, pewter-colored hair.

The cane, which again Tony had made the focal point of the picture, was made of clear, twisted Lucite strapped with silver threads and finished with a silver cuff placed where the handle began its curve. On the cuff, a large, braided, silver-banded crystal caught the light just enough to draw the eye to it. The cane looked like an elegant accessory to Jane's outfit, an accessory she had chosen just as carefully as she had chosen her shoes and handbag.

Standing gracefully framed by one of the arches of the elegant hotel lobby, Jane Roberts looked like a retired Powers model still in touch with her runway image.

"Oh, I must find a way to thank her for this," Clive said softly. "She came into my shop because her doctor told her she would have to use a cane all the time or risk serious injury. She was devastated, until I assured her that a beautiful cane is like an exquisite piece of jewelry, and if she chose it carefully, she would always feel good using it. I also told her she would discover that it would become a wonderful conversation starter.

"She's brought me some customers," he continued. "She even carries my business card with her because people are always asking her where she got her cane. And now it looks like she will bring me even more customers."

Motioning Tony over to a display case, he said, "Here are the other three models of those designer canes. They all have a Lucite base. But this one," Clive said, drawing it out of the case for Tony to see more closely, "is trimmed in bronze. It's similar in design to Jane Roberts' cane, but the jewel is made of sandstone rimmed in bronze."

Pointing inside the case, Clive added, "This next one is banded in black velvet, and on the cuff is an onyx stone rimmed in silver. And finally, here is this gold-beaded one. The jewel on the cuff is topaz. The canes are made in Italy. I'm retailing them for a hundred and ninety-nine dollars, which still gives me a pretty good mark-up, but I saw them advertised in a catalogue of a shop on Worth Avenue in Palm Beach for three hundred twenty-five dollars."

"They're unique, Clive. I think we should do a mailing in April, maybe a brochure picturing them all, to residential areas with homes valued at over a million dollars. They'd make the perfect gift for Mother's Day for those folks' mothers and mothers-in-law, wouldn't they?"

"Good idea," Clive said. "When I sell a few from this mailing, we can start working on that one."

Tony had finished the second postcard much like the first. The close-up picture of Jane's cane with a brief description beside it was featured on the message side with the name and address of Meanderings, and the message: *An exquisitely crafted accessory can swiftly transform your appearance from ordinary to extraordinary.*

"This picture, enlarged, would also make an eye-catching poster for your window, Clive, especially in time for Christmas," Tony suggested. "And you could present the other three canes next to it, maybe on a black velvet background. You might also ask Mr. Ferguson about putting up an easel in the lobby to hold a poster of either of these pictures."

"Do you think he would go for that, Tony? A lot of people go through this hotel lobby who probably don't know what I sell here."

"Why don't I ask him for you?"

"How much would a window picture and a couple of placards like that cost me, Tony?"

"I'll check with a couple of printers and work up an estimate for you, Clive, and I'll drop it off to you tomorrow. If you're ready to approve the proof for the hiking postcard, though, just initial this work order and I'll e-mail it to the printer later today."

Clive carried the work order to his desk and signed it, checking the box for a thousand postcards.

"I think I'd like to order a thousand of the Jane Roberts postcards, too, Tony. I have another mailing list of past customers I can send them to, also in time for Christmas. Same price as the other one?"

"Same price," Tony said, adding a thousand copies of the second postcard to the form Clive had just signed. "Just initial here, Clive, to indicate you have approved both proofs."

"Good, good. When will I have them to mail out, do you think?"

"I think probably by a week from today. That would be November 17," Tony answered, consulting his calendar again. "If there's any reason I can't do that, I'll let you know."

"As soon as I get them, Tony, I'll make sure Jane gets a generous supply to send to her friends and family. I am grateful to her and to you, too, of course. I'm so pleased to have met you, Tony," Clive said enthusiastically. "You've given me a bit of a new lease on life, you have. I'm really looking forward to our December meandering."

"I am, too, Clive. I guess I'll have to read up a little on the Ocala National Forest in the next few weeks, won't I?"

"If you like," Clive said, "or you can just relax and meander along with me to see what we can see."

"Hmm. What a novel idea," Tony said, chuckling.

Mr. Ferguson was behind the desk when Tony walked into the hotel lobby, so it was a perfect time to ask about putting up an easel and a poster in the lobby for Clive.

"You know, I think that's a great idea, Tony. I'd like to provide the easel, though, to be sure it complements the décor. Perhaps I should buy two easels and feature a poster for the café, too," Mr. Ferguson reasoned.

Immediately envisioning a color picture of one of Molly Malone's Irish Desserts on an easel in the lobby, Tony answered, "I think Sam might really go for that idea. He's thinking about adding a few new items to his menu next month, and I'm pretty sure he'd like to promote them that way. I'll be seeing him again later today, and I'll ask him if he wants me to make a poster for him like the one I'll be making for Clive.

"I'm also going to price a large, window-sized poster for Clive to attract customers from the street, especially for Christmas shopping. Is that something you might like to have for the front window of the hotel, too?" Tony asked.

"Perhaps," Ferguson considered, "maybe something we could put some tasteful Christmas decorations around. Why don't you give me a price and maybe sketch out what you think the window might look like? By the way, the ad you created for us will start in the art museum magazine in December, and I've decided to keep it running through January as well."

Driving away from the Fillmore, Tony was amazed at how good he felt. "I love it when my clients are so pleased with what I do,"

he said to the ELF. "I could hardly drag a compliment out of my boss at the agency, but so far, E.L.F. Promotions has only satisfied clients—all four of them."

Actually, he had six customers now that he had taken on Molly Malone's Irish Desserts, but he had put Frankie on hold as a client since he was a little distracted by his wedding and honeymoon plans.

Tony eased his car into a visitor's space in the Yacht Club parking lot and walked into the lobby. After flirting for a few minutes with the receptionist, he asked if the top chef was around. The receptionist made a call, and soon Amelia, the pretty executive chef, came down the stairs.

"Did you drop by just to admire me again, Tony," she asked with a saucy smile, "or to book a party for some big client of yours?"

"Admiring you is a given," Tony said, kissing her lightly on the cheek. "But the other thing I want is to pick your brain a little bit."

"You're welcome to all the brain I've got. Let's go sit over there." She led him to a circle of armed chairs around an appealing glass-topped coffee table at the far end of the lobby.

Tony hadn't seen Amelia since he used to book big client parties for ADPRO, so as briefly as he could, he brought her up to date on his life and career.

"So, now you're in business for yourself, Tony. How are you liking it?"

"Very much, so far. I have some very interesting clients, and I came to talk to you about one of them. I want to help her, but I need to know something about how business is done from your end, in the kitchens of good hotels and private clubs. I know if I want the best information, I'm wise to ask someone with the best experience."

"Flattery will get you everywhere, Tony. How can I help you?"

For the next few minutes, he filled in Amelia about Molly, her professional background, and her dream. Then, because Molly was so new to St. Petersburg, he asked Amelia if Molly was correct in assuming that big clubs, hotels, and fine restaurants in the area used suppliers like her for their desserts.

"She's right on, Tony. It used to be that our members came here to eat rich and heavy meals ending with a big dessert, a brandy, and sometimes the men liked to end with a good cigar. But times and tastes change. Cigars are bad for you, and you can't smoke them in the restaurant, anyway. Good brandy is very expensive. And a growing number of people think sugar is their enemy, so they don't eat it anymore, at least in public.

"Clubs like ours can't afford to keep our own pastry chef on staff because there isn't enough business to support one, but there is still enough interest in dessert for us to have a dessert cart and a dessert menu. The best answer for us is to buy our desserts, usually frozen, from a supplier just like Molly on an as-needed basis, and then add our own personal touch to the presentation.

"Really good commercial bakers who do something that isn't pedestrian are very hard to find, Tony. I'd be interested in sampling what she has to offer, especially if it isn't same old, same old. Something new always tends to tempt the otherwise un-temptable."

Reaching into her pocket, she drew out her business card. "Ask her to call me, please," she said, handing the card to Tony. "Molly Malone's Irish Desserts. Ever try any of them, Tony?"

"I've known her less than twenty-four hours, Amelia, so I haven't tasted any of her Irish desserts yet. But I tasted her brownies last night and her cinnamon buns this morning, and either one would make you want to make sure nothing bad ever happens to her."

"Be careful, my handsome friend," Amelia said, laughing. "The look in your eye when you describe her food is lecherous. Some things don't change, Tony. The best way to a man's heart is still by way of his stomach."

"Nah, I'm waiting for you to be available again, Amelia. You married that guy when I wasn't looking, but one day, you will be mine. And until then," he added, holding up her business card, "thanks for this! A possible appointment with you will really impress this new client."

"If she's good, I'll wind up the winner, or the Yacht Club's members will," Amelia said, allowing Tony to kiss her hand in a grand departing gesture. "I want to taste Molly Malone's Irish Cream Compote. Soon."

When he got home, Tony set his alarm clock for four-thirty and stretched out on the couch with Trainwreck curled up beside him. Before buying this couch, he had given it a trial run in the store, insisting that any couch he bought had to be a good napping couch. Napping had saved his father's sanity for years, and it worked for Tony, too, when he felt he was overloaded.

Fortunately, an hour's nap on that couch with a breeze wafting in off the bay through the open glass doors was as good as a full night's sleep to Tony, so when he called Molly at five o'clock, he was ready for an interesting evening.

They walked across the park together, enjoying the cool November weather and the local scenery. When they got to the Fillmore Cáfe, some of the ladies from the hotel were still gathered around a few tables.

Molly was intrigued, of course, that there were only three items on the menu, so Tony explained. "It's what Sam and his wife Mary can manage. With his built-in clientele here, the limited menu allows him to keep his doors open for them, and for any of the public that happen in, too. I've talked him into adding three specialty salads and a soup of the day at the lunch hour for the working people in the area, and he says they're going over really well. I'm putting together a small menu to be put out on the tables during lunch hour featuring just those items.

"Look at it this way, Molly. This three-entrée-only menu gives us all an opportunity to break out of another one of our boxes," Tony added. "Where is it written, except in our minds, that there must be more than three items on a restaurant menu for a restaurant to be successful?"

"Nowhere I can think of," she said amiably. "I think I'll live dangerously and order the meatloaf with mashed potatoes and gravy. I'm usually pretty much a salad person, but it isn't every day I go into business for myself."

"Or inaugurate your own brand," he said as he reached into his shirt pocket and handed her the business card mock-up he had created that morning for Molly Malone's Irish Desserts.

When she burst into tears, he watched in confusion. He never knew what to say when a woman cried, because he could never tell whether it was a good thing or a bad thing. But before he had to guess, she beamed at him through her tears.

"The fairy!" she whispered. "She looks like me! Oh, she's wonderful! I love it, I love it, I love it! When can I have more?"

"Probably in about five days. If you really like it, I'll do some finishing work on the fairy tonight and then send the file to the printer, and I'll ask them to send me a time estimate for it to be finished. It might be while I'm away at the end of the week, but I can have them delivered directly to you."

They talked for a few more minutes about the paper stock, the ink color, and the Irish blessing. Then when their plates had been cleared and their coffee poured, Tony said, "I have a couple of other interesting things to tell you, Molly."

First, he explained that he had talked with Sam and Mary about Molly possibly using this restaurant's kitchen at night for the first year until she got her business rolling. She could see if that idea interested her as soon as they finished their dinner. Then he told her about his conversation with Amelia at the Yacht Club and gave her Amelia's card.

"She said for you to call her as soon as possible," he said. "She'd like to see samples of some of your desserts. Is that normal?"

"Normal and reasonable," Molly answered. "It's called a

tasting. In another realm, it might be called an audition. What kind of clientele does the Yacht Club serve?"

"Rich," he said. "All ages and sizes, but all rich."

"How do you know Amelia?"

"One of my jobs for ADPRO—that's the ad agency I used to work for—was booking big client parties. Sometimes the agency hosted and sometimes the client hosted, but I usually worked out the details with the club manager, the liquor manager, and Amelia. She's terrific to work with."

"I wonder what she doesn't like about the supplier she has now?"

"She said something about being tired of same old, same old. That's why the Irish angle got her attention. She said people will order dessert if it's interesting enough, even when it's against their better judgment."

"Well, I certainly am excited to even have a chance at this account," Molly said, beaming. "The best way to build a commercial baking business is by references from your clients and by the reputation of the venues you serve. It sounds to me, my friend, as if you've arranged for me to have a chance to start at the top. Needless to say, I'm grateful. But I can't do much of a tasting without a place to work. Everyone else seems to be gone," she said, turning to survey all corners of the restaurant. "Do you think I can see the kitchen now?"

Tony tapped on the kitchen door and Sam opened it immediately. Tony introduced Molly, and right away, Mary took Molly by the arm to give her the grand tour.

"Mary's pretty excited about this idea, Tony," Sam said in a whisper. "I've been so preoccupied with keeping the bills paid I guess I haven't really noticed how tired she's been getting. She's really hoping this will work and that she may get some relief from pie-baking every day. If there's any way you can help me not blow this, pal, just do it."

Tony had never been all the way into the Fillmore Café's kitchen before, and he was surprised to see that Mary was using only about half the kitchen space. The entire back half of the quite large room was completely empty.

"I've been thinking since Tony talked to us earlier," Mary explained to Molly, "that maybe you wouldn't have to work nights if you could manage to set up your work space in the other half of this kitchen. I only use the front, and much of this space has gone to waste for almost ten years now. If you're willing to put in your own appliances, you could literally create a whole second kitchen in here just for your baking. And you could have access to it day or night."

In her mind, Molly was already designing her baking kitchen. She would want to measure, of course, but there would be room along the back wall for at least three ovens, two of which could be stacked, and one that would be part of a commercial-size range. A microwave could go above the range, and two refrigerators and two freezers could go at the other end. Between the refrigerators and the range, she could have a counter built to her height specifications on which she could comfortably mix and roll pastry. *If this is going to be my dream kitchen*, she thought, *I'm going to design it to work for me!* Along the side wall was room for plenty of pantry shelves, and in the center was room for an island with a sink and a dishwasher. It was perfect, except that she would need space to pack her orders for delivery.

"Is there another small room of any kind nearby?" she asked.

"Yeah, through here is a second storeroom," Sam said. He gestured for her to follow him through a door she hadn't even noticed. "We only use the front storeroom. This one is empty."

She walked just a few feet to a room about twelve by fourteen feet, which had both a window and a door.

"Where does that door go, do you know?" Molly asked Sam.

"Out to the alley. There's a door just like it in the room we use."

"And I could use this room, too?"

"If you need it," Sam said. "We have no plans for it."

"Can I look out in the alley?"

"Sure." Sam reached into his pocket for the key and unlocked the door. The alley was clean and wide enough for two cars to pass. Two enormous trashcans sat beside the door, and there was even a designated parking space.

"Anyone using that space?" she asked.

"No, not now," Sam said. "Norma, our waitress, walks to work, and Mary and I come to work and leave together in the same car. We park farther down the alley near the street. Our customers, those who drive, park on the street."

"Can I rent the parking space, too?"

"I guess there's no reason not to," Sam said, glancing at Mary for approval.

"Okay, let's just be sure I understand this perfectly," Molly said in her orderly, librarian-type manner. "You'll sublet me the back of your kitchen, from here to here," she indicated as she walked the space, "plus the storeroom and the designated parking space, for some mutually agreed-upon price, still undecided, from December 1 of this year until December 31 of next year. I'll be free, at my own expense, to install all of the appliances and add the built-ins I'll need, as long as I pay for them and they meet all the health department standards.

"I will have unlimited use of the storeroom, the back entrance, and the nearest parking space in the alley. And I can have access to my workspace day and night, as long as I don't get in your way when the restaurant is open."

Sam again looked to Mary for confirmation. Seeing her nod, he said, "That's a little more than Tony and I discussed, but we can live with that if you need it."

"What if I get so busy I have to hire a helper?"

"As long as your operation doesn't interfere with ours, no problem. Right, Mary?"

Mary nodded.

"Well, guys, I'm not a very good poker player," Molly said, "so I'm going to tell you right up front that I couldn't have found a more ideal setup for Molly Malone's Irish Desserts if I'd looked for six months. So all we have left to talk about is price."

Looking at Tony and hoping for understanding, Sam said, "How's six-fifty a month?"

Molly was incredulous. "Six hundred and fifty dollars?"

Oh, no, I've just blown the deal! "Well, I thought it would be worth that to you," Sam said, a little shaken.

At his stricken expression, Molly burst out laughing. "Sam, six hundred and fifty dollars for a space like this, right in the heart of the city, is way too little. I've been reading the ads, and I couldn't rent a totally empty space for under eight-fifty, and that's with no utilities included. I wouldn't even think of renting it for less than a thousand dollars a month, and even then, I might be taking advantage of your good nature."

From somewhere deep inside his chest, Sam emitted a long sigh."A grand a month would help us out a whole lot," he said, obviously relieved.

"You're sure it's all right with your landlord to sublet the space?" Molly asked before getting too much more excited.

"I talked to him this afternoon about it. He said as long as the room was being used for the same purpose I am renting it for, which in this case would be cooking food for sale, the management company would have no objection."

"Then we have a deal. I'll give you two months' rent right now, first and last. I will need to shop for the appliances right away and arrange to have them delivered and installed. I'll be here, of course, when all of that is happening. And I think—" she paused, looking up at the ceiling—"I think we can hang some heavy sheets of plastic from floor to ceiling to make sure the dust from the construction doesn't get in Mary's way or upset the health department. I'd like to try to get all this done in the next two weeks so I can officially open on December 1, if that works for you."

"That all sounds just fine, Molly," Mary said, somewhat relieved that Molly seemed to know exactly what she was doing and how to go about doing it. "Did Tony ask you about making the desserts for the Fillmore Café, too?"

"No," Molly said, looking at Tony, who simply shrugged his shoulders. "I guess he didn't have a chance. What kind of desserts did you have in mind?"

"I've been baking about ten fruit or custard or meringue pies a day for more years than I want to remember," Mary said, "and I'm really tired of it. I'd like to find another way to provide fresh-made desserts for our customers without having to work so hard."

"Well, I can make you three different kinds of pies every day," Molly said. "Why don't you get together an estimate of how much you're spending to make your desserts now, and I'll see if I can match it or come close. Will that work?"

"I sure hope so," Mary said. "I'll feel like I've been let out of jail if it does."

Molly perched on a stool beside one of the kitchen counters and took out her checkbook. "How would you like this check made out, Sam? To you personally, or to the Fillmore Café? Or do you have a different corporate name?"

"We're S & M, Inc.," Sam said, looking a little embarrassed. "Mary and I thought that corporate name would give the folks in the county licensing office a little laugh. Please make the check that way, if you don't mind."

Molly handed him a check for $2,000, with a notation that it was for the first month and last month's rent.

"I'll have my attorney draw up a sublease to S & M, Inc. for that same time period and bring it by for you to sign tomorrow at about this same time," Molly told them. "And if the fairies cooperate, I may know something by then about when some of the appliances might be delivered, too."

"Oh, my," Molly added, realizing she was a little breathless. "I've got so much to think about I can hardly contain it all."

CHAPTER ELEVEN

Still filled with energy after her conversation with Sam and Mary, Molly wasn't quite ready to go home and be alone. "Could we go for a little walk, Tony? Do you have time?"

He looked across the street at a newly opened gourmet coffee shop. "How about if we get a couple of lattes and go sit on a bench by the pier for a little while? The lights on the water always settle me down when I'm too wired to sleep."

"I'd like that. Even though Darth Vader is very tolerant of my many moods, which are usually pretty low key, I'm not sure he could handle my current energy level. I need a few more minutes to come down off cloud nine, or whatever number cloud I'm on."

They got their coffee, and then walked until they reached a black cast iron bench on the walkway to the Pier. Seated there facing the water, they could see the lights twinkling down on the bay from the condominium buildings around Vinoy Park, including their own building, those along the shoreline of Snell Isle, and even some from across the bay in Tampa.

"Beautiful, isn't it?" Molly said with a deep sigh. "I've never regretted buying my home in St. Petersburg. I've felt like I belong here, right from the beginning."

"It's the only place I've ever lived, and I'm perfectly happy here."

"I'm finding it a little hard to believe it's been less than twenty-four hours since I knocked on your door last night. I feel like Alice in Wonderland must have felt when she said, 'Things sure do happen fast around here.' But I've been waiting for things to start happening since I moved here, and now all I have to do, I guess, is keep up with them."

"Why did you need the extra storage room?" Tony asked. "There's plenty of room for shelving or cabinets in the main kitchen."

"For packing," she explained. "The desserts have to be transported from the place where they're made to the place where they'll be served. They will be packed in individual boxes and then stacked on trays that lock in place inside the delivery van. That's why having a designated parking space for a van right outside the door was such an unexpected blessing.

"Once the customers receive the boxed desserts, they store them in their freezers for defrosting as needed. Each restaurant or club then dresses the desserts for presentation and serves them on their own china or glassware. Sometimes I provide the garnishes, but generally, they provide their own special touches. I think, though, that I'll make some little marzipan shamrocks that some of the more expensive venues may want to use to enhance the Irish dessert theme."

"You sound pretty confident about it."

"I've been visualizing all of this in one stage or another for a very long time—several years, in fact. When I was in school in France, I used to imagine myself negotiating big contracts with hotel chains and having commercial bakeries operating in cities all over the world. But that's not what I want any more. I want to have my own small business that offers my Irish desserts, which I will create for my own pleasure and, in turn, for the pleasure of those who pay to eat them."

"Pretty good goal, Molly Malone," Tony said, patting her hand and then holding it in his. "I've no doubt you will make it."

"Did you spend time dreaming about owning your own agency

before you started it?"

"Not consciously, certainly. I thought I wanted to work only on national accounts for a big-name agency, and I had a hard time releasing that idea, actually. But now, I'm equally sure that for me to really love what I do and feel fully satisfied, I have to create advertising and promotions for my own pleasure, and in a way that genuinely benefits my clients. I think you and I have arrived at pretty much the same conclusions about the way we want to work, Molly."

"How big do you want your agency to grow, Tony? Will you have people working for you? Will you move your business out of your apartment?"

"Funny you should ask that, because those are the questions I've been asking myself today. I probably won't want or need to have anyone work for me for a while, unless it becomes necessary to maintain the quality of my work. But I will need more space, even to service just the accounts I have now. I looked at some space today that really appealed to me. It's just one office down from Meanderings."

"Where is Meanderings?"

"Oh, I forgot. You haven't had a tour of the Fillmore Hotel yet, have you? Along one side of the building, there are stores and businesses that can be entered from either the hotel lobby or the street. One of those stores is called Meanderings. It belongs to Clive Mason, a really charming Englishman. I know that's a funny word for one guy to use to describe another, but nothing else fits. Meanderings sells canes and walking staffs that are practically works of art."

"Oh, yes, I'm very familiar with walking staffs," Molly said. "Walking staffs can be either crude or elegant, but either way, they are works of art. Almost every man in Ireland uses one on his daily wanderings, and some women use them, too. I always thought I'd like to have one in my home just for decoration. My Gran did. Of course, it may have belonged to her husband or her father. People in Ireland never dispose of anything. Anyway, I liked it. Maybe I'll buy one from Clive."

"I hadn't thought of using one that way. I'm going meandering with Clive in the Ocala National Forest next month. I think I'll buy a staff for that trip, and then stand it in my office just to look at. It will probably make a good conversation starter, too."

"Oh, your office, Tony. You were saying you looked at office space today?"

"I did. A nice space. Plenty of room for a desk area for me and another room for all of my design equipment. There would be room in front, too, for a seating arrangement where I could have client meetings and give presentations. The rent is a thousand dollars a month, which is reasonable for the space. But I don't know whether I'm quite ready to commit to a lease yet.

"So," he continued, "I've decided to just let it rest until I get back from my friend Frankie's wedding, and then I'll decide whether to take that leap now or later. I still plan to keep a full office at home, though. I sometimes get my best ideas in the middle of the night."

"Tell me about it. Molly Malone's Irish Cream Compote became a culinary reality at about three o'clock one morning when I couldn't sleep. When and where is your friend getting married?"

"This coming weekend in Orlando. That's why I'll be asking the printer to deliver your cards to you at the Fillmore Café while I'm gone."

Tony watched with some amusement as she stretched and yawned like a tired but contented cat. "I suspect you'll sleep well enough now," he commented. "I think I'd better walk you home. You'll have a busy day tomorrow."

They got off the elevator and paused in front of the door to her condo. To his surprise, she rose up on her toes and kissed him squarely on the lips. "I don't know how to thank you, Tony. I'm too tired to think about how to do it properly right now, but I will. This has been, hands down, the very best day of my life."

Then she opened the door of her apartment, gathered an enthusiastic Darth Vader into her arms, and literally danced with him into her own living room.

Tony heard his phone ringing as he put his key in the door. Rushing to answer it, he took a few very tricky leaps over Trainwreck, who had innocently ambled out to greet him at the front door. Tony grabbed the phone before he could even catch his breath.

"Yo, Tony, you there?"

"Yeah, Dad, I'm here," Tony gasped. "I was just coming in the door when I heard the phone ringing and I almost fell over my cat. You okay, Dad?"

"Yeah, yeah. I'm fine. I know we just talked last week, but I couldn't wait to tell you my news now that I know it's true. Your Uncle Fred and I won the New York State Lottery."

"You won the lottery?" Tony sank down onto a stool in front of the kitchen counter.

"Well, not the whole big lottery, but we won two hundred and fifty thousand dollars."

"Two hundred and fifty thousand dollars?"

"I know. I was speechless, too, when we checked the numbers on Saturday, and I didn't want to call you until we actually got our check. Of course, Uncle Sam got his money before your Uncle Fred and I got ours, but still, the check is for a hundred and seventy-five thousand. That ain't chump change, huh?"

"No, Dad, it's not. Gosh, that's just great! I'm really happy for you. So you and Uncle Fred must be really excited. You guys got big plans for all that money?"

"Yeah, we have, and that's why I'm calling, Tone. We decided to fix up our kitchen. I called the decorator who did the living room for us last year, and she gave me an estimate of the cost for the remodel.

Then Fred and I decided to divide the rest of the money and share some of it with our kids. So I just put a check in the mail to you for thirty-six thousand dollars, Tony, and I wanted to let you know right away so you could be watching for it."

"What? You just sent me thirty-six thousand dollars?"

"Yeah. I figured just starting your own business, you would need new equipment. I don't know how much that stuff costs, but I hope this is going to help, Tony."

"It more than helps, Dad. It makes a huge difference. I just looked at a place today to rent for my office. It has everything I need and then some, but I was trying to decide whether to take it so soon after starting the agency. I guess I can do it now, without worrying about how I'm going to make the rent every month for the first year. The timing is just perfect."

"You don't like working at home anymore, Tony?"

"Oh, I do Dad, and I won't do anything to change my office here. I want to still be able to roll out of bed if I get an idea in the middle of the night and go right at it. But I need a place to meet clients that looks nice and is more professional, and I also need space for computers, printers, filing cabinets—stuff like that."

Then pausing to swallow the lump that suddenly came up in his throat, Tony went on in an unsteady voice. "You know, Dad, you already gave me twenty grand when I left home, and that was a heck of a gift. I don't really know how to say thanks for thirty-six thousand more. I just want you to know it's a really big and important gift coming right now."

"Wait, Tony, you never need to thank me. You were about the best kid a father could have ever had, and in the worst of circumstances. I don't think I could have handled your mother if you had been the kind of kid like a lot of them, either getting into trouble or making it. You helped me get through my life, day after day, for years. And you started to do it before you were really old enough to know how. It makes me really glad to be able to help you now.

"So," Luca went on, struggling to control the lump in his own throat, "maybe before we get too sappy with each other, we should just say thanks to the New York State Lottery."

"Well, yeah, thanks to them, too," Tony said with a shaky laugh.

"Have a good night's sleep, son, and then go rent your new office tomorrow. Honest, the check really is in the mail."

"Good night, Dad. I'll call you again when I get back from Frankie's wedding."

"Yeah, that'll be good. Have a good time, and give my second son a hug from me. Tell him I'm looking forward to meeting his Anna when I get down there in January. I sent him a check, too, by the way, so they can pick out something they want together."

"You're the best, Dad. Give my love to my rich uncle, too. Good night."

Tony sat stock still. *Unexpected income,* he thought. *Big time. And now I really have to find out how and why that works.*

About a month earlier, Tony had read an article in Financial Growth about what to do with unexpected income. The title of the article amused him at the time because he didn't have a job, so any income was unexpected. The gist of the article was that if and when unexpected income showed up in the form of gifts, found money, won money, rebates, old debts repaid that had long been written off, stock dividends, or any other similar channel, instead of wasting it or blowing it off on impulse, it would be wiser to put it into an "unexpected income" account and let the balance build until enough money accumulated to invest or buy something important.

For some reason, the message in that article continued to play around in the back of Tony's mind. One day, while at the bank across from the Fillmore Café coaxing the bank manager to let him put a couple of Sam's new menus in the employee break room, Tony had decided to open an account with $300 of unexpected income he had won in a poker game.

Every now and then, he and Frankie and a couple of other friends played poker at Frankie's house. Tony, who found poker just slightly boring, often lost his concentration and therefore also lost his money. Frankie had been taunting Tony about his perpetual poker losses the last couple of times they played, so for two or three weekends, Tony watched professional poker on television to sec what he could learn from the experts. He tried out some of the tricks he picked up on TV, and to his surprise, not to mention Frankie's, he won $300.

Opening the account with the winnings, Tony in a bold gesture announced to the pretty teller, "There. Now I'm ready to receive plenty more unexpected income!" After that, he forgot all about it. But a week or so later, just as the magazine article had suggested might happen, he got a check in the mail for $150 from a guy he used to work with at the ad agency. Tony didn't remember loaning the money, but the guy said that Tony had, and that he was sorry to have taken so long to repay it.

The next time Tony was in the bank taking an informal survey to see how many employees might order from the Fillmore Café if take-out were available at lunch time, he deposited the check in his unexpected income account. Looking at his new balance of $450, he again made the statement to no one in particular, "I'm ready any time for more unexpected income."

Now this huge check was coming to him from his father. It couldn't possibly have been more unexpected, so Tony decided to "Go to ELF!" to see what was going on.

"I need to talk to you, ELF," Tony said out loud. "I've got some big questions and I really need some answers."

A little light began to flicker on the counter next to the phone, and in just a few seconds, there sat the ELF.

"I have to know," Tony said, jumping straight into a conversation without even giving the ELF a greeting. "Why did opening an unexpected income account dump so much money in my lap in less than a month, all of it unexpected? Or are these 'windfalls' all just a coincidence?"

"Why don't you get yourself something to drink and come sit in the living room where you will be more comfortable?" the ELF suggested. "Because this may take a while. I'll meet you in there. No hurry, by the way, Tony. Do whatever you need to do first."

He knows everything, Tony thought, somewhat disconcerted. *He knows I want a beer, and apparently he knows I need to pee, too.*

The ELF smiled.

Tony got himself a cold beer and then used the bathroom in the hall on his way to the living room. As he sat down on the couch, a slightly miffed Trainwreck, still wary after Tony almost tripped over him, eyed Tony carefully to see if it was safe to jump into his lap.

The ELF was waiting, just as promised, legs dangling from the edge of the coffee table.

"The formula for getting anything you want is very simple, Tony," the ELF began. "In fact, all you have to remember is that it is as simple as A-B-C."

"The A in A-B-C stands for 'Ask,'" the ELF explained. "All the power in the universe can't help you get what you want until you ask for it. Asking for what you want is what begins the manifestation process.

"Sometimes you ask for things in words, sometimes you ask for things in thoughts, and sometimes you do things and your actions do the asking for you.

"When you opened your unexpected income account, that action alone told me that you wanted to attract more unexpected income," the ELF went on. "Then you made your asking even stronger when you told the bank teller that you were expecting more unexpected income. You with me so far, Tony?"

"I think so. If I take a specific action, it is the same to you as if

I ask for it in words."

"That's right. The A in A-B-C stands for 'Ask' and the B stands for 'Believe.' First, you ask me for something, and then it is essential that you believe that I'll give it to you. It's just like when you ask Frankie for a favor. When you ask Frankie for anything, you simply believe that he will do it for you, don't you Tony?"

"Yeah, that's true. Frankie and I have sort of an unspoken agreement. If either of us asks for anything, we believe absolutely that the other will give it. There are no exceptions, because one way or another, we always find a way."

"That's exactly the kind of agreement you made with me when you were born, Tony, but you've forgotten about it. Whenever you ask me for what you want and then believe that I will get it for you, I never fail you."

"And finally, the C in A-B-C stands for 'Collect.' Once you ask for something and believe that I will give it to you, you must also be ready, willing, and able to gratefully collect what you asked for when, where, and how I choose to deliver it."

"That's it?" Tony asked in amazement. "Opening the unexpected income account was the same as asking? Then when I just forgot about it and didn't try to micro-manage how I might receive unexpected income, that was the same as believing? And then by accepting the checks when they came in, that was collecting?"

"That's it exactly. But since I can see you still frowning, Tony, I'm guessing you don't quite believe it can be as simple as A-B-C. So let's go over it together one more time.

"First, you asked for unexpected income by simply opening an unexpected income account and using unexpected income you had already received. Then you also said in words to the bank teller that you expected to receive more unexpected income, which made your asking even stronger.

"Next, you showed me that you believed that I would give you what you asked for by getting out of my way and letting me decide when and where and how to deliver your unexpected income. Of course, the article that you read in Financial Growth had said that after you deposited your unexpected income you should just forget about it, and that certainly helped you do that.

"Finally, you collected, without resistance, your unexpected income when I delivered it to you. Can you see how that worked, Tony?" the ELF asked. "It really is as simple as A-B-C."

"Why would anyone not collect what they asked for when you were ready to deliver it?" Tony asked suspiciously.

"It happens all the time," the ELF said. "Here's one way you could have done that. You could have decided that the hundred and fifty dollars you got from your old buddy at ADPRO didn't qualify as unexpected income. After all, you loaned him the money, even though you had completely forgotten about it. If you had chosen to call that little windfall expected income, you would not have allowed yourself to collect what you asked me to get for you, which was unexpected income."

"The magazine article did point that out," Tony said. "I know it was my choice either way, but I surely didn't expect to receive that money."

"Another way you could have refused to collect delivery of that same money would have been to send it back to the man who borrowed it from you. You might have felt sorry for him because he had been out of work for so long, and you might have decided that he needed the money more than you did."

"You know, I actually considered doing that," Tony said. "But when I really thought about it, I felt like his dignity had taken enough of a blow by just being out of work for a couple of years. He didn't need me insulting him by giving him back the money. I know that, because my dignity suffered a lot of blows in all those months that I didn't have a job." Tony shuddered. "It wasn't fun."

"I was glad you made that choice, Tony, because it shows me you understand that you can accept his money without taking away his good. Believe me, Tony, there is plenty of good available for everyone.

"And tonight, you made another good decision like that. Other adult offspring might have offended their parents by refusing to collect a gift the size of the one Luca is giving you. You might have assumed that your father needed the money more than you do and refused his gift, but you didn't do that. You made a respectful choice by accepting your father's gift, Tony, and thereby, you gratefully collected the money you asked me to give you.

"I can tell you, Tony, that you made your father feel really good tonight. He and your uncle are celebrating with two of their friends at a local pub in Brooklyn right now, and they're both feeling proud and satisfied to have been able to do something so generous for their children. They're also plotting the numbers they will play in the next lottery, by the way."

"How come this system didn't work when I was so desperate for a job?" Tony asked. "I asked and asked and asked for a job for months. Why didn't it work then?"

"It didn't work because you exercised only the first step. When you asked for the job you wanted, instead of simply believing that I would get you the job, you continued to worry about when, where, and how the job would come to you. You never even came close to getting out of my way and simply believing that I would give you what you asked for, so you could never collect on your request.

"Getting what you want really is as easy as A-B-C, but learning to work with the process takes both practice and a willingness to give up some of your own control. However, when you actually experience how much easier it is to believe in me as your source of all supply, you will get used to practicing your A-B-Cs, because it is to your own great advantage to do so.

"Let me give you another example of how hard you sometimes make it for me to give you what you want," the ELF continued. "Every morning, without fail, Trainwreck yowls for his breakfast, right?"

"Yes, without fail," Tony said, absently scratching his cat's ears.

"And as he sees you heading for the cupboard where his food is, instead of getting out of your way and just letting you get his food, he decides to actively participate in the process with you, doesn't he? He keeps up a steady stream of noises to distract you. Then he tangles himself up so completely in your feet and legs that you can hardly get to the can opener, let alone put his food in his bowl."

"Yes," Tony said, chuckling. "That's pretty much the routine."

"How much faster would he get fed if, once he got your attention and asked for his breakfast, he believed that you would give it to him, as you always have before, and just sat by his bowl waiting to collect his breakfast?"

"Quite a bit faster, and he wouldn't risk getting stepped on, either."

"Well, what Trainwreck does to worry you because he's so anxious to get his breakfast, Tony, is exactly what you do to worry me when you ask for something, and then fret and worry and pace in my path while I'm in the process of providing it. At the very least, you delay the process. And most often, I just can't get you out of my way enough to finish my job."

"Ouch," Tony said, wincing when he clearly understood the ELF's example. "Let me go through this one more time, please, so that I can stop behaving that way. First, I ask clearly for what I want. Then I believe that you will give me anything I ask for as long as I leave you alone to do it. And finally, I agree to gratefully collect what I asked for when you choose to deliver it to me."

"That's right, that's exactly right," the ELF said delightedly. "For the most part, all of you who are right now in physical form do fine with the first part. You know how to ask. But then you have trouble believing that I will take care of everything from there. You just can't stay out of my way long enough for me to make it possible for you to collect what you asked for."

"Here's another example, Tony," the ELF went on. "A man is

praying right now, not very far from here in the Emergency Room of Tampa Bay Hospital. 'Please God,' he is asking; 'heal my broken arm.' And he really wants it healed. There is so much emotion around his asking that I know it is very important to him that his broken arm heal quickly and correctly. And I want very much to answer his prayer. But first, he has to believe that I will do it.

"Unfortunately, it looks like he's not going to do that, because he has already begun to bombard me with the way he thinks he should be treated. He doesn't want the doctor examining him to set his arm because she is a woman. He doesn't want a big, heavy cast put on his arm because it will make it hard for him to sleep at night. He doesn't want the healing to take longer than two months because he wants to play in a tennis tournament.

"I can't heal that man's arm, Tony, unless he believes that I will give him the perfectly healed arm he is asking me to give him. The woman doctor he is refusing to work with is one of the most skilled in the world at casting his kind of break. Because of the way his radius is broken, if it isn't put into a hard cast, it cannot mend properly. And as for the tournament, it is possible for him to make it if he lets me arrange for his healing, but if he insists on directing the healing process himself, he probably won't be ready in time for the tournament. He would do himself a big favor right now if he wouldn't insist on being in charge of things he doesn't really understand.

"And something else is very interesting about this particular man, Tony," the ELF explained. "Last week, he was making himself a sandwich and he cut his finger. It was inconvenient and it hurt a little bit, but he didn't make a big deal of it. He put a Band-Aid on it and just forgot about it. Obviously, he can believe that I am capable of healing a cut finger, but he's not sure I can heal a broken arm."

"So what will happen to him if he doesn't ever believe that you will heal his arm?" Tony asked. "Will it never heal, then?"

"Oh, his arm will heal. Broken arms are never fatal. But the way he will be able to use that arm, and how much strength it will have in the future, will depend on each choice he makes from now on. If his arm isn't set so the bone can heal properly, it is possible that he will never again be completely satisfied with the way his arm works."

"Believe me," Tony promised, "I'll take that information to heart. But right now, I'd like to change the subject, or at least take this subject in another direction. You said earlier that I asked you for thirty-six thousand dollars. I don't remember doing that."

"Before I answer that question completely, I have to tell you a little more about what is involved in the process of asking for what you want," the ELF said. "Believe me, this is very important for you to understand.

"As I said earlier, physical beings ask for things in three ways. The first way you ask for things is by your words—usually in some form of prayer or affirmation.

"The second way you ask for things is by your thoughts. If you think about wanting something, and you think about why you want it and what you will do when you get it, over and over and over again, that is a particularly effective form of asking.

"The third and most powerful way you ask for something is through your actions, especially if those actions are linked to strong feelings. When you are really excited about taking a step toward something you want, you literally vibrate toward it. Your energy is very high, and I can literally feel how intensely you want what you are asking me to give you."

"You know, all that really makes sense," Tony said. "And I don't question for a minute what you are saying about the ways I ask for things, but I still don't remember ever *saying* that I wanted thirty-six thousand dollars, or *thinking* about thirty-six thousand dollars, or taking any action coupled with feelings that would indicate that I wanted thirty-six thousand dollars."

"That is because sometimes you ask for a specific amount of money to buy things, Tony, and sometimes you ask for things that cost a specific amount of money."

"Hmm," Tony said. "Well, I have been thinking about buying things."

"Yes, you have. Through a combination of thoughts and actions over the last twenty-four hours, you have literally asked me for office space in the Fillmore Hotel for a year, plus very specific furnishings for that space—a sign, computers and software, a projector, a new kind of camera, and a viewing screen. You even looked up the cost of most of those things on the computer this afternoon."

"I did do all those things, but wow! You sure work fast," Tony said. "I only looked at that office space today. Does this A-B-C process always work that fast?"

"No, in fact, it rarely does. But what happened today is proof that it can, if the A-B-C steps are all executed perfectly.

"There are two primary reasons why the delivery of what you ask for is usually delayed," the ELF explained.

"We've talked about the first reason, and that is your failure to believe, without question, that I will give you what you ask for.

"The second is that quite often, you're not entirely sure what you want the first few times you ask. You may have a general idea, but you're a little short on specifics.

"Here's an example you will remember," the ELF said kindly. "A few years ago, you fell in love with a Lexus automobile. You liked the Lexus brand so much that you thought a lot about owning your own Lexus. You even cut out a picture of a Lexus and put it on your desk so that you would keep thinking about it. But you couldn't make up your mind what color you wanted, and what features you wanted on it, or even exactly which model Lexus you liked best. Do you remember that?"

"I do. I went back and forth about those details for weeks, and I changed the picture on my desk several times."

"Then one day, you opened up a document on your computer and wrote down, in detail, everything you wanted your Lexus to have, including the color, the model, and the back-up sensors. That was powerful asking, and within a week, you landed the Tampa Bay Ray's account for your agency and got a bonus. Remember?"

"I did, and I made the down payment on my Lexus with it, didn't I?"

"Yes, you did. And Tony," the ELF said with emphasis, "you could have had the Lexus sooner if you had decided on the details you wanted sooner. I can't deliver half an order. You have to ask for what you really want me to give you, and believe that I will give it to you before you can finally collect it."

"Today, however, "the ELF continued, "was a different story. What you asked me for today was crystal clear, and you had a lot of high energy around it. When you saw that rental space, you instantly visualized the way it would look when it was yours, not only specifically equipped and furnished but in actual operation, with customers sitting at the table viewing a Power Point presentation. It was very clear to me what office space and what equipment you wanted. That too, was powerful asking, Tony.

"Now stay with me, because this next part is just as important. Right after you walked through the office, checked some prices on your computer for equipment, and visualized it operational in your new office, what did you do next?"

"Well, let's see," Tony thought, mentally backtracking through his very busy day. "I decided to put any decision about renting the space on hold until I got back from Frankie's wedding. Then I put it out of my mind for the time being, went to the Yacht Club to see Angie, and came back here and took a nap."

"Or to put it another way," the ELF said, "you believed that the best thing you could do was just let go of it and let the details work themselves out."

"Which translates," Tony said, "to my completely getting out of your way and letting you be in charge of getting me all the things I wanted."

"You created zero resistance, Tony, which left me free to decide how, when, and where to get you the money to buy the things you want."

"Then my father called with thirty-six thousand dollars, which I'm guessing is exactly the price for the office space and the furniture and equipment I'll need."

"Bingo!" the ELF said, shimmering with joy, "plus a little extra for you to have some fun."

"Now here's where this all gets tricky for me, though," Tony said. "My father's winning lottery ticket was drawn several days ago, and I didn't look at the office space until today. And he certainly didn't know I needed pretty close to thirty-six thousand dollars. How do you explain that?"

"Well, the time factor needs explaining only from your perspective, Tony. From where I stand, there is no such thing as time. Everything happens at the same time.

"But the truth is, the exact amount your father decided to send you had nothing to do with your needs, at least in his mind. Because, as you say, he didn't even know about them. He told you how he settled on that amount. He and Fred decided how much it would cost to remodel their kitchen, and then they divided the rest of the money four ways—one quarter to each of them, and one quarter to each of their children. As far as your father was concerned, thirty-six thousand dollars just happened to be your share of his winnings."

"So it's just a 'coincidence' that my quarter of that money added up to the amount I needed to buy the stuff I had been asking for?"

"Because you see the things that happen in your human experience from an entirely different perspective than I do, Tony, you will never be able to completely explain what you call 'coincidences.' The best you can do is accept that sometimes your life unfolds in ways you can't quite explain. That's why it is so important that you believe that I will give you what you ask for and leave the when, where, and how up to me."

"I don't mean to be dense, or rude, for that matter," Tony said, "but the concept that getting anything I want is a simple as A-B-C just seems too simple."

"Well, I can't make it any more complicated for you, Tony. That's just the way it is. You can make it more complicated, though, if you choose to," the ELF quickly pointed out. "Human beings are especially good at complicating this abundantly simple process."

The ELF shook his head, causing his colors to shimmer up and down.

"Would you be interested in knowing why your father won the lottery this time, Tony, when he's been buying a ticket every week since the Florida Lottery began in 1988, and he's never won before?"

"Yeah, I'd be very interested in knowing that."

"Every time Luca bought a lottery ticket, he informed me by the simple act of buying the ticket that he would like to win the lottery. But at the same time he bought every one of those tickets, he would also say to himself, or to anyone who would listen, 'I don't know why I'm wasting my money on this ticket, because the chances of me winning the lottery are somewhere between slim and none.'"

"That's true," Tony said. "I've heard him say that myself."

"Time after time, he took a step toward what he wanted by buying the ticket, and at exactly the same time, he took a step back from what he wanted by believing there was almost no chance he would win. Almost everyone does the same thing, Tony—not just Luca. I call it 'yes-no thinking.' It's like trying to drive a bus with the gas and the brake on at the same time. It doesn't work.

"But this time was different, because this time, Luca was in a very good mood when he bought his weekly lottery ticket and thought to himself, I have a feeling this is my lucky ticket. I'm really ready to be a big winner this time. Then he put the ticket in his pocket and forgot about it. In fact, his winning ticket was for last Wednesday's drawing, but he didn't even look at it until Saturday to see if he'd won."

"That's really cool," Tony said. "You know, I think I'm going to find the asking and collecting part of this formula pretty easy, but it may take me some time to get the hang of believing that you will just give me anything I ask for."

"Think carefully about what you just said, Tony," the ELF said patiently, "because you just put the gas and the brakes on at the same time.

"Practice, practice, practice. Whenever you ask for something, then put it out of your mind immediately and believe that I will handle it for you. Work on one of your accounts, take a nap, watch a basketball game, go to a movie, do anything except concern yourself with how I will get you what you want. Once you get the hang of this idea, Tony, you'll be telling me that getting whatever you want is really as simple as A-B-C.

"Is there anything else you would like to ask before I go, Tony?" the ELF asked, still perched on the edge of the coffee table in Tony's living room.

"I suspect you know there is," Tony said with amusement. "Both Frankie and I would like to know if any of the things you're teaching us are written down anywhere so we could read more about them."

CHAPTER TWELVE

"Oh, yes," the ELF said. "There have been spiritual teachers in physical form on the earth for millennia. There are also some powerful teachers in non-physical form teaching on this plane. They can be accessed in various ways, some through human interpreters, some through deep soul writing, and some through concentrated meditation.

"At this particular time in eternity, when so many things across your planet are in a great state of change, Tony, an unusually large number of spiritual teachers from both realms are very busy helping those who wish to remember who they really are.

"One group of exceptional spiritual teachers currently in non-physical form call themselves Abraham. They have dictated a book I would very much recommend that you and Frankie read. It is called *Ask and It Is Given*, and its physical authors are Esther and Jerry Hicks. Abraham sends their teachings to Esther through blocks of thought, and she translates them into your language. Then she and her husband, Jerry, put the teachings into books. If you and Frankie read *Ask and It Is Given*, and then do some of the exercises in the back of the book, you will become a lot more comfortable with some of the things you've been learning from me."

"Abraham teaches what you have been teaching us?"

"Yes, but they use different terminology. What I call as easy as

A-B-C, Abraham calls The Law of Attraction. However, if you ask for what you want, believe without question that I will give it to you, and then collect it joyfully when it arrives, you will have practiced your A-B-Cs and cooperated with the Law of Attraction. The result will be the same: *Ask and It Is Given*."

"Do they call you ELF?"

"No, they don't. They call me your Inner Being. Have you still got the drawing of the iceberg that you wrote all of our names on?"

"I do."

"If you wouldn't mind getting it, I will show you what Abraham calls us."

"I'll be right back," Tony said.

In the file on top of his desk, Tony found the folder marked "The ELF," took out the picture of the iceberg, picked up a red Sharpie, and carried all of them into the living room.

"Okay, on the tip of the iceberg it says 'Tony Celentano,' right?" asked the ELF.

"Right."

"That represents you as a physical being, so no change there. Then, on the part of the iceberg below the water line, you wrote 'The ELF,' which is what I suggested you call me. Abraham calls me your Inner Being, so under 'The ELF,' please write 'Inner Being.' Then on the ocean, you wrote Eternal Life Force. Under the words Eternal Life Force, write 'All-There-Is.' It's very simple, Tony. When Abraham says 'Inner Being,' think 'the ELF,' and when Abraham says 'All-There-Is,' think 'Eternal Life Force.'"

TONY CELENTANO

THE ELF
-Inner Being

THE ETERNAL LIFE FORCE
-All-There-Is

"Why doesn't Abraham just use the same terminology you use? I mean, aren't you sort of their boss?"

"Individuals, both physical and non-physical, always make their own choices, Tony, and there's nothing wrong with Abraham's choice of names. I just prefer to use the Eternal Life Force rather than All There Is, because I am the life force that creates and sustains all life, and I am eternal.

"I also like to call myself the ELF because, in your language, that makes it easy for you to see exactly how I am an integral part of 'yoursELF.' Besides, I think the name and image of 'The ELF' is just plain fun. Look at me, Tony," the ELF said, grinning merrily. "Aren't I a fun guy when you get to know me?"

"You are a fun guy to be around, and you're teaching me how to be one, too. I like to be around you, and obviously, Trainwreck does, too," Tony said, scratching his cat's ears.

"One more answer to your question about names, Tony. Never let yourself get hung up on what people call me, please. Because there are as many ways people recognize me as there are people. And that's pretty much the way it is for you, too. Your father calls you 'Tone' or 'Son,' Frankie calls you 'Bro,' your ex-boss used to call you 'Hot Shot,' and I won't go into what your ex-girlfriend calls you."

Tony winced. "I haven't even seen anyone I could call an ex-girlfriend in several years, so you know more about that than I do. By the way," Tony added, looking down at the picture of the iceberg in his hand, "thanks for helping me put Abraham's terminology on this chart. I'll make a copy for Frankie, too, and walk him through it before he starts reading *Ask and It Is Given*."

"Now, while we're on the subject of good spiritual teachers, Tony," the ELF went on, "there is one more teacher on earth in human form whom I'd like you and Frankie to know about. His name is John McLaughlin, and he teaches not in a book, but on DVDs. In a course called *MIND Is Your Own Business*, he describes, in different ways, many of the same concepts you and I and Abraham have talked about, as well as other concepts we haven't even touched on yet."

"Does John McLaughlin call you the ELF?"

"Personally, he does, and he refers to me that way sometimes in *MIND Is Your Own Business*, too. But he also uses other names to describe me so that all people can relate to what he is saying. John teaches from the physical realm, of course, which will allow you to relate to him personally. He's a fun guy, too. He especially enjoys using humor to get his point across."

"I'll order them both right away," Tony said, "the book and the DVDs, and copies for Frankie, too. We should have them by the time he gets back from his honeymoon."

"Speaking of Frankie's wedding, Tony, that whole trip to Disney World offers you a very good opportunity to practice your A-B-Cs. Since I know what you are thinking and feeling, I can tell that you are pretty much dreading the idea of spending a day or two at Disney World, starting with the drive over there Thursday night with Frankie's sister and the baby. And you're still a little uneasy about Frankie getting married in so much of a hurry.

"Why not ask me to make Frankie's wedding and everything about it a nice experience for you? Then believe that I will do that, and just allow yourself to graciously collect a fun-filled weekend at your best friend's wedding."

"When will I stop being so surprised that you know everything I'm thinking and feeling?"

"When you get used to the idea that I am you, Tony, and that I love you unconditionally. When you really understand that, you'll also understand that I am delighted to give you everything you want, if you will just…"

"I've got it, I've got it," Tony interrupted. "You'll give me everything I want if I just practice my A-B-Cs."

Tony glanced at his watch for the first time in hours. "It's after midnight," he said in surprise.

"It's time for you to go to sleep now, Tony. You've had a very busy day, and tomorrow we have an office to rent."

And with a shake and a shimmer, the ELF slipped out of sight.

Saturday morning at nine o'clock, Tony and Frankie sat at a window table in the hotel's rooftop restaurant at Disney World.

"Are you all right, Frankie?"

Frankie chuckled. "I just knew you were going to ask me that."

"Well, Frankie, if I was getting married in four hours, wouldn't you ask me that?"

"Yes, and probably not so subtly. More likely, I'd be asking if you were sure you didn't want me to sneak you out through the restaurant kitchen, stuff you in the trunk of my car, and carry you away."

"Do you want me to sneak you out through the restaurant kitchen, stuff you in the trunk of my car, and carry you away?"

"No, I don't want that, Bro, honest. Today I'm about the happiest camper you're ever going to meet. An incredible woman wants to marry me and spend the rest of her life with me, and I'm just plain delighted about it."

"I'm really glad for you, Bro," Tony said, a little surprised at how much he meant it. "And if this marriage is what you want, then it's what I want for you, too."

"How was your trip over here with Julie and Andy, by the way?"

"It was really fun," Tony admitted. "Andy is a great little girl, and awfully smart. How old is she now, eight months? Julie was reading Dr. Suess to her, *The Cat in the Hat*. I would have thought Andy was way too young for that, but the rhyme tickled her, and she giggled in all the right places. She had Julie and me giggling right along with her."

"Yeah, she's a trip all right," her uncle said. "Last night, Anna and I took her to the parade so Julie and Mike could have a little time alone, and then we went for a ride on It's A Small World. She was fascinated the whole time, looking all around, smiling and babbling. It was fun.

"How are you holding up after a whole day at Disney World, Bro?" Frankie asked, changing the subject. "I know it's not your favorite place to be, and I've been so busy with our families, I've kind of left you on your own here."

Tony looked down at kids playing in the hotel pool and shook his head. "You know, I've only been here for a few hours at a time before this trip, and I admit I was dreading it, until the ELF suggested that I approach the trip differently. He told me to ask for the kind of experience I wanted to have, and then back off and let him give it to me.

"And I have to say, it's working. The one thing that surprises me most is that just about everyone is happy here. I mean, I expected to find over-excited, bratty kids running wild in the halls, and a snooty hotel staff, because after all, this is Disney World. But that's not the way it has turned out to be.

"And I had a really good time by myself yesterday, wandering around in the park. I checked out the way they market their merchandise, and wow! Even I found it hard to resist. I sent postcards to my dad and Uncle Fred, and bought a toy for Trainwreck. It's a squeaky Ratatouille."

"You've been talking to the ELF again?" Frankie asked with great interest.

"Yes, and I want like crazy to tell you all about it, but I have a feeling it would be better if I did that next Saturday. I think you're a little too preoccupied today to absorb deep spiritual concepts," Tony said with slight amusement. "But here's something that will interest you. I asked the ELF if any of what he is teaching us is written down anywhere, and he suggested a book we can read, and a set of DVDs we can watch. He says they will help us understand and practice using the stuff he is teaching us. So I ordered us each a copy of the book and the DVDs. I'll probably have them by next Saturday. I figure maybe we can watch some of the DVDs together on Saturday afternoons sometimes."

"Sounds cool," Frankie said. "I am really ready to know more."

"Me, too," Tony said, reaching into his back pocket and pulling out his cell phone. "But now, just for fun, I figured we could call Pete from here. I plugged the phone number of the Dome Café into my phone before I left. First Saturday morning in twenty years we haven't been there. We should make something special out of it, shouldn't we?"

"What a great idea," Frankie said. "Pete will be stoked."

Pete answered the phone.

"Hey Pete, how are you this morning? This is Tony Celentano."

"Yeah? Are you in Disney World, Tony?"

"You got it. Frankie and I are having a really good breakfast in a high-class hotel overlooking the Magic Kingdom. It's a nice change from that greasy Dome Café breakfast we usually have."

"Don't bust my chops about my food, Tony, huh? Man, it's good to hear from you. I was thinking about you guys off and on all morning. Seems odd around here today without my two favorite customers. How's the bridegroom?"

"Ask him yourself," Tony said, handing the phone to Frankie.

"Don't let him give you a hard time, Pete," Frankie said good-naturedly. "Breakfast is okay here, but these dainty little potato sticks and poached eggs will never replace Dome Fries and three over easy with hash."

"Aw, it's Tony's job to give me a hard time. Are you all right, Frankie?" Pete asked.

"Tony just asked me the same question. I don't know why you guys are so worried about me," Frankie said, laughing. "I'm not only fine; I'm better than fine. I'm gonna bring Anna in to meet you as soon as we get back from our honeymoon, Pete. She wants to see where I spend my Saturday mornings every week."

"I'd like to meet her, Frankie. I got a little wedding present for you. I'll give it to you when you come in."

"Thanks Pete. Have a good day now, and we'll see you next Saturday."

"Okay. Say goodbye to Tony, Frankie. So long."

"So," Frankie said, signaling the waitress for another cup of coffee. "Anything else new besides an ELF sighting?"

"Yeah, my old man won the New York Lottery."

"What? You're kidding! That's great. How much, Tony?"

"Two hundred fifty thousand. But he was in partnership with Uncle Fred, so their take, after Uncle Sam took his, came to around a hundred seventy-five grand."

"Boy, is that cool or what? What is your dad going to do with all that cash?"

Tony felt his eyes well up. "He's gonna split it with me," he said, staring really hard out the window for a moment.

Frankie stayed quiet, giving Tony time to get himself back together. Then he said, "Same question. What are you gonna do with all that dough?"

"Plow most of it into E.L.F. Promotions. I've already rented office space in the Fillmore," Tony said. "And when I get back, I'm going to pick out furniture and paint and carpeting. It's really perfect for me, Frankie. There are two rooms, one for working with clients, and one big enough for me to work on my computers and even bring in occasional freelancers if I need them. It has plenty of storage space, too, plus an entrance on the street and one from the hotel lobby. Which means, Bro, that it's time now for me to create my own 'brand.' I can't order a sign for the office until I do.

"I've been so busy creating everyone else's promotional material that I just made up some temporary cards for E.L.F. Promotions. Now, for lots of reasons, including creating my website, I'm going to have to decide what I want my own public image to be. I wish

I knew why, Frankie, that I find promoting myself so hard when I find promoting everyone else so easy.

"But, I don't have to worry about that today," he grinned, changing the subject. "Today I'm the best man at my best friend's wedding, and I'm not leaving your side until you say 'I do.' Speaking of which, it's ten o'clock and you aren't getting hitched for three hours. How are we going to kill the time in between?"

"Well, I can't speak for you. But since Anna and her mother and Julie and Crissy are getting their hair and makeup done, and Mike took Andy to breakfast with Snow White and the Seven Dwarfs, I'm going to do what I just love to do. The only thing here that Anna doesn't like to do at Disney World is ride Space Mountain, so that's my next stop. Do you still want to stick with me, Bro?"

"Just like glue, pal. I wouldn't miss seeing you turn that putrid shade of puke-green again. You remember the color you used to turn when we went on the roller coaster at Busch Gardens? If we're going on Space Mountain, we'd better go right now, so you'll have time to settle your stomach again before the wedding."

"That doesn't happen anymore, Bro. I'm a pro at rollercoaster riding now. But I'm looking forward to seeing how you hold out on the slopes. This baby makes that old rollercoaster we went on at Busch Gardens look like a kid slide in the neighborhood park."

"Hey, I'm Tony Celentano! How can you have any doubts about how I'll hold out?"

"Well, there's always that to contend with," Frankie said, sighing as he signed the check. Then tossing his arm around Tony's shoulder as they walked out of the restaurant, Frankie said, "I'm sure you'll do fine, pal. But don't worry. If you start to get squeamish on me, I'll just remind you to 'Go to ELF!'"

When Tony opened the door of his condo at seven o'clock that night, about the last thing he expected to see was Molly Malone sitting on his couch reading a book, and Trainwreck and Darth Vader curled up together on the floor sound asleep. He set his bag down and walked into the living room, amazed at the hugely cute scene of a six-pound dog and a nineteen-pound cat lovingly entwined.

Usually when he traveled out of town for just a few days, Tony left Trainwreck on his own with plenty of dry cat food, water, and litter. But since Molly had volunteered to feed Trainwreck, Tony had given her a key and his thanks for keeping Trainwreck clean and happily fed. Although he hadn't expected any miracles to happen while he was gone, clearly a miracle was asleep in front of him.

"How did you do that?" he asked incredulously.

"Well, I came in yesterday morning to feed Trainwreck, and he took off for his hiding place as soon as he saw me. I got to thinking how hard that would continue to be on him, since we're apparently going to be working together for a while, so I decided to try to make friends with him.

"Last night when I came to feed him, I brought a book with me. After I put his food down, I closed the door as if I was leaving, but then I tiptoed back to the couch to read, hoping he would think I was gone. It must have worked, because after a while, he came out of his hiding place and saw me sitting here.

"I started talking to him in a quiet voice and put my hand out for him to smell. Eventually he came closer, and when he did, I offered him a tuna fish ball I had made that afternoon. I just kept talking to him and feeding him by hand, and after a while, he let me scratch his ears.

"So I decided to go for broke. And when I came back for this morning's feeding, I brought Darth with me, hoping Trainwreck would think I had more tuna fish balls with me and wouldn't run away again. Even so, I was kind of surprised when he didn't run away. Instead, he held his ground and faced off with Darth.

"They did a fair amount of growling and hissing at each other at first, and I watched them very closely to be sure no one got hurt. It was a standoff for a while, but then Trainwreck backed off and just kind of looked at Darth, as if he was seeing him differently all of a sudden. After that, the growling and hissing changed to sniffing and smelling. To try to move their relationship along a little faster, I dropped your feather-on-a-stick toy directly between them. They both started batting at it, and before they knew what was happening, they were playing together.

"Tonight when I brought Darth back, they began to play and chase each other right away. When they finally tired each other out, they fell asleep just the way they are now. They were so cute together that I decided to wait for you to get back, hoping they wouldn't wake up until you got here."

"That's amazing," Tony said as he sat down on the couch beside her. "From now on, I guess they can have play dates. That's what Frankie's sister told me she calls it when she takes Andy to play with the baby down the street once or twice a week. It looks like these two would enjoy having play dates, too."

"How was the wedding?"

"You know, it was just great," Tony said, sitting back on the couch, still kind of surprised to hear himself say that. "It was so perfect for Frankie and Anna. They were married in a castle in front of a big, stone fireplace. Frankie and I stood there and watched the women come down a gorgeous staircase. Crissy, Anna's best friend, was the maid of honor. Julie, Frankie's sister, was a bridesmaid, and behind them, Minnie Mouse came down the stairs carrying Andy. Andy just smiled and kept patting Minnie's bow the whole time. And then, of course, Anna came down the stairs escorted by Mickey Mouse.

"It was just pure fantasy, Molly. Anna is an absolutely beautiful woman, and so tiny. Frankie is so tall, you get the impression that he'd just like to pick her up and carry her around all the time."

"Does he?" Molly asked, a bit of horror playing in her voice at the thought of it.

"Well, not in public anyway," Tony said, laughing. "But he did pick her up and put her in Cinderella's carriage. It was driven by two guys in full livery and pulled by two beautiful dapple-grey horses. As the carriage took off, the music on the loud speaker switched to 'Here Comes the Bride,' and people lined the streets to wave to them just as if they were real royalty. I have to admit, it was really something special."

"It sounds it," Molly sighed, feeling happy just hearing about it.

"Then the reception at the restaurant was amazing, too. You know, you really get caught up in the fantasy, Molly, and all of a sudden the ridiculous seems perfectly normal. Donald and Daisy Duck were there, and Cinderella. Anna was surprised and thrilled, because Frankie had arranged all that without her knowing it. We all drank champagne, I made a toast, Frankie and Anna cut the cake, and then they drove away to live happily ever after. And you know what?" he asked with a tone of real sentimentality in his voice. "I believe they will."

Thinking she would soon be overstaying her welcome, Molly said, "I'm sure you're tired by now, Tony. I'll take Darth and go home. It sounds to me like you had an adventure you won't forget anytime soon. Would you like me to make you a pot of tea before I go?"

"To tell you the truth, Molly, I'm still wired. I'd like some tea, and I don't suppose you have any…"

Molly chuckled. "I just happen to have a chocolate-mint marble pie in my refrigerator. Would you like a piece?"

"I would, if you'll have one with me. How about I make the tea and you go get the pie?"

"Deal. I won't disturb Darth until I'm ready to leave later. I'll be right back."

Tony sat a moment after she left, looking again at the pile of small animals sleeping soundly on the rug. "I guess fantasy does spill over into reality every now and then, doesn't it?" he murmured to the ELF before heading into the kitchen to make the tea.

Molly returned with a piece of chocolate mint pie and Tony soon finished the last bite.

"Would you like another piece?" Molly offered as Tony licked the fork.

"Yes, I'd like one. And no, I'm not going to have it. If I keep hanging around you, I'll weigh two hundred pounds. I'm making a mental memo to hit the weight room downstairs first thing in the morning. Now, tell me what you've been up to while I was living in Fantasy Land."

"Well, a lot actually. Friday I hired a carpenter, and he and I laid out the design for all the counters and shelving and the island in Sam and Mary's kitchen. Then, based on his measurements, I went to a restaurant supply company and ordered two ovens that will stack so I can add a third one below them if I ever need it. I also bought a range, two freezers and a refrigerator, a new food processor, and an industrial mixer.

"When I got home, there was a message on my phone from Amelia at the Yacht Club. I returned her call, and she asked me if I could prepare a dessert tasting for her tomorrow at three o'clock, four samples to start. So to be sure everything would be perfect for that tasting, yesterday I made six different Irish desserts and took them over to Sam's. He and Mary, Mr. Ferguson, Clive. and three women residents from the hotel tasted all six and voted for their favorite four. I will present those to Amelia tomorrow, although I'll take samples of the other two, also, in case she wants a bigger choice."

"I'll bet the hotel people were thrilled to be part of a dessert tasting. What a great idea."

"They were. The women, especially. They acted like little girls at a tea party," Molly said, chuckling. "And since three of the desserts were variations on pies, Mary and Sam cornered me to ask again if I was ready to contract to make their desserts every day for the Café. We cut a deal on a price per pie, with a fifty-pie weekly minimum, so Molly Malone's Irish Desserts has its first real customer. If all goes well with Amelia, I'll have another customer in the next few days."

"How long has it been since you knocked on my door?" Tony asked, trying to think through everything that had happened since. "It seems like at least a year or two."

"Exactly six nights ago," Molly answered, looking at her watch. "Right about now, as a matter of fact."

"It certainly has been an action-packed week, hasn't it? I really need to take time to get organized," Tony said. "If I don't, I'm in danger of letting someone down. Did your cards come, by the way?"

"Yes," Molly answered, reaching into her purse and handing him one. "What do you think?"

"What do you think? That's the important question."

"I think I feel really sorry for anyone whose name isn't Molly Malone, because this is just the most wonderful business card ever. It's funny how seeing it in print like this made it all so much more real for me," she said, grinning.

"Before I can get you more customers, I need to know a little more about the kind of customer you would like to have," Tony told her.

"Well, I would prefer to create for high end private clubs and restaurants, because they want their own exclusive desserts. On top of the regular desserts you see on any menu, the better restaurants want at least two, three, or four desserts their diners won't find anywhere else. I want exclusive desserts to become my specialty. The contract I ask them to sign will require a minimum order of those specialty desserts per month, and an up-front fee for exclusivity. Of course, if they get really busy or have a banquet or a wedding that bumps up the minimum order, then that becomes icing on the cake for me."

Tony groaned at the pun.

"Oops, sorry about that," Molly said, realizing what she had just said.

"The specialty desserts are almost always delivered frozen and are defrosted as needed by the sous chefs. The trick for me is to create a dessert that can be frozen and still taste just as good defrosted as it tasted when fresh."

"So how do you know what will work and what won't?"

"Experience helps, but trial and error are part of it, too. And then I always ask the fairies."

"You mentioned the fairies before, when you said they weren't helping you choose between being a librarian and being a pastry chef."

"And you showed me I was in a box that said I had to please other people before I could please myself," she said. "It could be that the problem is out of their realm, but the fairies never desert me when I'm baking."

Tony groaned again.

"Oh, dear. I wonder if I do that all the time. If so, no one else has ever picked up on it before. Gran taught me to cook with the fairies," Molly explained. "The Irish believe there are fairies to help with everything. Whenever I need help, I ask the fairies, and they help me make desserts that seem always to taste good, fresh or frozen."

Pausing for a minute to let that sink in, Tony realized that a few weeks ago, he would have thought this woman was just plain nuts. At the moment, though, her talk with the fairies didn't seem all that unusual.

"I'll start thinking about ways to get the attention of the other country clubs in the area, and some of the higher-end restaurants and hotels, too. If you get the Yacht Club account—and I'm sure you will—that will open some other doors for us. When will your new kitchen be ready?"

"I'm having the appliances delivered Friday, but it will take at least another week to get the kitchen exactly the way I want it. In the meantime, I'll start stocking my new freezers from my kitchen here.

Don't hold back, Tony. I'm jazzed enough to work all day every day and never even notice I've been doing it, at least not for a while."

Then she stood and stretched. "I need to go now, Tony, to get some sleep while I can. I'm so glad you had a good time. I'll leave the rest of that pie for you and Trainwreck to finish tomorrow."

Then she tiptoed over to the pile of sleeping animals, gently removed Darth Vader from under Trainwreck's paw, and cradled the still-sleeping dog in her arms. "We'll be back to play another day," she whispered to Trainwreck.

And we're both very glad you will, Tony thought as he closed the door behind them.

It was about the thousandth surprising thought he'd had in just one day.

CONCEPT V

Realizing . . .
Gratefulness is your most creative tool

CHAPTER THIRTEEN

Tony sat across from Mike Palmieri at Mike's desk ready to discuss the real estate firm's new promotional campaign.

"This may be different from anything you've ever done before, Tony," Mike explained, "so if I get into it and it doesn't seem like something you want to help me do, just say so.

"In all my advertising and on my letterhead and business cards, I've been using 'Mike Palmieri Real Estate, Where Houses Become Homes.' And I have to say, it has been good for me. But now I want to try something different, something that has more personal meaning for me."

"Such as?"

"Such as 'Mike Palmieri, The Grateful Realtor.'"

Mike let the silence expand until Tony spoke.

"That's really interesting, Mike," Tony said after reflecting on it for a moment. "I was letting myself think how I would feel if I picked up one of those free real estate magazines—you know, the kind with all thc realtors' listings pictured— and I read 'Mike Palmieri, The Grateful Realtor.' I have to say it would catch my interest. Are you willing to tell me more about it than just the tag line?"

"I am willing to tell you all about it, Tony," Mike said, walking over to the compact refrigerator in the corner of the office and taking out two cold bottles of water. He handed one to Tony and sat down in the chair next to him.

"A few years ago when I was still flipping little houses on the south side of town, I dated a woman who took me to church with her one Sunday. There was a guest speaker that day, a woman minister, and the first thing she said was, 'A homeless man who is living under a bridge in a cardboard box will begin to turn his life around the minute he becomes grateful for the shelter of the bridge and the protection of the box.'

"She talked then about why life never gets any better when all we do is complain about it, but once we shift our focus to what is good about our life, we're amazed at how quickly everything that matters to us improves. She said the regular practice of gratefulness increases our prosperity, improves our health, harmonizes our relationships, and deepens our spirituality.

"I knew the minute I heard that, Tony, that she was talking to me. I spent most of my time in those days complaining about everything that went wrong, and never paying attention when things went right.

"She had some items for sale in the lobby after the service, all relating to the practice of gratefulness. One was a computer program her husband had designed, an electronic gratefulness journal. I bought it, and I've been using it every day since. If you are going to ask me if it works, all I can tell you is that the size and quality of my business has more than tripled since I began making gratefulness the central energy of my life. And on top of that, I'm a much happier man."

Mike got up from his chair, went to the bookshelf, found the computer software package for the gratefulness journal, and handed it to Tony.

"John McLaughlin?" Tony said in surprise.

"Yes, it was his wife who gave the talk that day. I had never heard of Unity until then, but I've been going back to that church pretty often ever since."

"I think I just bought a DVD series by him," Tony said, still studying the software package.

"*MIND Is Your Own Business?*"

"Yeah, that's it. A friend recommended it. I ordered it this morning from Amazon."

"You're going to love it," Mike said. "McLaughlin used to be a realtor, so I can really relate to him personally. He uses some of his real estate experiences as examples, usually of what not to do. It really brings what he is teaching home to me."

"Small world, isn't it?" Tony said. "You still going with the same woman, Mike?

"No. Ditched the woman and kept the church, but I am still grateful to her," Mike said, grinning a little sheepishly. "I'll admit I don't go to church every Sunday, but sometimes I go to seminars or classes there during the week, and I really like their coffee shop and bookstore. They call it 'Wings.' I stop in pretty often when I'm at that end of town."

"Hmm, isn't that interesting?" Tony said, putting the software package down on Mike's desk.

"Funny, that's one of John McLaughlin's favorite lines. You'll hear him say it a lot on the DVDs," Mike said. "Isn't that interesting?"

"Okay, Mike, getting back to business," Tony said, opening his notebook and uncapping his pen. "I can design new business cards and stationery for you that say 'Mike Palmieri, The Grateful Realtor.' Do you want to change the company logo, too?"

"I think I would like to change it to something that conveys more about the kind of service I actually give, but I have no idea what it would look like. Buying and selling real estate is a scary experience for many people. They are usually making the most expensive purchase or sale they've ever made in their whole lives. I want them to understand at a glance that I know what I'm doing and that they can trust me, but I'd also like to get the idea across that I won't take them for granted and will be grateful for their business."

“Let me think about it and I’ll get back to you about the logo,” Tony said. “Other than cards and stationery, is there anything else you want, Mike?”

“Oh, yes. I’ve thought about this for a long time, Tony, and I’m prepared to spend some money to get what I want. We already have a website to showcase our listings, and except for changing the logo on it if you create a new one for us, I’m going to leave the website alone. I have a good rapport with the webmaster and I’m grateful for him.

“But something else I would like is a blog. One of the best ways we can serve our customers is to make sure they have plenty of good information so they can always make informed decisions. I have an employee, Jenny, who is a natural writer.”

Mike picked up a folder from the desk and put it in front of Tony. “Here are some samples of the kind of information we see ourselves posting on our blog. The posts run the gamut from information about changes in real estate law, how to tell if termites are a problem, and how to choose a mortgage broker, to helpful hints on simple home repairs, staging, Feng Shui, decorating, and landscaping. I want Jenny to slip in some information on the value of being grateful, too, every now and then. It will be kind of a ‘good house-buying, good house-keeping, good house-selling’ blog.

“I need you to teach us how to blog. I need you to set up the blog, design it, format it, and then show Jenny how to post on it at least once a week, maybe more. I’d also like you, or someone you recommend, to teach her, and me, how to promote it on social networking websites like Facebook, Twitter, and LinkedIn.”

“Creating a blog is no problem, Mike,” Tony said. “But paying for the kind of training you want by the hour could be very expensive. Plus it isn’t my specialty. I’d rather give you one price to create the blog and train Jenny how to use it. Then we can look into some other ways to teach you both to use social media to promote it. There are some good tele-seminars available, and St. Petersburg College offers some courses on how to effectively use sites like Facebook and Twitter. Of course, I'd be available to Jenny by phone or e-mail if she got into some kind of technical trouble."

"That would work for me. Just think it through and work up the price. I know you'll be fair with me, Tony. Now, for the biggest of the three projects," Mike said, getting up and pacing as he talked. "I have an e-mail list of somewhere between a hundred and fifty to two hundred people. These are mostly customers, but some are colleagues, some are suppliers, and some are just friends. I have many reasons to be grateful for all of them, and I want to express my gratitude in a unique way, more for my own sake than for theirs.

"My idea—and I'm counting on you to refine it, because I don't know exactly what I'm talking about except in concept—is to send an interesting, eye-catching e-mail greeting card to every person on the list once a month. The e-mail greeting card will include a coupon for a gift they can retrieve somewhere in the city. And I want that little gift, whatever it turns out to be each month, to be something nice enough or clever enough that most people who receive my e-mail will bother to go get the gift.

"The design of each month's message will be up to you. Seasonal is fine where appropriate. What I absolutely want included in every greeting, though, is my logo and my name, address, and telephone number, plus the line 'The Grateful Realtor,' as well as a coupon the recipient can redeem for a nice little free gift."

"Let me understand this, Mike, because it sounds very intriguing. You want me to design one e-mail greeting card a month for twelve months for you to send to a targeted list of a hundred and fifty to two hundred people. You want the greetings to be attractive and eye-catching, which probably means they should include some animation. Each greeting card will convey the message that you are 'The Grateful Realtor,' without naming specifically what you are grateful for, and each message will include a coupon redeemable for a nice little gift somewhere in the St. Petersburg area."

"That is very much what I have in mind, Tony."

"And you want me to come up with the twelve gifts, as well?"

"Yes, I do."

"How much are you willing to pay per merchant?"

"I'd like your input on that, too, Tony. But here are my thoughts. I will pay each of the twelve participating merchants a hundred dollars just to accept the coupons and supply the gift. I'd like to keep my contribution per gift to three dollars or less, but I'm hoping you can convince each merchant to provide something worth a little more than that to sweeten the pot for all of us. From my viewpoint, the participating merchant has everything to gain and nothing to lose. If no one redeems a coupon, the merchant will be a hundred dollars richer. However, the more people who redeem their coupons, the more chances the merchant will have to sell those people something else while they are in the store."

"Pretty shrewd, Mike," Tony admitted, "but it will be pricey. Just let me run a few figures here." Tony clicked onto the calculator in his iPhone and made a few entries.

"This is just in round figures," he told Mike a few minutes later, "but it will give you something to consider. I'm going to have to charge you around thirty-six hundred dollars just to produce twelve electronic animated messages and coupons. All the costs relating to the gifts will be at least another twenty-five hundred dollars. That's a lot of money to spend just to say thank you."

"Cheap at twice the price, Tony. Sincc I began to shift my focus to being grateful for all the blessings in my life, I have had so many amazing good things happen to me that I can't even remember them all, and they don't all have to do with money. I can't begin to explain how it works. You'll just have to discover it for yourself.

"I'm fine with those figures, Tony, and more if you need it. Besides," he said with a wide grin, "I'm glad to find out that all you're going to charge me is thirty-six hundred. Frankly, I was expecting you to charge me a lot more."

"Hmm, too bad I didn't know that," Tony said, grinning back at him. "But three hundred dollars per greeting card is fair for me. Once I get the format set up, the later messages will take less time to produce than the earlier ones do. That's what my business is about, Mike. I like providing top-quality advertising and promotional services for small business owners at reasonable prices. So far, it seems to be working out just fine, I'm happy to say."

"We're going to make a good team, Tony," Mike said. "There are too many coincidences surrounding our relationship already for it to be any other way. That is, if you still believe in coincidences—which I don't."

"Me either," Tony agreed. "Which project do you want me to start on first?"

"I think the logo first, because that will be part of everything else we do. I would like the first greeting card to go out in January, so I guess that project will be next, and then the blog."

"Okay, I'll come up with some ideas on these projects in that order, and get back to you by the end of the week."

Picking up the computer software box he had put down on Mike's desk, he added, "I think I'm going to order one of these electronic gratefulness journals myself, Mike. I'd better literally drown myself in the gratefulness experience while I'm working on your project so I can find out for myself what you are talking about."

"Smartest thing you'll ever do, Tony. Take it from 'The Grateful Realtor,'" Mike said as he walked Tony to the door.

Tony's first thought was to ask the ELF why being grateful had made such a difference in Mike Palmieri's life, but he didn't do it right away. In fact, he saw Mike on Monday, and it was Friday night before Tony had time to settle down in his own living room and 'Go to ELF!'

A little light shimmered over the coffee table, and the ELF appeared.

"So," the ELF said, "you want to know more about the power of gratefulness, Tony."

"Yeah, I do. But before we talk about that, I want to thank you for telling me to practice my A-B-Cs on Frankie's wedding weekend. I suppose you know I had a great time."

"Of course I know, because I was right there with you. We had fun, didn't we, especially on the down slide on Space Mountain? It's a good thing Frankie didn't know what you were thinking about him while your heart was almost leaping out of your chest," the ELF said, chuckling. "And thanks to you for mostly staying out of my way while I was getting your office furnished the way you asked me to. I appreciate that you let yourself believe I could handle the details while you worked over here on Mike's logo."

Tony didn't miss the twinkle in the ELF's eye. "Yeah, I decided I didn't need to be in that space every minute, since you could handle the furnishing of the office just fine without me. But that was hard for a control freak like me."

"You did fine, really fine, for a control freak like you."

"Do you like Mike's logo?" Tony asked.

"I do. Creating visual icons requires a special talent, because they have to literally tell a whole story in a very small space. And you have that kind of talent, Tony."

The logo Tony created for Mike was a simple circle with a little pitched roof over it, and inside the circle was a pair of hands clasped in a firm handshake. Mike's tag line, "Mike Palmieri, The Grateful Realtor," appeared below the circle.

"Your logo instantly conveys the concept of a successful real estate transaction, but the firm handshake also sends a message of trust, harmony, friendship, and even gratefulness," the ELF continued. "Those are all qualities buyers and sellers really want their realtor to have. Good job. Now, back to your original question,

Tony. What would you like to know about gratefulness?"

"The book you recommended, *Ask and It Is Given*, came in the mail while we were at Disney World. I've been reading it, mostly just before I go to sleep at night. I'm on the third chapter, but I also looked ahead at some of the exercises in the back of the book. There's something called a 'Rampage of Appreciation.' Is that what Mike is talking about? Are gratefulness and appreciation the same thing?"

"Abraham likes to use the word 'appreciation' instead of 'gratitude,' 'gratefulness,' 'thankfulness,' or even 'praise.' Because in your language, appreciation also can convey a meaning of 'added value.' And the act of giving thanks does create added value," the ELF explained.

"That makes sense, doesn't it? But which word do you like best?" Tony asked. "I'd kind of like to stay with your choice of words."

"In this case, the meanings of all those words are pretty close. But personally, I prefer the word 'gratefulness.' When you are really grateful, you feel so good you have a sense of great fullness. That concept pleases me," the ELF explained.

"Does being grateful really make you richer and healthier and all those other things Mike says it does?"

"It certainly can, because expressing gratefulness for what you have is a subtle or subconscious way of asking me to give you more that is just like it. You do it all the time."

"I do it without realizing it?"

"Much of the time, yes," the ELF answered. "When you finish working out in the morning, you may feel tired, but you also have good feelings about your strong, healthy, well-toned body. You are proud of it and grateful for it. That sense of gratefulness within you signals me that you want to continue to have a strong, healthy body. So I guide you toward activities that keep you healthy, and away from activities that don't.

"When you make a nice big deposit in the bank, you feel grateful for the increasing size of your bank balance, which lets me know you are ready to see it increase more and more often.

“When your customers show you they like your work, the way Clive did when he saw his postcards, for example, you send out vibrations of gratefulness for your satisfied customers, which tells me you want to experience more satisfied customers.

“One of the reasons that vibrations of gratefulness work so well and so fast, Tony, is because they are taking place at a subconscious level. So once you let me know that you would like to have more of what you just received, you seldom even think to get in the way of your own believing and collecting.”

“When I’m expressing my gratefulness subconsciously, who am I expressing it to?”

“Ah, that is a very good question. There is a really big difference between being grateful ‘to’ and being grateful ‘for,’ Tony. Being grateful ‘to’ creates negative energy, and being grateful ‘for’ creates positive energy.

“Let me give you an example. Someone does you a big favor and you immediately feel grateful ‘to’ him or her for it. That type of gratefulness carries with it a sense of indebtedness. Someday, it will be ‘payback’ time. The words you say to them as you thank them actually translate to some form of ‘I owe you one.’ Whenever you feel as if you owe someone for something, you are automatically creating debt, and debt conjures up a ‘feel bad’ energy that can easily keep you mired in more debt. Be very careful, Tony, of ever being grateful ‘to’ anyone unless you really do intend to pay them back.

“However, whenever you are grateful ‘for’ something, your joyful feelings bring forth a strong, ‘feel-good’ energy. Therefore, they attract more things for which to be grateful. I find that those who regularly express gratefulness ‘for’ life itself, for example, live in a constant state of wellbeing. They feel good about themselves and about everyone else, too.

“It will really help you a lot to get a handle on this concept, Tony.

Let me ask you. When you think about the money your father just sent you, do you feel grateful 'to,' or grateful 'for' him for sharing his winnings with you?"

"Both, I guess."

"That's an honest answer, but let's take a look at which feels better. Feeling grateful 'to' him is generated by your intellect, and I've heard you thinking that if he ever needs you, you'll be there for him. Those are thoughts of indebtedness, which can easily slip into more specific thoughts of indebtedness, such as, 'Someday Dad will need me to take care of him.' Thinking that way doesn't feel very good, does it Tony? Those negative feelings are me signaling you that you are thinking about a situation that you don't want, and Luca doesn't want, either. It will serve you both much better if you stop feeling grateful 'to' your father, Tony, and start feeling grateful 'for' him.

"When you feel grateful 'for' your father, those grateful thoughts are coming from your heart. They slip right into thoughts about what a good man Luca is, how much he has taught you through the years, how generous he is, how much you enjoy his sense of fun, and all kinds of other good things about him that you want to continue to experience. Thoughts like that make it possible for me to give you even more reasons to be grateful 'for' your father, Tony. And they are already on the way, I promise you. Are you feeling the difference, Tony, between being grateful 'to' and being grateful 'for'?"

"I am, and I think I also hear you saying that I can tell whether I am feeling grateful 'to' something or 'for' something by the way I feel. As long as I'm feeling really good about something, I'm actually feeling grateful 'for' it; therefore, I am automatically asking you to give me more of it," Tony answered.

"That's right. Being grateful is a very pure form of asking for more of the same, and since you have already collected whatever you are expressing gratefulness 'for,' it is easy for you to believe that you will be able to collect it again."

"Now," the ELF said, shifting around a little and flashing his colors again, "to bring this whole subject back to Mike Palmieri's e-mail greeting card project. He is asking you to create a vehicle through which he can express his gratefulness 'for' all the good things that have happened in his life. And because that is his only purpose, I will be able to give him many more things to be grateful for in the future."

"Hmm. I think I finally understand that."

"Any other questions?" the ELF asked, knowing full well there was one more.

"Is there anything else you can tell me that will help me to help Mike make his campaign a success?" Tony asked.

"Well, you're doing the very best thing right now, Tony, by asking me to help you fulfill Mike's true purpose as you create each greeting card for him. Also, you can ask me to help you fulfill your purpose, which is to serve another customer who is genuinely pleased with and grateful for your work. If you hold both of these desired outcomes in your heart while you develop this campaign, both you and Mike will be very happy with the results.

"But don't forget about your Bs and Cs, too, Tony," the Elf reminded him. "Believe that I will guide as you work with Mike, and keep yourself ready to gratefully collect a successful project.

"Now go and have fun with this project, because it has all the elements that you like to do most." And once again, the ELF shimmered out of sight.

In Woodlawn, Frankie pulled into his driveway behind Anna's car at exactly five-thirty. She didn't get home from work first every night, but when she did, she tended to launch herself into his arms the minute he came through the doorway. It was an experience Frankie had come very much to enjoy.

So when he opened the door and didn't see her little body flying in his direction, he was puzzled. Then he heard heart-wrenching sobs coming from the living room. *Oh, no, what's happened?* he wondered.

He found Anna sitting cross-legged on the couch, head in hands and crying as hard as he had ever seen a woman cry. Horrified, he sat down beside her and gently drew her into his lap. Putting her arms around his neck, she buried her head in his shoulder, and within a moment or two, her sobbing began to subside.

After she had cried herself out, Frankie reached into his pocket and pulled out his handkerchief. Gently, he wiped her face and then handed the handkerchief to her so she could blow her nose."What happened, sweetheart?" he asked softly.

"Patty-Cake died," she sniffled, beginning to cry softly again.

"Oh, Anna, I am so sorry," he said, drawing her head to his shoulder and gently stroking her hair.

Patty-Cake had been one of Anna's favorite patients at All Children's Hospital. At eight years old, she had been diagnosed with an incurable disease. She'd been in the hospital over a year, and both her bravery and her gentle spirit had captured Anna's heart. Wherever Anna and Frankie went, they always looked for little surprise presents to take to Patty-Cake. It was against the rules, but Anna didn't care. Patty-Cake had very little good in her life, and Anna's little surprises had pleased the child. A pretty shell from the beach. A little two-inch doll made entirely of cotton that Patty-Cake carried to X-rays and MRIs. A stress ball shaped like a pig that she squeezed when the pain from her disease became really bad. A pink, polka-dot hair bow. Anna and Frankie had even brought Patty-Cake some Mickey Mouse ears from Disney World. These very little presents had brought Patty-Cake very big smiles.

Anna started to talk, her breath still hitching. "Sh-sh-she t-t-told me th-this morning that she was going to leave the earth today because the angel came and sat on her bed and told her God was ready for her. She wasn't at all scared. She just wanted me to know. About an hour later, she went into a coma. A-a-and the angel did come for her," Anna stammered. "I saw her."

"You saw an angel?"

"Yes, I did. And not for the first time, either. They're so beautiful, and they come for the children so they won't be afraid. I know I shouldn't be sad, and in many ways, I'm not. Patty-Cake will not be in any more pain, and she won't be confined anymore to her body. But, oh, Frankie, I will miss her so much."

"You'll miss shopping for her, too," he said. Then, with some surprise, he realized he would, too.

"But now, I have to think about something else," Anna said. "Frankie, I want a dog."

"A dog?"

"I've never had a dog and I've always wanted one, and Patty-Cake never had a dog and she always wanted one. I can have a dog now, can't I, for me and for Patty-Cake?"

"I've never had a dog either," he said. "My childhood didn't allow for any additional complications. Shall we go look for one tonight?"

How sweet, she thought. *How sweet this man is.* "No, I think it would be better to wait until after we move so the dog doesn't have to adjust quickly to two new homes in a row. And besides, I haven't even researched what kind of dog I'd like yet." Anna kissed Frankie's cheek, giving thanks to the angels for him.

"I didn't know you researched dogs," Frankie said. "I thought you just went to the pound and picked one."

"That's a thought," Anna answered absently, obviously going over various breeds in her mind.

But apparently not a very good one, Frankie thought with amusement. "Well, if we're not going dog shopping, how about a sunset?"

"Do we have time?"

"Barely, but if we leave pretty soon, I think we can make it. If not, we'll just sit and watch the afterglow. Then I'll take you to the Fish House for dinner."

"It will only take me a minute to change," she said, slipping off his lap. Frankie could hear her muttering as she moved down the hall. "That means we'll need a fenced yard in the new house, and we'll have to find a kind vet. I'll start asking at work to see who likes…" And she disappeared into the bedroom.

Watching her go, his stomach began to settle down. *I know you're only pretending to feel better right now, Anna. But I'm going to do my best to see that you really do feel better before the night is over. And of course, you can have a dog. Two, if it will make you happy.*

CHAPTER FOURTEEN

Frankie and Tony were at the Dome Grill the next morning.

"It's hard to believe it has only been a week since we had breakfast together at the rooftop restaurant at Disney World," said Tony.

"Tell me about it. Anna and I got back from the cruise on Wednesday night, and I've been going full tilt ever since." Then he told Tony about coming home the night before and finding Anna in tears.

"She sees and talks to angels?" Tony asked. "Hmm. We talk to the ELF, Anna talks to angels, Clive talks to wood sprites, Molly talks to fairies. Our world is really expanding, isn't it, Frankie?"

"Fairies?" Frankie asked. "And who is Molly, by the way?"

"Oh, my, we do have to catch up!" Tony said, laughing. "Not only do I have to tell you about Molly and her fairies, but about practicing your A-B-Cs, and why it is better to be grateful 'for' something than to be grateful 'to' someone. You're simply going to have to get with the program, Bro."

"I can hardly wait," Frankie said a little irritably. Digging into his hash and eggs with a vengeance, he somehow felt way out of the loop.

Slowly and patiently, and as well as his memory served him, Tony filled Frankie in on his conversations with the ELF.

"According the ELF," Tony explained, "we can have whatever we want by doing just three things. We have to ask for what we want. We have to believe that he will give it to us and stay out of his way while he does, and finally, we have to gratefully collect whatever we asked for when he delivers it. Get it, Frankie? Ask, believe, collect—it's as simple as A-B-C.

"So I've been trying to think of an example to use to tell you what I understand about practicing our A-B-Cs," Tony said as he generously spread marmalade on his whole wheat toast. "And it occurred to me in the shower this morning that we practice our A-B-Cs every Saturday morning when we come here for breakfast."

"We do?"

"Sure, we do. We walk right in here and ask Pete for what we want, exactly, down to the way we want our eggs cooked and our hash crisped. Then we come and sit down here and jaw a while, and get completely out of Pete's way while he arranges for our breakfast to be cooked the way we like it. We never wander into the kitchen and look over the cook's shoulder and offer to help cook our meal. We never wonder if the eggs are fresh or if Pete made enough hash. We're never afraid the cook might be hung-over and not able to cook as well as usual. We believe without question that we're going to get our breakfast just the way we ordered it, and we never even think about how that's going to happen. And then we gratefully collect our breakfast as soon as Pete calls our number. Sometimes you go up and get it, sometimes I go up and get it, and every once in a while, Pete delivers it to us. We don't argue about how our food gets to us, we collect it when, where, and how it gets to us." Tony breathed a little sigh of relief when he realized how good his example really was. "Those are all the steps in practicing our A-B-Cs. Ask, believe, collect—easy as A-B-C."

"So when we want something and we say so, or think so, or whatever, we are actually placing our order with the ELF, just like we would in a restaurant? That sounds so cut and dried," Frankie said.

"That's pretty much what I said at first," Tony agreed. "But when I told the ELF that practicing my A-B-Cs to get what I want just sounded too simple, he said there was nothing he could do to make it more complicated."

"He's pretty funny, isn't he?"

Reaching down on the seat beside him, Tony handed Frankie a book and a DVD set. "Here's the stuff I told you I was ordering for us," Tony said, handing Frankie a copy of the book *Ask and It Is Given* and the DVD series *MIND Is Your Own Business*. "The ELF said these would help both of us, so I bought us each a copy. And I brought you a little chart so you can translate what Abraham, the authors of the book, call the ELF and the Eternal Life Force so you don't get confused by the different names they use. And by the way, the ELF said to tell you that if you have any questions, just 'Go to ELF!'"

"Have you read any of the book yet?"

"Yes, and I can't wait for you to start reading it, too, so we can talk about it. It's all the same stuff the ELF is saying, but Abraham explains things a little differently. And for me, they reinforce what the ELF says. There's so much to tell you, Frankie. If you're not in a hurry this afternoon, I'll tell you all about what the ELF taught me about gratefulness, too."

"How much do I owe you?" Frankie asked, glancing at the back of the book to see what Esther and Jerry Hicks look like.

"Nothing this time, Bro. It's a gift. If we get more assignments from the ELF that have a price tag, you can spring for those, okay?"

"Fine," Frankie said absently, looking at the cover of the DVD series. "Who is this McLaughlin guy?"

"Some Irish minister of a faith I only recently heard about. But don't worry, because he's not at all preachy. If it didn't say on the package he was a minister, you'd never know it. He's pretty interesting, and he's very funny. I just found out that Mike Palmieri is also watching this series, and he really likes the guy. And Molly was very impressed when she watched a couple of these DVDs with me Thursday night. By now, I think she's half in love with him."

"Molly again," Frankie frowned. "Give it up about Molly, Tony."

Tony reminded Frankie that he had met Molly and Darth Vader a couple of weeks before at the elevator on Tony's floor at his condo building.

"Oh, yeah," Frankie nodded. "The cute little redhead with the ditsy dog. I remember. But you said you didn't know her."

"I didn't, then," Tony explained, bringing Frankie up to date on how he got to know Molly, starting with the night she knocked on his door and ending with her creating peace between Trainwreck and Darth Vader.

"She sounds interesting."

"She is, and she bakes like a dream, even if she does consult the fairies while she's doing it."

"Did you ask the ELF about people talking to fairies and sprites?" Frankie asked, thinking, *And now I guess I can add angels.*

"Yes, and he explained that everyone here in human form knows, or senses to one degree or another, that there is a life force, a divine intelligence bigger than we are. But some people either prefer not to try to communicate with the life force itsELF, or they don't realize they can.

"Instead, they turn to other kinds of guides for help. But the ELF explained that all those guides are his personal messengers. He named some besides the fairies and the wood sprites, including angels, saints, spirit guides, and something called devas. Whatever these guides hear or sense, they communicate immediately and directly to the ELF. He says it happens in a nanosecond because they are all the same energy, anyway."

"There must be something the matter with me," Frankie said. "Because I've never talked to any invisible beings in my whole life, except for the ELF, of course, and that's only recently. But you know, come to think of it, my mother talked directly to God all the time. She included him in almost every conversation, so you felt like it was a three-way deal. I remember her saying to me, 'Your father just can't help himself, Frankie. But God, I know someday you'll take the need to drink away from him.' That's probably why I always assumed God wasn't listening, because if he was, surely she deserved to be heard. I wonder if she saw the angels that came to take her patients away at All Children's Hospital, too."

"Changing the subject," Tony said, stacking some of his dirty dishes to the side so that he could enjoy another mug of coffee. "If you and Anna are going to be home for any part of tomorrow, I'd like to stop by sometime and bring your Christmas stockings. I just got them back from the seamstress, and I have to say, they're killers."

"Yeah, we're going to be home all day. But some of my guys are coming by early to paint the trim on the house and help me clean out the garage. I did tell you we're going to sell this house and buy one together, didn't I?"

"No," Tony said, laughing. "You didn't mention that. So much is happening to both of us now that what used to seem like big news becomes barely a footnote. Anna doesn't like your house?"

"She likes it fine. I'm the one who doesn't like my house. Never did," Frankie said. "It wasn't my choice; it was Mom's, remember. And I want Anna and me to start fresh in a place that is just ours. One we both like, where we can make our own memories."

"So have you talked to a realtor?"

"Yeah, I talked to Mike Palmieri, the guy you recommended. He suggested we fix a few things, add some fresh paint, and clean out the closets, the garage, and the room in the attic, which he calls a bonus room. He said we should put it on the market right after Christmas."

"I still think it's strange to find out that Mike is watching the same set of DVDs we are, and that he has enjoyed other programs of John McLaughlin's before. As Alice in Wonderland said, 'Life just gets curiouser and curiouser.'"

"You still think Palmieri's a straight shooter?"

"More than ever," Tony said, thinking, *And I'm going to feel really, really bad if I turn out to be wrong.*

"Anyway, my guys will be gone by three or four o'clock," Frankie continued. "So how about you come over for dinner? I'll throw a few steaks on the grill. Anna makes a 'to-live-for' salad with spinach and strawberries and some kind of hot dressing. You can spend a few hours getting to know the Lovely Anna better. She's an angel herself."

"She won't mind that you invite me for dinner without asking her?"

"I'm sure she won't. She's been asking me when we were going to have you over to see the wedding pictures. By the way, I did tell her that you knit, and I showed her the sweater again that she had admired the night we met."

"And did she freak?"

"Yeah, but not in the way I expected. She was kind of mad at me for not telling her when her mother was here, because her mother would have enjoyed talking knitting with you. Anna seems to think it's perfectly normal for you to knit."

"Well, maybe you'll catch up with her one of these days, Bro," Tony said, grinning. "Anyway, I'd love to come to dinner tomorrow night. I'll bring a bottle of merlot to top off the steaks."

Then clearing his throat a little uncomfortably, Tony asked the question that had been on his mind since he drove to Disney World with Julie and little Andy. "Frankie, this really isn't any of my business, but are you and Anna thinking about having kids?"

"No, we're not, Tony," Frankie said thoughtfully. "We talked about it before we got married, of course, and each of us was relieved the other really didn't want to have children. We figure we're nearly forty, and among other things, we don't want to be sixty when our kids are in their twenties. So we've decided just to spoil Andy rotten, and any other kids Julie may decide to have, too. Anna, of course, spends her life around kids, and I've never had any pull to be a father. Can't say why, but it just doesn't speak to me.

We're getting a dog, though," he added. "She just told me she wants a dog."

"I guess there's a connection there somewhere," Tony said, smiling. "Okay, so I'll see you at six-thirty tomorrow then."

"Wait. Make it seven," Frankie said, changing his mind. "Just in case after the guys leave Anna and I want to … uh, take a nap."

"A nap?" Tony said, raising one eyebrow. Then he raised the other eyebrow. "Yeah, right. A nap."

Frankie grinned. "There are advantages to having your own woman 'in house,' you know. Which leads me to suggest that you bring Molly with you to dinner tomorrow night. She sounds like someone Anna would really enjoy meeting."

"Well, we're not dating," Tony said with a bit more emphasis than necessary. "We're just watching DVDs together and letting our animals have play dates. But I guess I could ask her."

Then grinning, he added, "If she says yes, I bet she'll offer to bring dessert."

"Even better. And come to think of it, ask her to bring Darth Vader. We might as well give Anna a little 'dog-fix' to tide her over until we get our own."

"I'll call you later and let you know, okay?" Tony said, heading to his parking space, Nice to have your own woman 'in house', huh? I'll bet Anna would kick his butt if she heard him talk like that!

Tony called Molly as soon as he got home. "Hey, Molly, it's Tony," he said, not really knowing whether he wanted her to say yes or no to Frankie's invitation.

"And how are you on this beautiful Saturday?" she answered, her voice pleasantly cheerful.

"I'm just fine. I just got back from having breakfast with Frankie."

"Oh, yes, your Saturday morning ritual. How are the newlyweds?"

"Apparently fine, at least according to the husband. Frankie and I were talking about my new customers, and I told him how I landed the Yacht Club account yesterday, specifically to promote Molly Malone's Irish Desserts as their newest menu item. Then he wanted to know a little more about you, so I told him about how we met and how you're working with Sam and Mary, and it occurred to him that you and Anna would probably enjoy knowing each other. He asked me to bring you with me to their house for dinner tomorrow night. Would you like to go?"

"I would. I'd like that very much. Do you think they would be offended if I offered to bring dessert?"

"Well, I'd be lying to you, Molly, if I didn't tell you that Frankie and I were sort of counting on it, because Anna doesn't make anything but salads. He says she makes really good salads, but that's it."

"Does Frankie have a favorite dessert, do you know?"

"Hmm. Well, I know he loves German chocolate cake, because his mother used to make him one for his birthday every year."

"I'll see what I can do," Molly said, already assembling in her mind the ingredients for German chocolate cake. "What time should I be ready?"

"We'll leave around six-thirty, okay? Frankie's cooking steaks on the grill, so don't get dressed up. Oh, and Molly? They're thinking about getting a dog of some kind but don't know what kind yet, so Frankie was wondering if you'd bring Darth Vader for Anna to play with, just to see if he's the kind of dog she would like, too."

"Oh," she said with some amusement. "Darth Vader has never been invited out to dinner before. I'll have to give him a bath especially for the occasion, even though he won't like that part a bit."

Before he put Frankie and Anna's finished Christmas stockings in the box, Tony looked at them one more time. Definitely the best I've done yet, he thought, very pleased.

By trial and error, he had found that the best gift box for his now-famous Christmas stockings was a white florist box. The day before, he had picked up one from the florist next to the hotel, and he now layered it with tissue paper. He was ready to layer in the first stocking when Molly rang his doorbell.

"Oh, may I see them before you put them in the box?" Molly asked excitedly after their greeting.

Setting down her bakery box, she let Darth Vader off his leash to play with Trainwreck, and sat down on the floor in front of the coffee table to admire the stockings. "They are works of art, Tony," she said, sighing. "Such a talent you have!"

Smiling, he very carefully wrapped each Christmas stocking in tissue paper, laid them in the box, and tied the box with a wide red ribbon. The package was almost as pretty as its contents. "Ready?" Tony asked.

"Sure. Come here, Darth," Molly called, and the little dog trotted up to get his leash put back on. Gently scratching Trainwreck's ears to say goodbye, she and Tony walked out, each carrying a white box containing examples of their individual artistic talents.

When they pulled up in front of Frankie and Anna's house, Tony sat in the car a moment admiring the view. He hadn't been there for well over a year, except for poker games, which were always held after dark. The house looked quite different now. To go along with Frankie's cleaning and maintenance, Anna had added some personal touches.

The community of Woodlawn featured older homes of mixed architectural styles. Frankie's was a cream-colored frame house, and the fresh blue-grey paint on the trim glistened. The front door, a slightly darker shade of blue-grey, boasted a lovely brass door knocker. A brass mailbox beside the door wore a high shine, and the porch sported a pretty new banister. Two handsome rocking chairs sat side by side on the porch, and several lush flowering plants hung from the rafters.

A small garden with a comfortable bench in the center had been added in the middle of the front yard, and window boxes filled with impatiens graced the front windows. *Great curb appeal*, Tony thought, his artistic eye pleased. *Good job, Anna!*

Molly took in the whole scene with delight, and then caught her breath when Anna answered the door. Even to another woman, Anna was strikingly beautiful, and her sundress, which Tony recognized as the one she had worn for her wedding, suited her perfectly. Tony kissed Anna warmly on the cheek and introduced her to Molly and Darth Vader.

With Darth serving as an instant ice-breaker, Tony realized he was excess baggage as Anna and Molly walked toward the kitchen engrossed in easy conversation. Tony placed his white box on the hall table and headed outside to look for Frankie.

"Hey, Bro," Frankie said. "Did Molly come with you?"

"She did, and the two women are deep in the 'getting to know all about you' process. You need any help out here?"

"The day a good German boy needs the help of an Italian to broil a steak will be a sad day for Deutschland," Frankie said good-naturedly. "Sit down and get a beer from the cooler, and I'll tell you about my latest conversation with the ELF."

Tony settled himself at the picnic table across from Frankie while the grill was still getting hot.

"Anna went shopping for salad stuff this afternoon and I came out here on the patio to catch some rays," said Frankie. "I thought it might be a good time, so I asked the ELF if we could talk, and he appeared and sat right on the table in front of me.

"I asked him to explain about Anna and her angels. He told me pretty much what he told you. He said the Eternal Life Force has to constantly rearrange the universe to meet all the billions of requests he gets every day, not just from human beings but from animals, too, and that various beings who are not in physical form help him keep in touch with all that needs to be done. These beings are all individual expressions of him, as you and I are. They just don't have bodies, and to us, they are invisible.

"He explained that some people talk directly to the Eternal Life Force, who most call God. Others talk to the ELF, or their inner being, or higher self, or the Christ within. And still others talk to different invisible beings such as fairies, sprites, spirit guides, the voice, devas, angels, or saints. It doesn't matter a bit what kind of guide we talk to, he said, because the results are always the same. Talking to any of the ELF's messengers is exactly like talking directly to him.

"The angels that come when someone dies, he said, are there simply to bring comfort to the one who is leaving his or her human body behind. They are like escorts from one plane of existence to the other. And he said those same angels help babies come into their bodies when they are born. He also told me we each have a guardian angel with us all the time while we are here to help us in lots of other ways.

"He used an example that really convinced me, Bro," Frankie said, leaving his grill to heat and joining Tony at the table. "The other day, I was driving my van behind a truck when a large sheet of cardboard flew off the back of the truck and onto my windshield. In just a second, it was like being blinded. I couldn't see where I was going or how to pull over and stop the van. And then for no reason that I could see—there was no wind and nothing else natural to dislodge it—the cardboard gently slid down the hood and off to the side of the road. The ELF said that was the work of my guardian angel."

"Did you ask him about your mother's conversations with God?"

"He brought it up, because he knew it was on my mind, I guess, and he went back to talking about practicing our A-B-Cs to explain why God never seemed to hear my mother.

"He assured me that he heard her every time she said things like 'And I know, God, that someday you will do this or that,' but her prayers were couched in the future. If our requests or prayers ask for things to happen in the future, then whatever we are praying for will always remain in the future."

"I know I keep repeating this, but it's complicated, isn't it?" Tony asked.

"He says it's amazingly simple, and we make it complicated, but that we'll figure it all out soon enough."

Just at that moment, Anna and Molly came out of the house with paper plates, cups, and tableware.

"Are we going to be able to eat out here?" Anna asked Frankie, explaining to the others that sometimes they had mosquito invasions.

"Seems fine so far. Will you all be warm enough to eat outside?" Frankie asked.

"Yes!" the other three chorused.

After dinner when the air grew a little cool, they gathered in the living room for coffee and what Frankie soon would call "the best German chocolate cake I've ever eaten." The women had coffee, but knowing what Molly had in her bakery box, Tony had stopped at a convenience store and picked up half a gallon of milk for himself and Frankie. *Women never do seem to understand*, he thought, *that chocolate cake requires cold milk to make the cake taste even better.*

When they had finished exclaiming over Molly's dessert, Tony went to the hall for Frankie and Anna's wedding present.

"My word, I wasn't expecting anything like this," Anna exclaimed at her first look. "When Frankie said you were knitting us Christmas stockings, I pictured white stockings with candy-apple-red and Gumby-green reindeer worked into the pattern. These aren't just Christmas stockings, they're heirlooms."

With what could only be called reverence, she held up each one to study it in detail.

"They need to last, Anna, for at least fifty or sixty more years," Tony said quietly, noticing that Frankie's tear-veiled eyes remained riveted on Anna.

"But," he added in an effort to lift the mood, "your real wedding present is inside Frankie's stocking."

Anna slid her hand inside and pulled out a small mailing tube, which she handed to Frankie. Popping off the top, he drew out something that looked like a certificate. Reading it to himself and slowly drawing in his breath, he handed the paper to Anna.

"Twenty shares of Walt Disney stock in the name of Franklin and Anna Doerrer. You mean the real Walt Disney?" she asked incredulously.

"The real thing," Tony said, uncommonly pleased with the gift he had chosen. "I figure you two are going to drop enough money at Disney World over the next twenty or thirty years to contribute plenty to the value of that stock before you retire."

"Look at it, Molly," Anna said, drawing Molly into the conversation. "It's a real stock certificate, but it's got a picture of Mickey Mouse in all four corners. Isn't that cool?"

"I guess we'll be getting a safety deposit box tomorrow," Frankie said, taking back the certificate to have another look. "I don't know what to say, Bro. You've left me speechless. First the picture of *Rocky Horror,*" he said, pointing to the framed picture in the hallway, "then those amazing Christmas stockings, and now this. They're just all so … so special."

"Well, it's a good thing you're the kind of guy who mates for life, Frankie," Tony said, "because I wouldn't want to go through making all these choices again, ever." Then he ducked as Frankie reached over to cuff him on the side of the head—Frankie's way, of course, of saying "I love you, too, Bro."

Tony and Molly's walk to their car was long enough for Darth to handle his personal needs. Meanwhile, the ELF, sitting in one of the rockers on the front porch, heard Anna inside the house and Molly outside the house, say in unison, "Now that was just about a perfect evening."

Exactly what the men were thinking.

CHAPTER FIFTEEN

"How did you enjoy the Grand Prix last week?" Frankie asked Tony as they ate their Saturday morning breakfast at the Dome Grill.

The Formula 1 motor race through the downtown streets of St. Petersburg was world famous. "Oh, it was cool, especially since it was free. Those front row seats on my balcony are killers," Tony said, grinning. "The race probably annoys some of the condo owners around there because the sound booth is right under our units and we can hear every race being called, but I think it's fabulous. Of course, I couldn't get my car out of the parking lot for three days, but that was okay. I walked to the office. It didn't inconvenience me.

"I'm sorry you and Anna didn't want to come, but I also know that fast cars have never been your thing, Bro. Actually, we could have had almost as much fun without the race. It turned out to be a great group of people who came to watch it with me."

"Who did wind up coming? Not that you couldn't sell those seats if you wanted to."

"Mike Palmieri and his girlfriend came. He, of course, knows where the front row seats are in that building, so he asked if they could come and watch the race with me. And since I was going to be entertaining anyway, I called Bill Lee. Remember the guy who was my Big Brother?"

"Yeah, you said he took you to your first car show."

"He did. It was one of the best days of my life. He and his wife came over from Tampa. And Molly was there, too. She made us a picnic supper, even though we picnicked on the eleventh floor, and Mike brought up some extra chairs from one of the community rooms. There were six of us on the balcony watching the race together. It was great."

"I was in Palmieri's office signing my listing yesterday," Frankie said, "and he was bragging on the logo you did for him. I thought it was really good and I told him so. I would pick him out of a crowd in a heartbeat with that logo and the line 'The Grateful Realtor.' But now, Bro, I want to know how you really feel about going off into the woods with Clive this afternoon."

"You know, when I posted this trip on my calendar, the first week in December seemed like a long way off, but here it is. The timing turns out to be perfect, actually. I'm really ready for this little break in my routine. I've never been to the Ocala National Forest, have you?"

"No, but some friends of mine go up there camping. You're not camping, are you, Bro?"

"Who, me?" Tony asked, recoiling in surprise. "I don't camp. You know that. Clive says we're staying at the Bass Champions Restaurant and Lounge in Salt Springs tonight. Isn't that interesting? Then tomorrow morning, we'll start meandering at seven o'clock, hoping to see some evidence of deer. I brought a good heavy jacket. I think it will be brisk in the forest that early in the morning, but it will be an adventure."

"And you bought a walking stick?"

"I did. It's in the office. That's where I'm meeting Clive, so you can come see it when we leave here if you like. It's really gorgeous. It's made of blue ash. I'm planning to use it as a decoration in my new office after this weekend."

"You don't expect to become a regular meanderer, then?"

"Uh, no," Tony answered fairly emphatically. "So what's new

with you, Bro? Those three new contracts working out for you?"

"Yeah, those were great customer leads from Mike Palmieri. I pitched all three and got all three contracts. One of the new buildings we're cleaning is the one you live in. We're doing the pool, the gym, the hallways, the elevators, the lobby, and the meeting rooms three times a week, and the windows perpetually. I'm really grateful that you thought to ask him about that, even if it means I don't need to hire you to find more work for me right away."

"I'll get your money some other way. You know me; I'm tenacious."

"I put on a new crew, and I really like every one of the new guys. Times are tough for a lot of guys, you know? Most of them used to work in construction. They're glad to get clean, honest work for decent pay, and I'm stoked to get better help than I could hire normally. This recession seems to be working more for me than against me. And yes, ELF, I am grateful, and you know it."

"Now Frankie, you're beginning to sound like your mother, talking to God and me in the same conversation."

"Ask me if I care what I sound like. My life is too good to worry about things like that. Now, I've got something else to ask you about," Frankie said, leaning slightly forward across the table. "I got a call from my Uncle Lawrence in Connecticut. He's my father's brother. I only met him when he came down for Dad's funeral, and I've never met his wife. But you know, I don't have much family, so when Anna suggested we send them a wedding announcement, I said fine.

"So he calls and he's really sentimental. He's got no kids of his own. He never got a chance to know Julie and me, his only niece and nephew, and he wondered if Anna and I would like to come up to his place for Christmas."

"Hmm. Would you?"

"I think we might," Frankie said. "He sent pictures, and his place in Madison looks wonderful. He keeps a couple of horses and some cats, dogs, and chickens. And it might snow," he said. "Anna, of course, saw plenty of snow in Denver, but I've never seen it, have you?"

"No, I haven't. Dad keeps asking me every year to come to New York for Christmas so he can show me Rockefeller Center and Radio City Music Hall, and he says I'd go nuts over the animated store windows. I guess they're really somethin' else, but I've never taken him up on it."

"Well, here's what I was thinking, Tony. Anna would like to stop on the way for a day at Williamsburg, Virginia. She's always wanted to go there at Christmastime. It's all decorated like it was in colonial times, and she thinks it will be interesting. So I thought if you came with us, you and I could switch off and drive right through to Williamsburg, then we could stay a night in a hotel, clean up, visit Williamsburg, get a real night's sleep, and then I could drop you off at your dad's place on the way to see Uncle Lawrence. I could pick you up again on the way back, and we could do almost the same thing coming back, because Anna wants to visit Savannah, too."

"How long do you plan to be gone?"

"If we drive the way I'm thinking, probably twelve days, but that would work out okay for me, because Christmas is on a Saturday. So my crews will only have to clean the big buildings once between Thursday and Monday. We'd leave on a Friday and be back sometime on the Tuesday or Wednesday after Christmas. Could you do that, too, do you think?"

It's nice now that I'm my own boss, isn't it? Tony thought. "I'm pretty sure I could work that out. My customers won't want much from me between Christmas and New Year's, although I've got some good-sized promotions coming up right after the first of the year. Let me talk to Dad and see what he has planned. How soon do you have to know?"

"Oh, by next week will be fine. This is still just the first weekend in December."

"Okay, I'll let you know next Saturday. Now, you wanna come see my walking stick before it gets used in the Ocala National Forest?"

"I'll meet you in the lobby of the Fillmore in ten minutes," Frankie said. "I want to touch base with Mr. Ferguson, if I can. He has three tenants going out this week, and he wants me to give him an estimate for deep-cleaning their apartments. Maybe he can get me in to see at least one of them today so that I can get an idea of what that's going to take."

Sitting comfortably together, each with his back against a tall tree, Clive and Tony ate the lunch the inn had packed for them that morning.

"I gather you don't spend much time in the woods, Tony," Clive said seriously.

"Clive, the only other woods I've ever been in is a piece of land about the size of a basketball court with trees on it, and that was over twenty years ago."

"Hardly woods then, was it? In the city I suppose?"

"Right in the middle of the city. But it was big enough to hide a couple of teenage boys who wanted to get away from some pretty bad stuff going on at home. My friend Frankie and I called it Sherwood Forest, and we went there when we needed a safe place to think things out."

"Sherwood Forest? I didn't know Yank kids knew much about Robin Hood. He was my hero when I was a kid," Clive chuckled. "Rob from the rich and give to the poor. It all seemed so sensible to me."

"Us, too," Tony admitted. "I guess that's one of the reasons we called our secret space Sherwood Forest."

"Well, then, we have something about our childhood in common, don't we, even though we were a whole ocean apart?" Clive said, getting up and stowing the trash from lunch in his knapsack. "Shall we just have a look, Tony, at what's to see on the way back, then?"

They had come halfway on their "meandering," according to Clive's plan, and they planned to return by a different path to the place they had parked the car that morning. It had been only forty degrees Fahrenheit when they left the inn, but now it had warmed up to the mid-sixties, and Tony had stowed his heavy jacket in his backpack. He was comfortable in jeans and a long-sleeved sweatshirt. The walking staff, he had to admit, made the hiking quite pleasant.

They were standing at the junction of two paths. Even though Tony was relatively sure Clive knew which one to take, he asked if the wood sprites were giving Clive any clues about the better path to choose.

"Just listen," Clive suggested.

Tony listened. All he heard was the usual crackle typical of any wooded area—branches rubbing together, grasses rustling—except for one loud bird.

Clive pointed down one of the paths about fifteen yards to a bird sitting on an almost-bare branch singing its heart out. "It's calling us," Clive said, "so let's go the way the bird invites us to go. Do you believe in spirit guides, Tony?"

"As a matter of fact, I do. I believe different kinds of spirit guides assist different people when they need it," Tony answered, a little surprised to hear himself discussing the subject with such apparent ease. "Who do you call on for help in the city, Clive, where there are no wood sprites?"

"St. Christopher, actually. I used to ask him to guide me just when I was traveling. Then when I decided to open the shop and stop traveling so much, I wondered if he would stick around with me, and he did. If I'm confused about something, I ask him to straighten me out, and he helps me find my way. Or if I lose something, he helps me find it. If the problem is bigger than that, though, I just tell him what the problem is and leave it alone as much as I can so he can solve it his way. Frankly, Tony, I wonder what people do if they don't get some help from the spirit world. I suppose they just bump around feeling confused all the time.

"Now, let's have a look here," Clive said as he pointed to a hole in the ground. Since they started their meandering earlier in the day, Clive had been educating Tony about the creatures of the woods. They had seen deer tracks and heard the call of wild turkeys. They had seen abandoned bird nests, shed snake skins, spider webs, and things that lived under rocks.

"This is a fox squirrel hole," Clive explained. "They're nocturnal creatures. He's probably having a good nap about now. And over there in that scrub palm is a scrub jay."

Tony looked in the direction of a little blue bird sitting in a patch of sunlight warbling away. "They only live in Florida," Clive went on, as if it were his duty to teach Tony all he could in a short period of time.

"How do you know so much about Florida wildlife, Clive? You grew up a long way from here."

"Yes, but I've lived here thirty-five years, and I've always been fascinated by the creatures that live here, too. I read a lot, I meander a lot, and I talk to friends with similar interests. It's just what I do."

Several hours later, as they approached Tony's car and began to put their gear into the trunk, Tony realized how much he had enjoyed the whole meandering experience, including the dart game in the inn's pub the night before when Clive had trounced him soundly.

"I've really had a good time this weekend, Clive. I've had my eyes opened to a whole world of things. There's a lot of variety to life, isn't there?"

"I don't know how anyone could spend any time in nature and not believe that there is a creative intelligence beyond our ability to fully comprehend, because none of us could ever have thought up such a world, or managed to keep it all going. But the good news is that we don't have to understand it all, do we? We each just have to understand our own little bit."

"That piece of homespun philosophy should be put up on a banner and hung at the entrance to every city and town," Tony said, laughing. "Let's see, 'Welcome to Our Town, where you never have to understand it all, you just have to understand your own little bit.' I'm gonna have to come up with something wonderful to do with that."

"Be my guest, my friend," Clive said, chuckling as he walked around to his side of the car. "You're the advertising man."

When Tony and Frankie met again the next Saturday at the Dome Grill, each was full of news. "You first, Bro," Frankie said. "I want to hear about your meandering."

"Well, it was certainly different. I wouldn't want to do it every weekend, but Clive is such an interesting guy in his own way, I really enjoyed it. I'm no woodsman though, at least according to Clive."

"I doubt he'll make you into one, either," Frankie said knowingly. "How does Clive support himself? Surely he doesn't do it by selling canes and walking sticks."

"You'd be surprised. He does a good little business there, and he's only got himself to support. He has no family except his mother. 'Mum,' he calls her. She still lives in England."

"How do you promote the sale of canes? To doctors' offices?"

"You know, that's not a bad idea, Frankie. I'll keep that market in mind. So far, all I've done for him is create a few postcards, one that he's mailed out to members of the hiking clubs and bird-watching clubs he belongs to, and another one that he's mailed out to his old customers. And I made him a poster for the hotel lobby, and a display for his front window. But while we were driving back last Sunday, I talked to him about doing something else that has the potential to make him a lot more money.

"He came to my office while I was still moving in and showed me a cane he had just received that telescopes. It can fold down into itself until it's about the size of a cigar. It's just the right size for a woman to put into her purse or a man into his inside coat pocket. It opens in segments, and you twist each segment as you pull it out to lock it in place. It's a pretty clever design, actually.

"Clive tells me most elderly people need the help of a cane only for balance when they get tired or begin to feel ill. Otherwise, they don't like to use one. This kind of cane can be carried wherever they go without anyone knowing it, and they don't have to use it unless they need to."

"And you think there's a market for that?"

"I do, and I think it's a growing market. Remember, America is aging, just like us," Tony said, winking at Frankie. "I talked to Clive about using the Internet to promote his business, which would vastly expand his customer base. An ad would go out by e-mail to people all over the country in a demographic of sixty-five years of age and older, and with annual incomes in excess of fifty thousand dollars.

"I have an appointment tomorrow to visit the factory that makes these canes. Believe it or not, they are in Lutz, just north of Tampa. I talked to the factory owner by phone, and he told me they ship to individuals, so he's willing to ship right from the factory any orders we generate. Before I get Clive any more involved in my idea than he already is, I want to see for myself how clean their production line is, how much inventory they carry at any one time, and what kind of quality control measures are in place. Because someone could get really hurt if the cane didn't lock properly. And I want to see what their shipping procedure looks like."

"And if you like their operation?"

"Then I'll explore buying the e-mail lists from a company that will send our ads out in what is called an e-mail blast. We can contract for so many addresses and so many blasts, depending on what seems reasonable and affordable. My part will be to design a killer ad that will bring in the orders, and Clive's part will be to keep purchasing mailing lists until he's exhausted his market, if that ever happens. It could take years and provide him with a very consistent income."

"Now that's clever. How much will Clive's up-front costs be?"

"Don't know yet. It depends on how much the mailing lists cost."

"You're really having fun coming up with these promotional campaigns, aren't you, Bro?" Frankie asked.

"You know, I am, because I'm doing exactly what I want to do. I was just talking to the ELF about it yesterday. The last time we talked, he asked me to take some time to figure out what I wanted, and then he would talk to me about it. But he cautioned me to keep it simple. I did think about it. When I thought I knew what I wanted, I decided to 'Go to ELF!' and find out if I was on the right track. It was only five-thirty in the morning, but there he was, right on the rail of my balcony.

"What I want," I told the ELF, "is to make enough money to have all the things I want whenever I want them, by using my skills to help independent business men and women have all the things they want whenever they want them."

"What did he say?"

"He sighed, and I got the message right away that there was something wrong with my statement. Then I felt this great surge of love come over me. I guess he wanted me to know I wasn't about to be judged, just redirected. He explained to me that in the first part of the statement, I wasn't specific enough to get what I wanted, and in the second part, I was too specific to get what I wanted."

"'When you wrote this mission statement, or intention, or whatever it is, Tony, you completely forgot to practice your A-B-Cs,' the ELF explained. "'When you say you want to earn enough money to buy all the things you want, I can tell right away that you haven't the foggiest idea how much money that would be or what it is you are going to want. And if you don't know what you want, then neither do I. Before you ask me for something, you at least need to know what you are asking for and why you want it.

"'Then in the second part of your statement, you say you want to make that undisclosed amount of money by using your skills to help independent business men and women make their money. This will shock you, I know, Tony, but if you had come up with this statement a month ago, you would not have received your father's thirty-six thousand dollars, because you are clearly stating that the only way you want to receive money is to earn it by using your own skills.'"

"Ouch," Frankie said.

"Yeah, that's the way I felt. Like I had my hand slapped. So I asked him if he was upset with me."

"And what did he say to that?"

"He said no, of course he wasn't upset with me. He was never upset with me, and he didn't want me to be upset with myself, either. Then he gave me a tool to help me decide more specifically what I want and why I want it. It's called Life Design, and it's actually pretty simple, Bro. I brought a pad with me if you want me to show you how to use it."

"Of course I do."

Frankie put their dirty dishes on the tray and set the tray on an empty table while Tony took their coffee mugs to refill. Then he handed Frankie a legal pad and a pen.

"This Life Design process is based on four questions," Tony explained. "What do I want? Why do I want it? How will I feel when I get it? Why do I believe I can have it? So, write those four things on your pad, Frankie, leaving about half a page in between each question."

"What are they again?"

"At the top of the page write, 'What do I want?' Now go down to the middle of the page and write, 'Why do I want it?' Then at the top of the next page write, 'How will I feel when I get it?' And on the middle of that page write, 'Why do I believe I can have it?'

"So, what do you want, Bro," Tony continued, "or at least, what do you think you want?"

"I want to sell my house and buy one that Anna and I like better."

"Okay, then under 'What do I want?' write that down."

When Frankie finished writing, Tony said, "Now move down to the next question, 'Why do I want it?' and list all the reasons you want to sell your house and buy a different one."

Frankie wrote:

I want to sell my house so that I have enough cash to buy a bigger house without taking on a lot more debt.

I want to buy a newer house in very good condition so I don't have to make constant repairs.

I want to live in a more upscale neighborhood.

I want to buy a house that has three bedrooms instead of two.

I want to buy a house with at least one fireplace.

I want to buy a house that has a big fenced back yard with a porch or patio, and plenty of room for the dog to run.

"Is that the kind of thing you're talking about?" Frankie asked.

"Yes, exactly," Tony said. "Now go to the next question, 'How will I feel when I sell my house and buy a new one?' Then start listing how you will feel."

Frankie began to write again:

When I sell my house, I will feel free because I won't have to worry about so many repairs anymore.

I will feel happy that Anna and I will be able to choose our house together.

I will feel proud when I invite my friends to visit our new home.

I will feel excited because for the first time I will choose where I want to live and who will live there with me.

I will feel grateful for the money I make from the sale of my house.

"Very good, Frankie. Now the last question is 'Why do I believe I can sell my house?' Write down the reasons you believe you can sell your house."

Frankie wrote:

I believe I can sell my house in Woodlawn quickly because it is an attractive area of town and houses in my neighborhood usually sell pretty quickly.

Because the house I own will suit many kinds of buyers.

Because there are good schools in the area where I live.

Because I have a really good realtor working for me.

Because I know how to practice my A-B-Cs.

"Is that enough?" Frankie asked.

"The ELF said it's enough when you feel it's enough. How do you like the process?"

"Well, it makes you think, doesn't it? I had thought about why I wanted to sell the house, but never about how I would feel when it sold. And I was surprised at how strongly I believe it will sell, and soon. Pretty soon I'm going to have to replace one of my vans. I think I'll use Life Design to find out if I really want another one just like the one I have or if it is time for a change."

"According to the ELF, that's exactly the purpose of making these Life Design sheets," Tony explained. "So we can clarify in our own minds what we really want. He also said if we can't come up with enough 'whys' for what we think we want, we probably don't want it. I created a Life Design sheet for a software package I thought I wanted, but I couldn't come up with more than two 'whys,'" Tony continued. "Apparently I don't really want it, and if I ever do, I guess the 'whys' will have increased by then. That one use of this process, alone, saved me time and kept me from wasting money."

"Well, now, as John McLaughlin says on our DVDs, isn't that interesting?" Frankie said, winking at Tony.

"Yeah," Tony said, chuckling. "Isn't it, though?"

Frankie started to hand Tony back his pad. "Keep that pad, Bro," Tony said, "to remind you of the four questions of Life Design: What do I want? Why do I want it? How will I feel when I get it? Why do I believe I can have it? And the ELF also said that as soon as we decide what we really want, to be sure to ask him for it, believe that he will get it for us, and then prepare ourselves to collect it. I love the way he gets really colorful whenever he says, 'Remember, Tony, getting what you really want is as simple as A-B-C.'"

Tony settled back with his coffee. "Now, to completely change the subject, are you still planning to take the trip to Connecticut for Christmas?"

"Yes, which brings me to my question. Are you going with us?"

"I am," Tony said. "Dad was ecstatic about my coming. It seems that Uncle Fred is planning to visit his daughter this Christmas, so I don't even have to go to a hotel. I can stay in Uncle Fred's room. Dad's now busy setting up a full sightseeing tour for when I get there. So just tell me when to be packed and ready."

"We're planning to leave on Friday the seventeenth after breakfast. I figured since we won't be around the next morning, all three of us could have breakfast here with Pete before we go. You know, wish him a Merry Christmas from his two best customers. The next Saturday is Christmas Day, and he won't be open, anyway.

"I've got all the maps and mileages," he continued. "With you and me switching off driving, I figure we can drive straight through to Williamsburg, stopping for meals and stuff but not staying at a hotel until Saturday night. That leg of the trip is around seven hundred and fifty miles. Anna booked us a room at the Williamsburg Inn in Williamsburg for Saturday and Sunday. Then we'll drive to your Dad's on Monday, and Anna and I will go right on to Madison that night. It's about three hundred miles from Williamsburg to New York City, and another hundred miles to Madison."

"So then I can tell Dad to expect me on Monday the twentieth?"

"Yeah, and you can call him along the way, too, but I would expect we could be in New York City by late afternoon. He lives in Brooklyn, right?"

"Yeah, that's right. Is Anna excited about the trip?"

"Out of her mind," Frankie replied. "Ordering us cold-weather clothes on the Internet and making sure she has presents for everyone, even though she doesn't know them or even much about them. Women live in a different world, Tony, but as long as all I have to do is help pay the bills and she's happy, it's all okay with me. Did you hear John McLaughlin say on the DVD that the secret to a happy life is a happy wife? The guy knows what he is talking about."

"By the way," Tony asked, "did I also tell you I asked the ELF if he had any suggestions about what to give my father for Christmas?"

"No. What did he say?"

"What he always says: If I know enough to ask the question, I already know the answer."

"Annoying, isn't it?" Frankie winced, having been told the same thing himself several times.

"You got that right. But you know, Frankie, I realized very quickly that I did know the answer. I had noticed a few years ago when Dad sent me pictures of his apartment that he had cut out some of my old magazine ads and thumb-tacked them onto his bedroom wall, just like he used to keep my old drawings when I was a kid. And I realized then that I've never created any kind of original art just for him. It crossed my mind to draw something special for him, but then the thought went right out of my mind. Funny, isn't it, how I remembered those magazine cut-outs in his bedroom almost as soon as I finished my conversation with the ELF?"

"I hate to keep repeating myself, but isn't that interesting?" Frankie smirked. "So are you drawing him something special?"

"It's all done. I created a drawing of a bridge that is a combination of the Brooklyn Bridge, which he can see from the windows of his apartment in New York, and the Sunshine Skyway Bridge, which he can see from his condominium balcony down here. Then I sketched him sitting up on the superstructure of the bridge knitting, like he's knitting the two bridges together. It's pretty cool, if I do say so myself."

"How are we getting it in the van?" Frankie asked, thinking of all the things Anna planned to take with them. "Or are you shipping it ahead?"

"Don't look so panicked, Bro," Tony said with a grin, remembering the whole episode in Carrabba's when he had brought Frankie and Anna their engagement present. "I'll just carry it in a tube in my suitcase and take it to a framer while I'm there. Dad can even pick out his own frame. Now, what's on your mind today, Frankie? So far, I've been doing all the talking."

"Actually, I've got appreciation on my mind."

"Oh?"

"Yeah, I was reading in *Ask and It Is Given* all the reasons for starting a 'Rampage of Appreciation,' and what got me in the gut was the statement that I should practice appreciation when my thoughts are taking me in a negative direction.

"I haven't said any of this to Anna, because she's so excited about the trip and having such a good time, but planning this trip dug up some old stuff for me, Tony. I mean, I'm looking forward to meeting Uncle Lawrence and getting to know him better. I've always felt a little strange about not having any family except Julie, when everyone else seems to have a lot of family. But the subject of family or Christmas or something sent my mind catapulting back to how Mom always tried to make something good out of Christmas, but never succeeded. I started having both sad and mad thoughts at the same time, which used to be the only two kinds of thoughts I ever had. I was just plain feeling awful and pretending I wasn't, for Anna's sake, when I read about a 'Rampage of Appreciation.'"

"Why didn't you call me? You coulda talked it out with me, Frankie. You've done that for me before when the old memories made me crazy. Lots of times."

"It started while you were meandering with Clive. I know I could have called you on your cell phone, but I decided to do what the book said first, to see if it would help.

"The directions said to look around the room I was sitting in and begin thinking of things to be grateful for right there. My mother came right to my mind. I am, after all, still living in her house, and she loved it and made it a home. You know, I blamed her, Tony, for putting up with my father and forcing us all into a life that was awful most of the time. But she did her best, under the circumstances, to keep the house clean and nice, even if there was a good chance he'd smash everything to pieces. When he did, she just went out and bought more stuff. I felt very grateful for my mother's attempts to keep our home nice, and grateful she finally got a house she liked that nobody could smash up and ruin for her."

"Then did you feel better?"

"I really did. So then I let myself think about my father to see if there was anything about him I could be grateful for, and there was. I thought of a few good times with him, like one weekend when he stayed sober and we all went to the Florida State Fair. It wasn't much, but it was a different kind of memory, because all four of us had a really good time. He won a gigantic teddy bear for Julie, and he and I shot at some targets together. He was pretty good, too.

"Then I realized that as mean and drunk as he could be most of the time, he always earned a living, and my mother, Julie, and I were never cold or hungry. We had a miserable time at home, but we didn't miss out on anything at school. I skateboarded. I belonged to the swim club. I was on the track team and had a membership at the gym. I had good trendy clothes. I got a class ring. I went to the prom. I had my own car when I was seventeen. And even when he died, my father provided for us. I couldn't have started my company without the money his insurance policy paid out. The 'Rampage of Appreciation' created this huge catharsis for me, Tony. It was amazing."

"That really is amazing, because even the mention of his name used to cause you real hard pain," Tony said, touched to the bone by the benevolent look on Frankie's face when he talked this way about his father.

"Well, my point here, Bro, is that I sat there for hours being grateful for thousands of blessings, including, most of all, you and Anna and Julie. And you know what happened?"

"No, but I sure want to find out."

"The pain stopped. I realized that an old tape had been running in my head for years, constantly beating the drum of my terrible childhood. It was kind of a 'Why me?' song that never shut up, day or night. And now it's gone. I can't explain it. It's just gone, and I feel like I let go of a five hundred pound weight in my head. I just couldn't wait to tell you, because you're the only person I know who might possibly understand how good that could feel."

"Yeah, I can imagine, Frankie. It must be huge."

Reaching his big, calloused workman's hand across the table and laying it on top of Tony's arm, Frankie said, "You ought to try it, Bro. You really ought to try it. Because I just know you're still running some kind of tape like that of your own."

CONCEPT VI

Realizing . . .
The answers you seek are inside your heart

CHAPTER SIXTEEN

Tony drove around town doing errands. To be sure he had done everything he had promised each of his clients before he left on his Christmas trip to visit Luca, he ran a mental inventory.

The Fillmore Café was doing well. Molly's desserts had proven to be a draw, and the addition of soup and salad at lunch was working. Sam had started to develop a nice little lunch take-out business as well, and Molly's rent every month meant the café was no longer on the financial ropes. All in all, Tony was pleased with the way his first account had prospered under the guidance of E.L.F. Promotions, and there was nothing new for him to do for Sam at the moment.

The Fillmore Hotel was full and had five people on its waiting list, thanks to the ads in the Fine Arts Museum publication, so that account was on hold for a while, too.

Meanderings had done a lively little business in designer canes and walking staffs for holiday gift-giving, so Clive could afford to visit his mum in England for Christmas. Tony had liked the way the collapsible cane factory in Lutz did business, so he had researched the purchase of e-mail lists and had given the information to Clive to consider for a promotional campaign in February. The up-front investment for that project would run in the range of $2,000 for both the ad and start-up mailing list of 5,000 people in Florida and Arizona. Clive was pondering it, and had told Tony he would make a decision during the holidays.

Molly had two new accounts Tony had found for her. One was a caterer who did parties only on Snell Island, and her business would balloon during the holidays. Sometimes her firm catered three or four parties a day of over fifty guests each. The Yacht Club planned to break out Molly's desserts on New Year's Eve, so she had one whole freezer stocked for that account. Of course, she baked for the Fillmore Café every day, and supplied another small restaurant in Gulfport with exclusive desserts. She wanted at least two more steady accounts for the coming year, but for now, she was a satisfied client.

Tony had designed a clever e-mail for the Yacht Club to remind members to make their reservations for Christmas and New Year's Eve. He had also designed attention-grabbing table cards for them to promote Molly Malone's Irish Desserts. They hadn't ordered any more work from him since, but Tony planned a visit to the club manager soon after he returned from New York. He had a few new ideas to keep their members coming in throughout the year.

That left Mike Palmieri. Tony made a note to call him as soon as he got to the office.

Just as he parked on the street in front of the Fillmore, he grinned as he noted the next "coincidence" occurring between him and his biggest client. Mike was getting out of his car two parking spaces ahead.

"Hi, Mike. What brings you to my neck of the woods?" Tony asked, meeting Mike on the sidewalk.

"I didn't know this was your neck of the woods," Mike said, shaking Tony's hand. "Your office is in this hotel?"

"Right here," Tony said, pointing to the storefront directly in front of them. "No sign yet, though. The shoemaker's children never have shoes, and all that. Customers first, you know." Tony looked a little sheepish.

"Well, I'm here because I have a client living in this hotel," Mike explained. "I've had her house on the market, and we've got a contract on it."

"When you finish with your client, would you have time to stop by for a few minutes? I have your January and February greeting cards done, and I'd like to show them to you before I go out of town for Christmas."

"I have time right now, and I'm anxious to see them. My appointment with my client is anytime between two and four, and it's only two-thirty now. Let's go look."

In his office, Tony opened his laptop, pulled up the file with the January greeting card, and let Mike take it all in. The card was round, mimicking the round shape of the new logo. Inside the circle was a wintery-looking street scene with deep clouds and gray shadows. A little button read, "Click on the clock to turn on the lights." With one mouse click, light flooded the picture from the clock tower, street lights, store windows, headlights, and even the moon. Below the circle and slightly to the right, a coupon read, "In appreciation for the bright light you are in my life, I would like to give you a small gift."

Then there was a picture of a small LED flashlight about three inches long, and two lines of copy below the picture described the light and some of its uses. Below the picture were the words, "Please take this coupon to Office Depot at any of the locations listed below to pick up your special gift." Below the coupon, "Happy New Year" was written in script, followed by Mike's new logo, name, address, phone number, and the tag line "The Grateful Realtor."

"I'm speechless, Tony," Mike said, "and that doesn't happen very often, trust me. This is wonderful."

"Thanks," Tony said, handing Mike one of the flashlights. "I had hoped it was what you wanted. Now that you've lived with the new logo for a few weeks, is it still working for you?"

"You bet. I love the new logo, and so far, so does everyone who has seen it. And this little flashlight is just the kind of gift I was hoping for. How much will these cost?"

"They retail for four dollars each, but your cost will be two dollars each, plus the sales tax. Office Depot will absorb the other two dollars, and their general manager told me that he hopes to bill you for all two hundred redeemed coupons. These flashlights come in white, like this one, or in red, black or silver—customer's choice—and Office Depot guarantees them."

"Wow, I'm really impressed, Tony. Now, I hate to sound greedy, but did you say you had the February greeting card done, too?"

Tony clicked to another screen on his laptop, and there it was. The February greeting card was shaped like a heart, the center of the heart was red but with no message on it until a sign popped up in the center. "Click here for my Valentine message to you," read the sign. With one mouse click, the heart filled up with dozens of little candy hearts in pastel colors bearing messages: Be Mine, Yum Yum, I Love You, You're Cool, Cloud Nine, and Puppy Love. The coupon read, "I'm sending you a little present for Valentine's Day." Below that was a picture of a red glass heart-shaped paperweight, and a few lines of description along with the instruction to redeem the coupon at any of the Pier 1 Imports locations listed below.

While Mike read the card in detail, Tony reached into the out box on his desk and handed Mike a paperweight like the one described in the coupon.

"They have enough of these in stock?" Mike asked, turning the paperweight over in his hand to examine it more closely.

"Each store has five hundred in stock, and they can get more from their Clearwater and Sarasota stores if they need to. These will cost you almost your entire three dollars, and the store is still eating more than half the retail cost of the paperweight, which is six ninety-five. I thought they were exceptionally nice, though. I bought one myself," Tony said, pointing to a pile of papers anchored by a heart paperweight on the credenza.

"They look like they cost much more, don't they?" Mike said. "I am ecstatic, Tony. I can't wait to see the other ten messages."

"Well, I don't have all of the greeting cards created yet, but here's a list of the gifts I'm suggesting for all twelve months. I can get you samples of most of them. Some of them you may have to redeem on site, though, like one of Molly Malone's Irish Desserts for the month of March."

"I met Molly at your Grand Prix party and I've already sampled her desserts. That one will really be some treat for my customers. And I like that these merchants are spread all over town, so at least some will be super-convenient for everyone," Mike commented as he surveyed the gift list.

"I think you'll find this campaign has a synergistic effect, Mike. As each customer redeems one coupon and really likes the little gift, he or she will start watching for the next coupon. And even though I know this isn't your real purpose, some of them will be reminded to call you when they want to buy or sell real estate."

"I'll take some of that, too, if that's how it works out, and I will continue to be grateful for it," Mike said, shaking Tony's hand. "Bill me for these two right away, will you, Tony?"

"Oh, I can do better than that," Tony said, from his out box extracting an envelope with Mike's name on it.

"I prefer to deliver my invoices in person." He grinned and handed Mike his bill. "I'll e-mail these files to you as soon as you leave so you can send them out whenever you like."

"I'll cut you a check right away," Mike said, grinning back at him. "You said you are going out of town for the holidays, Tony? I was going to invite you to my open house."

"You know Frankie and Anna Doerrer? Frankie said he was listing their house with you."

"Oh, yes. Great couple. I forgot that Frankie said he was a friend of yours."

"Frankie is my oldest friend, and Anna is, of course, a new one. We're driving north together to visit family in New York and Connecticut. We're leaving on the seventeenth, but we'll be back before New Year's."

"Well, then, have a great trip, and I'll see you when you get back."

"I'll be working on your blog in January, Mike, and I'll have two more greeting cards for you by the end of that month. You have a great holiday, too, and good luck with your contract. You can get to the hotel lobby right from here," Tony said, pointing to the inside door.

Tony sat in his home office and sighed, absently scratching Trainwreck's ears while consulting his to-do list. He would be leaving for New York in four days, and even though he would have enjoyed a lazy do-nothing day, he still had things to do.

He was almost packed for the trip. His father's present was ready, and so was the nice wool scarf he had knit for his uncle. He was packing Anna and Frankie's presents, too. Since Tony wouldn't be with them on Christmas, they had agreed to celebrate Christmas together in Savannah on the way back. Tony didn't own much in the way of cold-weather clothes, but he planned on layering shirts and sweaters, and he could always buy a coat in New York if he needed one. Today, the temperature in New York City and the temperature in Tampa were identical, but he knew that could change quickly.

All of his client work was up to date, and when Mike's check came in, there would be enough money in the company account to pay all the bills for January. If Clive decided to go ahead with the marketing of the collapsible canes, that work would pay a good part of February's bills. But the truth was that E.L.F. Promotions could not survive long with only six accounts, three of which had already gone into hiatus.

He had written that into his marketing plan. Small businesses would be loyal, he knew, but no single company would need his services all the time. That was the reason he had set a goal to have a client base of twenty-five to thirty active small businesses he could serve as needed.

An interesting side benefit of finding the gifts for Mike's clients was that some of these businesses were potential clients for E.L.F. Promotions, too. The owners of the plant nursery, which would offer a hanging plant in June for Mike's promotion, were interested in talking to Tony about a spring ad campaign for their business.

Sweet Cheeks Candy and Beauty Bar would be providing a jar of red, white, and blue jelly beans in July, and the owner wanted to talk to Tony after the first of the year, as well. The business was generally promoted in October, December, and February, for obvious reasons, but the owner was open to listening if Tony had other ideas.

The most fun potential client, though, was Gallagher's Pumpkin and Christmas Tree Patch, which sold fresh pumpkins only from September through October. It would supply six-inch pumpkins in October for Mike's clients. From Tony, though, the owner was interested in banners, flyers, print ads, and any other suggestions for selling pumpkins that Tony could conjure up, and was also open to whatever possibilities Tony could recommend for the Christmas tree lot the owner operated in November and December. Tony had some potential small business clients in the pipeline, but not nearly enough, so he decided on three steps to take to let the ELF know he was asking for business, and he would complete them all before he left on the trip. He hoped the trip would be so interesting it would keep him out of the ELF's hair so he would avoid interfering once he did the asking.

Today he would do some Life Design sheets to clarify some of the things he wanted and why he wanted them. Later, he would get out *Ask and It Is Given* and read the directions for a "Rampage of Appreciation." Frankie had convinced Tony that gratefulness was a truly healing process, and Mike Palmieri was convinced of the same thing. Finally, Tony decided, he would spend all he next day in his office designing his own "brand." He was beginning to feel embarrassed that he used temporary business cards and billed his clients on plain white stationery, not to mention still having no sign for his office door. He simply needed to ignore the clutchy feeling in his stomach when he thought about promoting E.L.F. Promotions. It was crazy, and he just needed to push through it.

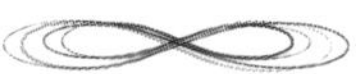

The next morning, Tony got out of bed and became his own client. Wanting no excuses for delaying his process, he changed his mind about going to his office and started right where he was in his home office. He had played with designs for weeks, so he picked one and systematically built a 'brand' for E.L.F. Promotions, including a logo, business cards, stationery, invoices, and a simple statement that defined his message and purpose.

The finished package was polished, professional, and high-end. And boring. Something was missing and he knew it. If he had designed this package for a client, he would have tossed it all before even showing it to the client, because it didn't thrill him. What was wrong? He didn't know, and it troubled him deeply. Why could he never seem to do for himself what he did so easily for his clients?

He made himself a sandwich and a pot of coffee. After eating, he carried his coffee into the living room. The longing in his heart to find the answer to his own question was so strong and so real that the ELF shimmered onto the edge of the coffee table without even being asked.

"What the hell's the matter with me?" Tony asked the ELF, immediately apologizing for his language.

The ELF chuckled. "Heaven and hell are human concepts, Tony," the ELF explained. "There's no hell where I am, thank goodness. But because I am you, I can feel your hell, and it isn't a good feeling."

"I just don't get it," Tony said. "I'm full of energy and ideas.

I guess you heard me talking to Frankie last Saturday. I'm having fun with this business, I'm learning, and my clients are happy. But I can't make enough money to stay alive with only six clients, and I can't conjure up the energy to promote myself. Why not?"

"I hate to keep repeating myself," the ELF said, "but you're never given a question for which you don't already know the answer. You just don't want to look at it."

"I don't know where to look," Tony said simply. "I can't identify a single box I've created that needs breaking up. I'm not holding back with this business. In fact, I'm way out on a limb sometimes."

"The answer is in your heart, Tony, and you avoid going to your heart with great creativity."

"Hearts hurt."

"Sometimes, but they hurt only when you've left something painful in them that you won't allow to escape."

"I'm not going back there, and you can't make me. I said I wouldn't and I won't," Tony said stubbornly.

Then he realized to whom he was talking. "Can you make me?"

"No, nor would I if I could," the ELF said, "but I know what is there. I was there when you locked it up and thought you threw away the key. You're almost forty years old, Tony. A piece of your heart has remained closed for nearly thirty years. If you allow it to, your body will serve you for at least another forty or fifty years. Do you want to spend those years asking the same empty question over and over? Let's see, how did you put it? Oh, yes. 'What the hell is the matter with me?' You can't get out of your own hell, Tony, until you allow your heart to open up and give you directions."

Tony sat in silence, his feelings washing over him. Pondering the ELF's question, he made a decision. "No, I don't want to waste my life wondering what's wrong with me," he told the ELF. "I don't want to miss out on anything. But I can't go back there alone. I mean, I just can't. I'm not even sure I can do it with you."

"I am you, Tony. I'm always with you. Keep in mind that hurt and pain are part of the human experience, but it isn't necessary to suffer from them for very long. You've been suffering with your pain way too long. When you locked it away, you dulled it, but you didn't extinguish it. You can walk through it now and come out the other side for good. Are you ready?"

Stark terror nipped at Tony's gut. "Bring it on," he said bravely, "bring it on."

Leaning his head back on the couch, he closed his eyes and very cautiously let his mind travel back to the day Denny was killed.

Tony was telling the lady who had called on the telephone that she had a wrong number when he heard his mother scream. He dropped the telephone and ran outside. No one was in the yard, but he saw people in the street. The scene began to unravel itself in stages.

Denny's little body, twisted in an inhuman way, was splayed out on the pavement. Beside him, a few feet away, Tony's dog lay perfectly still. A man, the driver of the van, was trying to keep people away from Denny. His mother was screaming at the top of her lungs, and wouldn't—or couldn't—stop. When Tony turned his head, he saw his father running toward them as fast as he could, calling out his wife's name.

Tony rushed to his mother and tried to hold her, but she shoved him away. When his father reached her, she shoved him away, too. Tony and his father tried again and again, but she wouldn't let them touch her. She just screamed and screamed. Then an ambulance came. His parents got into the ambulance with Denny. Their neighbor, a woman whose name Tony couldn't remember, said she would take him home with her. His father kissed him goodbye, and the ambulance doors closed. Tony begged to go with them, but nobody listened. Nobody heard.

Tony was alone and too young to do anything.

He went to school that week, each afternoon returning home to wait for his family to return. At the end of the week, his father did come home, dull with grief. He told Tony his brother was dead and his mother was in a special hospital where she would stay for a while.

His father went to visit her every day, but Tony wasn't allowed to go. Every time his father came home from a visit, he looked sadder.

Tony did the only thing he knew to do. He took care of his father. He cleaned the house as well as he could, he went to the corner store and bought bread and bologna and cheese, and he made his father sandwiches. He got up and went to school every day, and more importantly, he never complained. One thing his father didn't need was complaints from him.

Tony was very happy when his father said his mother would be home the next day. After school, Tony cleaned up his parents' bedroom. He washed and dried the sheets. It took him a long time to make the bed, he remembered, and he hadn't been fond of making beds ever since.

When his mother came home that night, he ran to her and hugged her. She didn't hug him back; she pushed him away and went to her room.

"She's so tired," his father explained. "Give her time, Tony. Give her time."

And so Tony did. He talked to her sometimes about what was going on in school and in the neighborhood, but she didn't seem to hear. Sometimes he tried kissing her cheek, but she turned away.

Then the violence started. She began screaming every night, and breaking furniture, and throwing things at his father. It was quite a while, though, before Tony realized how much he hated it.

Now, Tony felt his whole body stiffen. Opening his eyes, he looked at the ELF. His body began to tremble, but the ELF held his gaze. In a moment, Tony took a deep breath and went back into his memory.

It was his eleventh birthday, not that it made a difference. His mother didn't remember, and his busy and exhausted father didn't, either. Tony went to bed that night accepting that his birthday was just another terrible day like all the others. He had closed his eyes and begged sleep to come when a terrible, awful question began to consume him. He had been on the edge of asking it before—not that anyone would listen—but he'd always been able to push it away. Now the question wouldn't go away, and he felt it filling up not only his mind, but his heart and body, too.

He threw the covers off and screamed at the top of his lungs. "Denny is dead, but what about me, Mama? What about me? Why don't you come back and just love me, Mama? Why can't you just love me?"

But she didn't come or answer him, and he cried himself to sleep knowing she never would.

Sitting in his own living room twenty-seven years later, Tony was overwhelmed by that same awful, confused feeling he had felt as a little boy. He still needed an answer to the burning question he had tucked away in his heart all those years earlier, and the thought consumed him.

That was when he heard the noise. Starting as a growl in his gut, it grew into a thunderous roar in his throat. Springing to his feet, he let the sound explode like the cry of a wounded animal, searing his throat and rattling his eardrums. Then he sank down onto the couch, his body spent. His head in his hands, he let the tears flow—hot, silent, burning tears—a raging deluge that left him empty and weak. And cleansed.

Lifting his head, he looked at the ELF. "Why wasn't I enough for my mother? Did she ever love me? Or did she stop loving me when Denny was born? Or did it happen when he died?"

"There's something you don't know about your mother," the ELF said kindly. "You don't know, because she never told anyone—not her parents, not even your father. Your mother's favorite brother, Art, was killed when she was fifteen and he was seventeen. He was out joyriding with a friend. They took a corner too fast and slammed into a tree, and Art was killed instantly. About two hours before he had left for that ride, Art had asked your mother to go to a movie with him that night, and she had turned him down. So he went out with his friend instead.

"I'm sure you can figure out that she blamed herself one-hundred percent for Art's death. No matter how many times she went over the story of his death in her mind, it always wound up that it was her fault, because it wouldn't have happened, she concluded, if she had gone to a movie with him in the first place. Her feelings of guilt grew so large that many times she considered killing herself. Finally, she decided she had to make a choice: die and get it over with, or bury the memory and go on living. She chose to bury the memory.

"She married your father, whom she truly did love. Then she had you, and she more than loved you, Tony; she adored you. She never planned on having Denny. You were the only child she had ever wanted, she said, and you were more than she deserved. But Denny was born anyway, and everything about him terrified her. He was such a happy child—the one all of you called Sunshine Yellow—that she decided he was a sign that something awful was going to happen to finally punish her for Art's death. Those dark, fearful thoughts licked away at her sanity, and when Denny was killed, she died with him, on one level. Right there in the street as she looked at Denny's twisted little body, her massive guilt and her need to blame herself for both his death and Art's was so huge that she closed her heart completely to herself, to you, to your father, to me, and to life itself.

"The night you screamed in your bed, your mother couldn't hear you physically, mentally, or emotionally. Her heart was slammed shut, her mind completely distorted by her horrendous guilt. No one else existed on this planet, or off it, either, for your mother, Tony. No one.

"I heard you, of course. I felt your terror. I felt your huge hurt. I vibrated with your screams. And I felt you tuck away in your heart the question of whether your mother had ever loved you so you would never have to ask it again. And then, slowly over the years, based on all the wrong evidence, you made up your own answer. You decided that you weren't good enough for your own mother to love, and therefore, you would never be good enough for anyone else to love, including yourself."

"Is that why I haven't been able to promote my own work?"

"Of course. It's also why you're almost forty years old, Tony, and have deeply loved only two people: your father and Frankie. It's time to let up on yourself now, Tony. You need to begin to see yourself the way others see you, which is only half as amazing as the way I see you."

"Are there other people who feel like I have felt? That something way beyond their control happened to them to make them believe something huge was wrong with them?"

"I would venture a guess, Tony, that at least eighty percent of you who are in physical form have completely forgotten you are marvelous beings with unlimited potential. 'I'm not good enough' is a terrible blight on the human spirit, and it is pervasive in your society."

"Well, surely all those people weren't rejected by their mothers when they were kids," Tony said.

"Everyone who is here in physical form has a life story to tell. No two stories are alike in detail, but many are alike in general. Those who have decided that they aren't 'good enough' have felt seriously put down and rejected by a parent, or grandparent, or sibling, or teacher, or first love, or best friend, or even by me. A few were victims of someone who hurt them intentionally, but by far the greater number was hurt by someone like your mother, who was so deeply mired in her own pain that she didn't even know who you were anymore.

"Let me assure you, Tony—and remember who you are talking to—in or out of this world, there is nothing wrong with you, and there never was. What you have all these years believed was a betrayal had absolutely nothing to do with you, personally. The only person your mother rejected was herself. She simply checked out of life as she had known it up until then, and she went to a place where no one else could follow her."

The ELF sat quietly and let Tony absorb that information.

Finally, Tony emerged from his thoughts. "Well, I do feel somewhat better. You knew I would. I'm not all the way up to feeling good yet, but who knows? I'm willing to believe it can happen."

"Are you at least ready to accept, then, that there is nothing 'the hell' the matter with you?"

"Well, I didn't think you could say anything to make me smile tonight, but yeah, I guess there's nothing the hell the matter with me. Really. I don't know about letting myself love people, though—I mean besides my father and Frankie. It just seems too . . . dangerous."

As if on cue, Trainwreck jumped into Tony's lap and began climbing up his chest, the way he had when Tony had peeled him off the telephone pole. Tony slipped his arm under his cat to support him and let him nestle his head into his neck. At the same time, Tony ran his hand down the cat's back and stopped at the bald place. Trainwreck began to purr his deepest, gravelliest purr.

"I guess you went through some heavy hurtin' and came out all right, didn't you, Buddy?" Tony said to Trainwreck, scratching his back at the base of his tail where he liked it best. "And as I remember, it didn't take you even an hour after we met for you to fall in love with me."

Looking right at the ELF, Tony said, "You made him do this, didn't you?"

"No, I did not," the ELF said emphatically. "Humans think they are smarter than animals because humans can talk, but animals have instincts far superior to humans. Trainwreck could sense you needed a demonstration of unconditional love, and he was just the cat to give it to you."

"Do I have to do anything else?"

"For what purpose?" the ELF asked, wanting Tony to think through his question more completely.

"To really get the message that it's all right for me to promote my work and that I can do it as well for E.L.F. Promotions as I can for my clients. And I guess," Tony said, clearing his throat three or four times, "to let myself risk loving a few more people."

"It depends on how much of a hurry you're in," the ELF said kindly. "It will happen on its own, now that you understand you were never consciously rejected by your mother. But you can speed it up a little if you want. You can make it happen faster and better."

"How? I like the idea of faster and better," Tony said.

"I've already given you the tools, Tony. And you've done a very good job of ignoring them. But now I think you may be willing to use them."

"What tools?"

"You've watched the DVDs, MIND Is Your Own Business?"

"You know I have. Three times. Once by myself, once on Saturday afternoons with Frankie, and once with Molly. And Molly and I are getting ready to watch them all over again."

"Why haven't you used the affirmations, then?"

"Affirmations? Those sentences on that little white card? Is that what you're talking about? How on earth can reading those sentences over and over again make me think I'm good enough to love and be loved for the rest of my life?"

"I'll try to explain to you how and why affirmations work," the ELF said, "but you'll need a piece of paper and a ballpoint pen."

"Okay," Tony said, giving Trainwreck an extra little scratch and putting him down on the floor. Then he went to his office and got a notepad and a pen.

Your Twelve Spiritual Awakening Affirmations

I am a perfect creation of The Eternal Life Force.

There is no other person on this planet exactly like me.

I am intimately connected to all of the power of the Universe.

The Eternal Life Force loves me all the time.

I am who I am and I allow others to be who they are.

I am a limitless being.

I ask for what I want and I receive it.

I am a healthy, wealthy child of the Eternal Life Force.

Love, peace and joy abound in my life.

I am filled with a sense of wellbeing.

I am joyful and I am grateful.

Things always work out for me.

"All right," the ELF said when he saw that Tony was ready. "In block letters about an inch high, please write the word 'bad.'"

After Tony finished, the ELF said, "Now right overlaid on the word 'bad,' write the word 'good.'"

"Got it."

"Now I want you to trace over the word 'good' with your pen until I tell you to stop," the ELF instructed.

Several minutes later, the ELF said, "You can stop now, Tony. Now tell me. What word do you see written on your paper?"

"Good," Tony answered.

"Can you see the original word you wrote under the letters of the word 'good'?"

Tony looked carefully. He even stood up and put the paper directly under a lamp to get better visibility, but he couldn't see a trace of the word 'bad,' even though he knew he had written it there originally.

"No, I can't see any of the original letters of the word 'bad.' I've traced over them."

"Well, let's look at what you did. You wrote the word 'bad' and then you overlaid it with the word 'good'. But writing the word 'good' once didn't block out the word 'bad,' did it? You had to trace the letters in the word good over and over and over again before 'good' obliterated 'bad.' That's the way affirmations work in your mind, Tony," the ELF continued. "You have an ingrained belief that you've held for years that says you're not good enough. When you state affirmations that you are good enough, and you repeat them often enough, you eventually will replace your long-standing belief that you're not good enough with a new belief that you are good enough.

"Nothing will seem to change the first few times you say these affirmations. In fact, the words are so different from your current belief system that you won't even believe them at first. But if you keep repeating them, you will come eventually to believe the truth about yourself. You will see yourself not only the way I see you, but also the way you saw yourself when you decided to be born as

Tony Celentano."

"And repeating these sentences over and over again is the fast way to feel better about myself?"

"'Fast' is relative, Tony," the ELF said, chuckling. "And it's hard for me to even work with the concept of fast and slow, because as I told you, in my realm everything happens at once. But I've seen what happens when people use these affirmations, if they repeat them twelve times a day for twelve weeks exactly as written. I can promise you will begin to feel better, happier, and more confident sooner than you would think.

"I want you to know, Tony, even though John McLaughlin is the teacher offering these affirmations, he didn't write them or decide how often you should repeat them. I did. I gave him these affirmations, and all of them together are especially designed to replace the belief of 'not good enough' with a deep, abiding understanding of how really wonderful you are right now in your physical form. These particular affirmations are such an important tool that I asked John to agree to provide them free to anyone, anytime, anywhere. And he has always done that."

"He's an interesting guy, isn't he?" Tony asked.

"He's a man with a talent for teaching difficult concepts in an easy-to-accept way. And I like that he uses humor as one of his teaching tools. If you humans would laugh a lot more, your life experiences would go a lot more smoothly. You can meet him if you like, Tony. He lives in Clearwater."

"You're kidding me."

"No, I'm not. Just give him a call."

Now, isn't that interesting? Tony thought. "So is this my assignment?" Tony asked as he retrieved the card from his DVD package. "To repeat these affirmations twelve times a day for twelve weeks?"

Tony sat back down and looked the ELF right in the eye. "Thanks for caring," he said simply.

“One of those affirmations relates to that, doesn’t it, Tony? The one that says, ‘The Eternal Life Force loves me all the time.’ Believe it, Tony. Believe them all. Now it’s time for you to get some sleep, and when you wake, you’ll find you already feel a lot better.”

With a brief show of brilliant color, the ELF faded away.

Tony put the card listing the affirmations down on the coffee table, gathered Trainwreck in his arms again, and carried him to bed.

“We’ll begin repeating those affirmations tomorrow,” he told Trainwreck sleepily. “And since you’re such a smarty-pants, you can say them with me.”

They slept deeply and dreamlessly for the next twelve hours

CHAPTER SEVENTEEN

On Friday morning at eight o'clock, packed and ready to leave on their trip, Frankie, Anna, and Tony piled out of Frankie's van in front of the Dome Café, laughing at Tony's latest lame Christmas joke.

"What do you call someone who is afraid of Santa Claus?" Tony had asked from the back seat.

Anna bit. "I don't know. What do you call someone who is afraid of Santa Claus?"

"Claustrophobic."

"Sick," Frankie said. "Ugh!"

"I got a million of 'em, Bro," Tony quipped.

"That's what I'm afraid of," Frankie said to Anna. "This could be a long thousand miles."

"It's two thousand miles, round-trip," she said, correcting him.

"Yeah, that's if we decide to bring him back," Frankie replied, expecting a good punch from Tony. But instead, they all burst out laughing at the confused expression on Pete's face when they walked through the door.

"No, you didn't lose a whole day out of your life, Pete," Frankie told him with a grin. "It's still Friday. We're a day early this week."

"Oh, thank God. You guys gave me a real start there." Then remembering his manners, he smiled warmly. "And you've brought the Lovely Anna with you. Merry Christmas."

"And to you, Pete," Anna answered cordially.

"What's up guys?" Pete asked.

"We're leaving today to visit our relatives in New York and Connecticut," Frankie explained, "so we decided to bring your Christmas present today. It's a chance for you to see us one more time and drool over the Lovely Anna."

"Well, I really like the last part," Pete said, turning again to Anna. "I know what these two meatballs want for breakfast, because they never change. But what would you like, pretty lady?"

"I think I'll try your blueberry pancakes with a bowl of fruit on the side, and coffee," Anna said.

Pete rang up all three orders, gave them each a mug for their coffee, and refused their money.

"My treat today," he said. "I don't want to give you fellas big heads or nothing—not that I have to do much to do that, of course—but I'm really touched that you came in to see me before you left. So Merry Christmas from me, too."

"Okay, so now you're going to embarrass us into giving you your real present," Tony said, shaking his head and pulling an envelope from his jacket pocket. "Take your wife out for a really nice dinner on us, Pete," Tony said, passing Pete a gift certificate for Ruth's Chris Steakhouse. "But be sure you think of us romping around in the snow up north while you're eating."

Sitting at their usual table, Tony commented on how well everything fit into the van after they loaded it, even leaving room to tip the seats back so they could get some sleep.

"It is amazing," Frankie said, "since Anna packed most of the state of Florida to take with us. But I'm glad it worked out that way, too, because now when you're driving, I can climb into the back seat and sleep with Anna."

"And while you are driving…" Tony began.

"…you can lie back in the front seat and go to sleep where I can keep my eye on you," Frankie said, finishing Tony's sentence for him.

"Hmm. You used to be more willing to share, Bro," Tony said.

"Yeah, right—my basketball and my baseball glove."

"And Mary Alice Finnegan."

"Who was Mary Alice Finnegan, Frankie?" Anna asked sweetly.

"Just a mutual friend," Frankie said, sending Tony a murderous look. And then to change the subject, he took their itinerary out of his pocket and began to discuss the route.

Anna's hand shot out and covered Frankie's, slapping the itinerary down onto the table.

"Who was Mary Alice Finnegan, Tony?"

Tony looked at Frankie, who nodded helplessly.

"She was a waitress in this restaurant, actually. Frankie and I were in our twenties, and I say with no modesty at all, we were a handsome pair of guys. He was so blond and I was so dark that when we walked into a room together, we turned heads every time.

"Pete used to keep a couple of waitresses in here in those days. They didn't serve the food then, either, but they'd drop by and talk to the customers, bring extra napkins and condiments, push the desserts, stuff like that. Mary Alice was clearly besotted with us. She found a dozen reasons to stop by every time we were here. Mayonnaise, ketchup, mustard, and A1 sauce—stuff just kept coming. It got in our way of talking to each other, so we decided to take up her interest in us in another way.

"The first week, I went to the restroom and Frankie asked her out. Then the next week, he went to the restroom and I asked her out. Since she didn't want either one of us to know about the other, she stopped coming by the table so often for fear that one or the other of us would mention we had seen her during the week. We really enjoyed having our uninterrupted Saturday morning breakfasts back again," Tony said.

"She was a nice enough girl, but not the type to pull either of our chains. So after a few weeks, we started to realize we were acting like a couple of sleaze balls," Frankie added. "The next week, we called her over to our table and told her we had been playing a game with her and were sorry, but neither of us was interested in a serious relationship, and we hoped she would understand."

"And did she?" Anna asked.

"Are you kidding?" they exclaimed in unison.

"You've heard of being mad as a wet hen?" Tony asked. "Well, she was mad as a wet ostrich. She called us every name in the book, including a few we'd never heard before, and loud enough for the whole restaurant, including Pete, to hear. Then she stormed out of here never to return."

"Not one of my prouder moments," Frankie said. "I suppose we could blame it on our youth, but the fact is, we were really just a couple of slugs."

"Hmm…" Anna said.

"Hmm…? Is that all you have to say about it?" Frankie asked hopefully.

"It should be," she answered. "I should let you wallow in guilt for the rest of your lives for what you think you did to that poor girl. But I love you both, so I feel duty-bound to point out something that has obviously escaped you so far. Mary Alice Finnegan wasn't exactly the victim you seem to have made of her. Since she assumed you were two-timing each other, she apparently had no qualms about two-timing each of you, either."

"Son of a bitch," Tony said. "I never thought of that!"

"Yeah, I guess it shows how bright we were—in fact are," Frankie said, chuckling. "But, I'm not sure that negates our lousy actions entirely, so let's change the subject."

Turning to Anna, he said, "Are you ready yet to talk about this itinerary?"

"Yes, sweetheart, I'm ready," she said, patting his hand in consolation. "You've both suffered long enough."

But because 'the sisterhood' is eternal, Anna sent out a little silent salute to the spirit of Mary Alice Finnegan, who once gave two young Casanovas a little taste of their own medicine.

Frankie drove as far as Gainesville, Florida, on that beautiful December day. Tony had subscribed to some Abraham CDs, so they listened to those, pausing them every now and then to talk about something Abraham said. Anna had surprised them with John McLaughlin's affirmation CD, so they also played that CD off and on, repeating the affirmations together.

Not knowing if Frankie had told Anna about his and Tony's relationship with the ELF, Tony shared with them what the ELF had told him about how affirmations work, but he said he had heard it from a friend. So far, he'd been following the ELF's instructions for three days and had missed none of his twelve daily repetitions.

After they stopped for lunch and filled up with gas, Tony took the wheel while Frankie and Anna napped in the back seat. For some reason Tony didn't bother to consider, his mind drifted to Molly. She had come a long way since the night she had knocked on his door desperate for help in making a decision about whether to go back to her old work or start her own company. Now she had five good, paying customers. Her kitchen was fully established in the Fillmore Café, and Sam and Mary had just about adopted her. She was planning to spend Christmas with them, and she and Mary would work part of the day serving meals to homeless people at the St. Vincent de Paul soup kitchen.

I'll bet it will be the first time they've been served by a chef trained in Montmartre, Tony thought, chuckling to himself. *I wonder if I could ever convince myself to serve meals in a soup kitchen. Certainly it's not an idea that I've ever thought of before, but things like that happen with Molly. You wind up doing stuff you've never thought of before.*

She had talked him into going with her to a restaurant supply warehouse. He knew restaurants used big vessels for cooking, but some of the pots and pans he saw there were ginormous. And she had introduced him to some kitchen tools he didn't know existed. He liked melon, so she bought him a melon baller. Sometimes he put fresh mushrooms in his salad, and she bought him a mushroom brush and taught him how to clean mushrooms.

They both liked to do artsy things, so they had fallen into the habit of going to street shows by local artists. They went to an exhibition of Steuben glass at the Fine Arts Museum, foreign films at the Tampa Theatre, and outdoor performances by the American Stage Company at Demen's Landing.

On the spur of the moment, they had decided to rent a booth together at a small-business owners' fair at Tropicana Field. Molly had picked up a customer there, and Tony had gathered dozens of business cards for later follow up.

Lately, they had been letting their animals have more play dates than they had at first, and always at his apartment, because Darth Vader traveled better than Trainwreck did. Tony had become used to Molly cooking in his kitchen while he worked in his office. He liked most of the CDs she brought with her and the way she set the table for their dinners together. When Molly cooked, he ate in his own home the way he would have eaten in a five-star restaurant.

I wonder how we have become so comfortable together without my even realizing it, he thought. Am I missing her? Hmm...could be.

Molly had talked him into putting up a Christmas tree, which Trainwreck found very interesting. They had put colored lights and balls on the tree, and the cat spent hours lying on his back under the tree watching the lights go on and off and pawing the ornaments on the bottom branches. Both of their condos smelled delicious, because she had baked gingerbread ornaments for their trees.

She also talked him into painting the logos of each of his clients on some ornaments, saying it would help him remember the first Christmas he owned E.L.F. Promotions. The logos turned out so well that he illustrated them on his computer, printed them off as decals, put the decals on Christmas ornaments, and delivered them to each of his clients as impromptu Christmas gifts.

Tony's thoughts shifted to Trainwreck having so much fun playing with the ornaments. He was glad he had bought the tree, but also glad he had decided to take it down just before he left, because he was afraid the cat might pull it over on himself and get hurt.

He had left two cans of gourmet tuna for Trainwreck's Christmas dinner, and toys under Molly's tree for both the cat and the dog. Molly and Darth would keep Trainwreck entertained while Tony was away, but still, this trip would be the longest time he'd been away from his cat since they had became roommates.

Celentano, he thought, *you're getting a little sloppy about your cat, aren't you? Nevertheless, he still didn't like the thought of Trainwreck being unhappy while he was gone.*

To thank her for taking care of Trainwreck while he was away, Tony had given Molly her own blog site and taught her how to use it. Then he had spent a whole afternoon with her taking pictures to go with her blogs. He had photographed her measuring liquids and solids, sifting dry ingredients, creaming butter, melting chocolate, rolling dough, and molding candy garnishes. Then they had made tablescapes to showcase ten of her latest Irish desserts. Finally, they had driven around town and he had taken pictures of each of her customer's places of business.

I'd better start being a little more careful with my time, Tony realized. *Now that I think of it, I gave away about a thousand dollars worth of billing hours without a thought.* He hadn't meant for his gift to include all that. In fact, he had intended to give her only the masthead for her blog and a little training on how to use it. But Molly had been so excited about all the things she could do with the blog, he had kept showing her more.

She had such a good time taking those pictures, staging those desserts, and playacting with the camera, he remembered. *And if*

I'm really honest, so did I.

Suddenly, Tony felt a hard thump on his back. "Ow! What'd you do that for, Frankie?" Tony growled, reacting in annoyance.

"Because we've been trying to get your attention and you're obviously not awake," Frankie responded with equal annoyance. "What kind of mental voyage were you on, for Pete's sake? Would you have even recognized a semi if it had been coming toward us?"

Yeah, what kind of a voyage was I on? Tony wondered. But what he said was, "What exactly can I do for you?"

"We'd like to stop, go to the bathroom, and get something to eat," Frankie said. "You've been driving for almost four hours."

Wow, Tony thought. *Four hours? Have I been thinking about Molly and Trainwreck for four hours?*

As he pulled the van off at the next exit, he read aloud from the interstate sign listing their options for places to eat.

"American Pie?"

"No," they said.

"Ming's Sushi Bar?"

"No."

"Cracker Barrel?"

"Yes!" Tony and Frankie answered in unison. "You bet!"

Anna giggled. "It's fine with me," she said. "They have really good soup and great vegetables, but what is it about the Cracker Barrel that obviously appeals so much to both of you?"

"Oh, I don't know," Frankie said. "Meatloaf with mashed potatoes and gravy, maybe?"

"Chicken-fried steak?" Tony offered.

"Hot roast beef sandwiches with mashed potatoes and gravy?"

"Potato casserole," Frankie and Tony said in unison.

Frankie opened the back door, plucked Anna off the seat, and set down her onto the ground in front of him.

"Men," she complained, looking up at him. "The only thing you enjoy better than sex is clogging your arteries with fat-filled food."

Immediately she found herself sitting on the seat of the van again, Frankie's hands around her waist and her legs dangling three feet above the ground.

"Now that you mention it," Frankie said, leering, "how about you and I stay in the van for a little sex? Tony can go on into the Cracker Barrel and clog his arteries by himself."

"Steady, big fella," she said, giving his nose a sharp little twist as she slipped efficiently down to the ground by herself. "I want a bathroom and my dinner, in that order."

"Nice try," Tony said, slinging his arm around Frankie's shoulder.

They watched with mutual appreciation as she strode toward the restaurant at a brisk clip. "Yeah, she's crazy about me," Frankie said. "She just doesn't want to embarrass you, that's all."

"Sure, that's the only possible explanation, pal," Tony agreed with a deep chuckle.

Sitting on a hillside the next night in Williamsburg, Virginia, listening to a chorus of very fine voices singing Christmas carols, Tony and Frankie each had an epiphany.

Funny, listening to this stuff doesn't hurt anymore, Frankie thought.

Christmas had always been a tough time for Frankie. Other kids seemed to love it very much, but in his house, holidays, and especially Christmas, were always a mess. His mother had tried but it had never worked, because when other people were happy, it seemed to upset his father more than ever. On most Christmases, Frankie, his mother, and Julie had wound up eating frozen turkey dinners, because the smell of a turkey cooking drove his father wild. Then all three of them went to bed early so they would be asleep when his father came home. But ever since his first 'Rampage of Appreciation' when he started focusing on the good side of his parents, Frankie had been able to allow things into his life that he had always rejected in the past.

Right this minute, he thought the four-hundred voice choir that Anna had wanted so much to hear sounded very nice. But mostly, he just loved the look on her face as she listened, her little body swathed in a red plaid blanket as she sipped delicately from the cup of hot chocolate he had poured from the thermos. He put his arm around her and drew her close. *I like the way Christmas feels with Anna*, he thought. And nothing that had ever happened on Christmases past seemed to matter anymore.

Sitting next to him, Tony was having similar thoughts. Until he met Frankie, he had thought he was the only kid in the world who had lousy Christmases. The holiday didn't even exist in his house, because ornaments were only more things for his mother to throw at his father. The best Luca could do for Tony was to buy him something he really wanted, like records or clothes or sporting equipment. Beyond that, Tony was on his own to do whatever he liked about Christmas, which wasn't much. Tony didn't like holidays in general, but Christmas was the pits. The Christmas spirit everyone talked about had eluded him.

However, since the ELF had encouraged him to face his unconscious belief that he wasn't good enough for his own mother to love, he had come to the realization that she simply had lost the capacity to love anything, not just him. Now he found his own heart opening to new experiences.

Sitting in this lovely place with his good friends on a beautiful winter night, he listened to the songs that always before had made him feel sick inside. But nothing bad was happening inside him now.

Imagine that, he thought. Tony knew he'd never relate to the words these carolers were singing. Their story wasn't his story, but he could enjoy the music and tap into the joy of the people around him, especially Frankie and Anna. He liked to look at them sharing a blanket and a life so contentedly. Both he and Frankie were changing for the better since they had met the ELF.

The only thing that's missing, Tony thought, again with great surprise, *is Molly.* She would love, love, love all the pageantry and the music here tonight. And she would definitely love the Williamsburg Inn. Very likely, she would convince the management to let her experience cooking in an outdoor kitchen over an open fire.

I guess I'm going to have to look at the fact that she's getting inside of me without my knowing it, Tony thought, *but...not quite yet.*

Then he did what he had learned to do long ago. He set that thought aside and simply enjoyed the moment.

Tony woke up in his uncle's bedroom in Brooklyn feeling a little disoriented. Looking out the window, he saw the outline of the Brooklyn Bridge through a dark grey haze. It looked cold out there as dawn was breaking, and it probably was.

Slowly he surveyed the room. No decorator touches here; everything was brown. The walls were brown, the ceiling was brown, the floors were brown, the bedspread was brown, the curtains were brown. *I feel like I'm inside a paper bag*, thought Tony.

The room contained very few personal items. A picture of his cousin Veronica, Fred's only daughter whom Tony had never met, sat on an otherwise unadorned dresser. Above the headboard of the bed was a crucifix, and back in a little alcove between the bathroom and the closet was a small statue of some sort.

Tony checked his watch; it was only seven o'clock. He and his father were going to breakfast at eight-thirty, so Tony didn't have to get up for at least another hour.

They'd had a nice little talk the night before, but Tony had somehow felt a little awkward about it. He wasn't a kid anymore, but he had felt like one at first. He didn't know how to relate to Luca, adult to adult, but he guessed he'd find out over the next few days.

To his surprise, a little shimmer of light flashed next to him and the ELF appeared, sitting cross-legged on the bedspread beside him.

"You want to know how to relate to your father?" the ELF asked.

"I do, but I didn't expect you to help me with that," Tony said.

"Well, you and Luca are about to have a really interesting time, Tony, and I want you to be comfortable enough to thoroughly enjoy it. You'll be talking about a lot of different things you and he don't know about each other yet, but you're going to like finding out about them. I also want to tell you it's all right for you to tell your father what I told you about your mother. Don't rush it, though. But Luca needs to know, as much as you did, why he lost her so suddenly. If you just wait, you'll know exactly when to talk with him about it."

"I was wondering about that. It has made a difference to me knowing it wasn't just Denny's death that made her shut us all out of her life. But you know that, of course."

"Yes, you're coming along just fine, Tony. I'm proud of you. And the other thing I want to tell you is to plan to have fun. This will be a really wonderful trip for you, Tony, if you will relax and let it be."

"How am I doing with staying out of your way while you get me some new customers?"

The ELF shimmered wildly. "You were doing fine until you asked that question," he said. "Trust me, Tony, the when, where, and how are still up to me." Then the ELF chuckled good-naturedly and faded out of sight.

Tony stretched contentedly and then swore softly as his uncle's cat startled him by jumping up on the bed. His father had told him the night before that Fred had found Subway in the subway when he was barely weaned and that he always slept in Fred's room. He hoped Tony wouldn't mind and, of course, Tony didn't. To make Subway feel welcome, Tony lifted the covers and let the cat get under them. When Tony snuggled down for a few more minutes of sleep before the alarm sounded, Subway curled up against him, apparently seeking body heat.

Tony could have sworn, as he drifted off to sleep, that he heard the words, "Trainwreck sent me."

Tony and Luca sat comfortably together having breakfast at a little neighborhood restaurant in Brooklyn.

"I really like your apartment, Dad," Tony said, not daring to add what he was thinking: *Except for the bedroom*. "The decorator you hired was top-notch. But I've been curious why you and Uncle Fred invested so much money in a rental apartment. I understand about feathering your own nest, but that's pretty expensive feathering."

"Oh, it's not a rental anymore, Tony. They converted to condos about three years ago, and Fred and I bought it. It wasn't cheap, but we thought it was a good investment, and the monthly mortgage payment is about the same as we were paying for rent. When we got that loan, we also had the living room decorated. Then when we won the lottery, we had the kitchen remodeled, too."

"That's great," Tony said. "Are you through decorating?"

"For the moment, yes. Someday we may decorate our bedrooms, but it doesn't seem like a priority yet. Now let me show you some things we can do for the next two days, Tony." Luca took a little notebook out of his pocket, along with a few brochures.

After breakfast today, he suggested, they would take the subway into Manhattan and sightsee until they were tired. After that, they would have dinner at Rockefeller Center, and end the night seeing the Rockettes at Radio City Music Hall. Luca had purchased the hard-to-get Christmas show tickets the minute he heard Tony was coming to New York.

Tony hadn't drunk his second cup of coffee yet. He was still sleepy and chilled, and he was having trouble adjusting to the way everyone in New York seemed to run around frantically, so he wasn't exactly jumping the gun to leave the restaurant. *These*

Yankees probably have to run around like crazy just to keep from freezing to death, he thought.

But his father, he noticed, was up and ready for anything. Tony had been especially pleased to find Luca in such good shape in every way. He appeared happy and healthy, and most of all, to Tony's surprise, he appeared content.

I wonder how he's come to grips with this Christmas thing, Tony thought. *He used to hate it as much as I did*. But Tony decided it wasn't time to ask about that.

The store windows, he had to admit, were spectacular: Macy's, Bloomingdales, Bergdorf Goodman, Saks. It was hard to choose a favorite. Everything in Tony's mind and heart that admired impeccable design was satisfied by those perfectly animated Christmas scenes. Even the non-animated decorations in the shops carrying couture fashions and imported shoes and handbags captured his attention. Luca enjoyed watching Tony search out all the design elements, and he loved having Tony explain why one thing or another was done with particular excellence.

They had lunch at the Guggenheim Museum, where Luca earlier had discovered a traveling exhibition of the works of artist William Stout, the famous dinosaur illustrator and one of Tony's favorites. They spent several hours enjoying the exhibits, and in the gift shop, Tony found himself buying a tiny crystal fairy for Molly. She would love it, he just knew.

Then Luca took Tony to his favorite yarn store, which was two stories high. Except for the sales clerks, he and his dad were the only men in the store. It didn't bother them; they were in knitter's paradise. Luca bought yarn to make a stole for someone named Molly—his lady friend from bingo, he explained. Tony bought yarn to knit a throw for the leather sofa in his new office. He wasn't crazy about carrying yarn around all day, though, so he had the store ship it to his home in Florida.

They took a New York City bus to Rockefeller Center, and

as they walked around the area, Tony pointed out various famous works of art and architecture. As Luca saw the same sculptures and frescos he had seen many times before, but through Tony's eyes, he was moved by his son's appreciation for the art and the artists.

The huge sculpture of Atlas carrying the world on his back brought back some interesting memories for Tony. In design school, Tony explained to Luca, one of his assignments had been to draw and redraw that sculpture from multiple perspectives, as it might be used in various kinds of advertisements. "I wasn't very fond of Atlas at the time," Tony told his father, "but I can see now that he's really pretty spectacular."

They watched skaters—big and little, young and old—until they began to feel really cold standing at the rim of the rink. Then they settled into an early dinner at A.J. Maxwell's Steak House.

When the waiter brought them coffee and a brandy to top off their meal, Tony noted they still had an hour and a half until the show started at Radio City Music Hall. Because six o'clock was early for most New Yorkers to have dinner, the restaurant wasn't crowded yet. As Tony settled back in the booth, he decided to stay right where he was, warm and contented, until show time.

It was the perfect time to poke around in his father's mind a little.

"I can't help but notice," Tony began cautiously, "that you don't seem to be 'put off,' I guess would be a good term, by everything Christmas anymore. I seem to remember that you and I agreed for years to just ignore all this holiday cheer."

"Yeah, funny, isn't it? I've been noticing the same thing about you, Tony."

"Ah, but I noticed you first, Dad, so you get to explain first. Wassup?"

"Gosh, Tone, I don't know where to start with this. I figured we'd have this conversation sometime this weekend, but … well, okay, let me ask you. Do you believe …" Luca paused to find the right words. "I don't know just how to put this. Do you believe in God or anything like that?"

"I do, yes. I believe in something like God."

"It's pretty hard to explain, you know, but I'm going to start by telling you a little bit about how I lived when you were a kid. Maybe it will help you understand how I live now. In those days, I lived two lives, Tony. I lived one where I went to work and came home, and kept the house going and kept you going, and tried not to get killed by your mother. That's the life you and everybody else could see.

"But I lived another life, too, Tony, and it wasn't an unhappy one. After I finally accepted that your mother was never going to get better unless a miracle happened, I found a way to do what I used to think of as my 'duty' stuff—taking care of her, the house, you and whatever you needed. Then when all that was done for the day, I would simply escape from it all and be by myself.

"I set myself up in my little study so I could literally live in there if I wanted to. I could read, deal with our finances, watch TV, bring you in for talks, and knit. I even slept in there many nights. That one room was my personal sanctuary. Since your mother yelled from the time I came home until she exhausted herself and fell asleep, I had a soundproof door put on that room, Tony. And I had one put on your room, too."

"You did?"

"Yeah. You never seemed to realize that when you shut your bedroom door it shut out your mother's screaming, too, but it did. It was quiet in your room, wasn't it, Tony? You could read in there, or do your homework, or watch your TV. Your room was kind of your sanctuary, too, wasn't it?"

Tony was really surprised. "That's true. When I went into my room and shut the door, I couldn't hear her screaming. You mean you fixed it so I couldn't hear her?"

"Yeah, I did. I didn't make a big thing of it. I just figured you needed your sleep and you needed a certain amount of protection from her screaming, too. I guess you were close to eleven when I had the door changed. By then, you were big enough to come get me if you needed anything, so I figured it was safe enough for me to just escape into my sanctuary and let you escape into yours. Remember the doorbell next to my door that you rang if you wanted to come in? That was because I would never have heard you if you'd just knocked."

Tony felt a new understanding creep into his heart. If he couldn't have heard his mother's screams, then she couldn't have heard his screams, either. He remembered that when he had let himself relive the night he had screamed to his mother asking why she never came back to love him, the ELF had said, "Your mother didn't ignore you when you screamed. She just couldn't hear you because both her ears and her heart were closed to you."

Tony came back from his mental side trip to hear his father saying, "I never knew what to call it, but I had what I thought of as my invisible friend. I just knew that when I asked my invisible friend a question, something inside of me answered. So when I couldn't figure out how to do something, I just sat there knitting and told my story to the invisible friend in my head. After a while, it would give me a clue as to how to solve my problem.

"See, I didn't have many real—or maybe I should say human—friends, Tone. I had a good relationship with some of the guys at work, and my boss knew what was going on with us at home. I couldn't go in with a bandage on my nose or forehead or cheek every other week without giving some explanation. The people at the *Times* were real good to me, under the circumstances.

"But I wasn't free to do things with the guys after work. I couldn't join the company bowling team or go to a ball game with them on a Saturday, and so my work friendships didn't extend into personal ones. The only friend I had, really, until you got old enough to talk to me, was my invisible friend. And you know, somehow most of the time, it was enough.

"When I moved to New York, everything here was very strange to me," Luca went on, signaling the waiter for another cup of coffee. "It was a big shift, all right. You can see how different it is here. Lots and lots of people all moving very fast, and subways and busses and taxis and traffic. Plus, I didn't go to work every day anymore, so finding things I liked to do to keep me busy took a while. Then, of course, living in what was your uncle's apartment at the time, my room was still my sanctuary. So I kept talking to my invisible friend, and it kept helping me find answers.

"One of the things I figured out, and I know it was with help from my invisible friend, was that it was time for me to discover who Luca Celentano was. Not Luca my father's son, or Helen's husband, or Tony's father, or the *Times* manager, but who I was when I had no other title except Luca Celentano. I wasn't bound by 'duty stuff' anymore, except to keep my own space clean. A housekeeper cleaned the apartment, Fred and I ate in restaurants, and I was free to let as many new things into my life as I could accept.

"So I began to explore New York, sometimes with Fred, sometimes on my own. And because I wanted to begin where I would not be a total stranger, I started with all things Italian. I ate in Italian restaurants and talked to the waiters and owners and cooks. I went to movies and plays with Italian themes. Did you see *Mamma Mia*, by the way, Tony? That Meryl Streep—she's really somethin' else!

"Anyway, I even dragged Fred to the opera, *The Marriage of Figaro* and *La Traviata*, and to hear Pavarotti sing at the Met. He had a voice, and something else about him, too, that could bring you to tears, Tony. Too bad he died."

"Yeah, it is," Tony agreed, slightly amused at the way his father jumped around from subject to subject. Tony had forgotten how Luca had always done that, adding little tag lines to whatever he was talking about.

"But the first Christmas after I came to New York, Fred was buzzing around decorating the apartment from top to bottom, and I was miserable. In fact, it was the only time I ever thought of moving back to Florida in all these years. Obviously, you can't go anywhere in this town that Christmas isn't right in your face, except maybe Chinatown and the New York Deli. Did you know, Tone, that Chinese restaurants do a big business on Christmas because almost no other restaurants are open?"

"I never thought of it," Tony answered, grinning, because he could remember very clearly eating Chinese takeout with Frankie on a few Christmases when they were kids hiding out together and watching movies on Frankie's VCR.

"So I did what I always do," Luca continued. "I talked to my invisible friend about it, and got the same answer I got when I asked about finding out who Luca Celentano is. It was time to let new things into my life. And so I just escaped from Fred and went into Manhattan on my own, like we did today, and I let myself try to 'experience' Christmas like everybody else did. It made me sad at first, but then I went into Macy's and stood and watched the kids with Santa Claus, and I sat in a neighborhood coffee shop and listened to people talk about their Christmas plans, and I looked at all the animated windows. And by the end of the day, trying on the idea that Christmas could be fun didn't seem so impossible.

"And it gets a little better every year. This is the seventh year I've spent a whole day in Manhattan looking at store windows and coming to Rockefeller Center. I've really liked doing it with you, Tone, but I don't mind doing it by myself, either. Christmas is a season I can enjoy just because it makes so many other people happy. Believe it or not, I start early. I even come down here for the Macy's Thanksgiving Day parade, if we don't go to Fred's daughter's house for Thanksgiving."

"It's a lot easier when you're not fighting it, isn't it?" Tony said. "This is the first year, actually, that I've let myself begin to enjoy Christmas even a little bit. And I think, like you, that I will get to like it better as time goes on. I certainly enjoyed today, Dad."

Tony reached over to touch his father's arm. Luca had never been affectionate with him, except for one time that Tony could remember. But he noticed his father didn't pull away from his affectionate touch now. Instead, Luca laid his own hand over Tony's and smiled.

"Now, please tell me a little more about your invisible friend, can you, Dad? How do you know when you're talking to yourself and just making up things in your own mind, or when it is your invisible friend talking to you?"

"I just know, Tony," Luca said, "because I finally figured out that when I'm trying to make up answers all by myself or trying to solve my own problems, I usually feet pretty bad. But when my invisible friend is guiding me toward the best answers, I start to feel really good. So I wait until I start to feel good about what I'm thinking, and I know my invisible friend approves.

"I have something else to tell you, too, Tony, and when I do, I suppose you're really going to be ready to have me committed. But I figure I might as well be hung for a sheep as a lamb, as my father used to say. So here goes. You see, I've been reading this book, and it's full of the wisdom of people who aren't here on earth. It's written by what they call non-physical beings."

Tony's hand stopped somewhere between the table and his mouth, the brandy snifter he held appearing to hang in midair.

"What is the name of the book, Dad?" Tony asked quietly.

"Please don't look at me that way, Tony. I can't stand it. I'd hoped you'd understand, but maybe we'd better change the subject."

"Sorry, Dad," Tony said, returning his glass to the table. "But I really want to know. What is the name of the book?"

"*Ask and It Is Given*," Luca said, looking down at the table. "It was written by a woman named Esther Hicks. She writes whatever the non-physical beings tell her to write. Just please don't think I've lost my mind, Tony, because I haven't. Instead," he said, reaching across the table and groping for Tony's hand, "I finally found my sanity." Luca hoped against hope that he wasn't losing his son.

"Who told you about that book?" Tony asked, unable to corral the multitude of questions tumbling through his mind.

"Molly did," Luca answered.

"Molly!"

"Yeah, Molly. She's that really nice lady I told you about. We met playing bingo at the Catholic church."

"You're going to the Catholic church now?"

Luca chuckled. "Only to play Bingo, son. Look, I still think we'd better just change the subject."

"No, Dad, we'd better not. Now let me tell you how I came to read the same book, and how it, among other things, has helped me find my sanity, too."

Tony told his father his whole story, starting with the day he thought he would lose everything he owned and the ELF appeared in his living room.

"Wow," Luca said. "Just like my invisible friend, which Abraham calls my 'Inner Being.'"

They talked about what they had learned from Abraham until it was time to leave for Radio City.

"Great show!" Luca said as he and Tony climbed into a cab in a long line of cabs waiting at the exit of Radio City Music Hall.

Then whispering, Luca asked. "You sure you don't want to take the subway home, Tony? This is gonna cost you."

"I'm sure, Dad. My treat. My best client just paid his bill, so I can afford the cab fare. And if you're half as tired as I am, you don't want to ride the subway tonight, either."

"Well, you're right about that," Luca said, stretching out his short legs full length and laying his head back on the seat. "I'm not as young as I used to be, you know."

"Oh, you're wrong, Dad. You're much younger than you used to be, in thousands of different ways."

Luca smiled. "Some legs on those Rockettes, huh, Tony?"

CHAPTER EIGHTEEN

When they got back to Luca's apartment, the message light was blinking on his phone. Luca punched the "listen" button and he and Tony both recognized Frankie's voice.

"Hey, Mr. Celentano, Tony. It's Frankie. I tried your cell phone, Tony, but you must have it turned off. Hey, it's really beautiful here at Uncle Lawrence's, and we're having a great time. We were telling him about you guys, and he remembers meeting both of you at my father's funeral. He says you were staying down there for the winter, Mr. Celentano, and you were really kind to him. You helped him figure out some stuff about my father that made him feel better.

"Anyway, they'd like to know, and so would Anna and I, if you would like to come up here to their farm in Madison and spend Christmas Eve and Christmas Day with us. They have plenty of room. I checked the trains and there's one leaving Grand Central at three-thirty on the afternoon of the twenty-fourth. Anna and I would meet you at the station in Madison."

The message cut off, but then another one started.

"It's me again," Frankie's voice went on. "So if you get in before midnight tonight, call me back on my cell phone and let me know, and if not, call me in the morning, okay? Don't worry about how early you call. Anna is having fun milking cows, feeding horses and chickens, and playing with the puppies, so we'll be up and eating breakfast by six o'clock. Man, I'm glad I don't live on a farm all the time, but it is fun to play at. Hope you decide to co… " The message ended again.

"Whadaya think, Tone?" Luca asked.

"Do you have any special plans for us for Christmas Eve and Christmas Day?"

"No, I just figured we'd play it by ear."

"Does your ear like the sound of going to Connecticut?"

"I remember I really liked Frankie's uncle. He was so sad and so confused. He'd never been able to have a relationship with his brother since they were boys and he felt terrible about it. I'm glad to hear I helped him some. So, yeah, I think I'd like that, Tony," Luca went on. "I've never been on a farm, and I wouldn't mind watching Anna milk a cow, either. She's so tiny that the cow, in comparison, must look like a buffalo when she's milking it."

"At six o'clock in the morning, you're going to be looking at them by yourself, Dad," Tony said, laughing. "I'll still be cutting Zs."

"There must be some woman on the planet who can get you up at that hour, Tony. She just hasn't shown up yet," Luca said, laughing.

"Well, if she ever does, I'll miss her, because I'll already be married to a late sleeper."

Married? How did that word pop up? he thought. *More likely, I'll be sleeping late by myself for the rest of my life.* But Molly crept into his mind at that exact moment. He could actually picture her sleeping beside him, and for a few minutes, he let her just rest there.

"It's too late to call Frankie back now," Luca said. "We'll call him in the morning."

Then clapping Tony on the back, Luca said, "This was a great day, Tone. One of the best I've ever had." With that, he headed off for bed.

As Tony made his way to Fred's bedroom, Subway wound himself around Tony's legs. A handsome tuxedo cat, Subway was equal parts black and white with a very pretty black face, green eyes, and snow-white whiskers.

Reaching down to pick him up, it occurred to Tony that Subway might be missing Fred the way Tony was missing Trainwreck. "Well, never mind, old boy," Tony said, scratching Subway on the back at the base of his tail where Trainwreck most liked to be scratched. "We'll all get back to our right places soon. But for tonight, we'll just have to comfort each other."

The next day, they called Frankie and accepted his aunt and uncle's invitation. Then, knowing they would need to take Luca's gift to a framer before they left for Connecticut, Tony suggested that they exchange their Christmas presents early.

Luca gave Tony a beautiful sweater, the first one he had made using one of the new textured yarns. Jet-black shot with silver, it looked fabulous on Tony. *Molly will love this*, he thought. *Well, there she is again, already on my mind this morning.*

Then Tony gave Luca the drawing he had made of his father knitting the hybrid bridge together. Luca was speechless. Together, they went into his bedroom to decide where to place the drawing. Taking down the magazine cutouts of Tony's ads thumb-tacked to the wall, Luca was preparing to tack up the new graphic when Tony stopped him.

"Dad, I went on the Internet and found a framer just six blocks from here. It's a national chain that I know does good work. The frame is part of your present from me, so let's just walk over there together and I'll help you pick out a frame and mat right now. Then I'll feel like you have your whole present, okay?"

At the shop, Luca was glad Tony was there to help choose a frame. "So many choices," Luca said, bewildered. Tony guided him easily through the selection of a double mat and a simple frame, and he also arranged to have the completed artwork delivered to Luca's apartment during the week between Christmas and New Year's Day.

On the way back, they stopped at a deli for what Luca called a real New York breakfast: scrambled eggs, lox and bagels with a generous slab of cream cheese, and big thick mugs of coffee. "So has Uncle Fred read *Ask and It Is Given*, too?" Tony asked as the waiter poured their second cup of coffee.

"No," Luca said with a wry smile. "I started to talk to him about my I.B. once, but he stopped me cold."

"Your I.B.?"

"Inner Being. That's what Abraham calls my invisible friend. I do, too, now, but it's easier just to use his initials. To me, it fits him, and it feels good to finally give my invisible friend a name. You know, Tone," he went on, "Fred and I were raised Catholic as kids, and it's always meant something to Fred to be Catholic. He was in a boys' choir when he was a kid, and they sang at a lot of masses. God, he had a beautiful soprano voice! Then he became an acolyte, and he enjoyed what I call all the trappings of the church. But it never did a thing for me, even as a little kid.

"The church was always noisy and sometimes smelly. People were forever getting up and getting down and 'disturbing God,' I used to think, and the priest spoke in Latin, so I couldn't understand what he said. I never felt anything that I might call holy in church. I stopped going as soon as I left home.

"But Fred stayed, especially after he married Greta. She was Catholic, too, and they raised Veronica to be Catholic. He still goes to church every Sunday and on Holy Days of Obligation. He didn't care for the idea of me talking to my I.B. He said he didn't really want to hear about it. But he does the same things we do, Tony, he just doesn't know it."

"How's that?"

"Well, he keeps a crucifix hanging on the wall over his bed, and he's always calling on Jesus for help with his loved ones, Veronica and her family, and even Subway. When Fred gets really excited about something, like the day the housekeeper left the window open and Subway got out on the fire escape, he calls for Jesus, Mary, *and Joseph.*

"And he talks to the saints. He asks St. Anthony to help him find things, and he asks St. Christopher to watch over him, even when he just takes the subway. I read in the *New York Times*, by the way, that for some reason, St. Christopher has fallen out of favor with Catholics. But that doesn't seem to stop Fred from trusting him. And whenever he can't figure something out with his finances, he talks to St. Jude, the saint of the impossible. Now, if Jesus and the saints aren't non-physical, who is?"

Luca shook his head and finished off his bagel. "Did you notice the shrine to St. Theresa in his room, Tony?"

"Not at first, I didn't. It's back in that little alcove, isn't it? I didn't know exactly what it was."

"Yeah, that's where it is. It's a shrine to St. Theresa like our mother kept. St. Theresa was known for spreading love by offering flowers to everyone. Mama called her 'the Little Flower,' and she always put a vase of flowers in front of the statue. Fred brought the statue with him from his old home, and he grows pansies and lilies-of-the-valley in a window box off his bedroom so he can put fresh flowers before St. Theresa every day. In the winter, he uses cuttings from a holly bush downstairs.

"I told him he could keep the statue in the living room if he wanted to, but he says our mother had left it to him because she knew he would appreciate it and I wouldn't, so he prefers to keep it in his own room."

"Does that hurt your feelings, Dad?"

"No, I figure he's got his thing and I've got mine. He keeps the Little Flower in his room for his personal enjoyment, and I keep my I.B. with me in mine. Nothin' wrong with that," Luca said, and Tony believed him. "It sure is nice to be able to talk to you about it, though, Tone. Besides you, Molly is the only person who even comes close to understanding why my I.B. is so important to me."

"Hmm…now tell me about Molly," Tony said, accepting his third cup of coffee from the pleasant waitress. *I'd better leave her an especially good tip*, Tony thought. They'd been there quite a while this morning, and they weren't nearly ready to leave yet.

"Well, as I told you, I met Molly at bingo. One thing Fred and I do together is play bingo. I enjoy the game and the people, and it doesn't matter to me that it's in the Catholic Church. Fred, on the other hand, goes because it is in the Catholic Church. Go figure.

"Anyway, we started noticing these two nice-looking ladies, always together, who came to bingo almost every Friday night. So we got there early one night and waited for them to sit down so we could sit at their table. We started to talk to them over bingo, and then we invited them out afterward for a cup of coffee. Turns out they're sisters who also share a condo just a few blocks from here.

"After we shared a few more bingo nights, we started going to movies together and to concerts in Central Park, and we all had fun. Fortunately, Fred liked Sally best and I was really drawn to Molly. After a few months, Fred and I had a talk about our new lady friends and decided to lay our cards on the table. We invited them for pizza at our condo one night right after we had it decorated. We told them straight out that we'd like to take our relationship with them to a more personal level, but they should understand we weren't interested in marriage, either one of us.

"They looked at each other and began to laugh. They said they had talked about the same thing and wondered, since we always went out in pairs, how Sally was going to let Fred know that she would like to see him alone sometimes, and Molly the same thing with me. And by the way, they weren't interested in marriage, either, but everything else was possible.

"So we've been dating, both single and double, ever since. If we want to be alone, we just go to different apartments. Usually I go home with Molly, and Fred and Sally stay at our place. Molly's good for me, Tone, and I'm good for her, and we both really love this Abraham stuff. She ordered their CDs, and we spend some evenings listening to Abraham and talking about what a great world we've created for ourselves. She knew I was nervous about talking to you about it, and she'll be so glad to hear that you really understand Abraham. Unbelievable!"

"I'd like to meet her, Dad," Tony said. "Why don't you call them and invite them to dinner tonight? I can stand in for Fred temporarily, although I know it won't be the same for Sally."

"Sally's away visiting her kids, but if you wouldn't mind having dinner with just Molly and me, that would be really swell. Better, in fact, than if Sally and Fred were here, because we can't talk about Abraham with either of them. Since they won't be here, we won't have to watch what we say."

Tony handed Luca his cell phone. "Call Molly and ask her, Dad. We'll figure out a good restaurant to go to later."

Luca called Molly and made plans for a dinner date. Then he returned Tony's phone and they left the deli.

"You got a girl yet, Tony?" Luca asked as they walked back to the apartment.

"Well, a week ago I would have said no. But the truth is, there's someone I've been missing on this trip, so maybe the answer is yes. I promise I'll tell you all about her on the train up to Connecticut Friday. She's a very interesting lady."

"What's her name?"

"Believe it or not, her name is Molly." Tony smiled, trying to remember back to when he still believed in coincidences.

He could have sworn he heard the ELF laugh.

When they got back to Luca's apartment, it was still hours before they were to meet Molly for dinner. Tony felt the nudge he had been waiting for from the ELF that told him it was time to talk to his father about Helen.

Since they still had a day and half until they left for Connecticut, plus a three-hour train ride, Tony and Luca decided to knit a couple of wool scarves to take to Frankie's aunt and uncle for Christmas. Luca pulled out enough wool from his stash for two scarves, one skein in dark grey and another exactly like it in light grey, with smaller amounts of teal and turquoise yarns to use for accents. He also had a case of needles he'd been collecting for years, and Tony chose a couple. Then Luca lit a fire in the fireplace, made them a pot of hot chocolate, and they settled down for a good session of knitting and talking.

"When Molly and Sally have a knitting session like this, they call it a Stitch and Bitch," Luca said, chuckling.

"Molly sounds like she has a good sense of humor."

"You bet," Luca said. "They both do. I'm not in the market anymore for anyone in my life without a sense of humor, Tone. Humor is the grease that turns the earth on its axis, and I'm taking personal responsibility to see that it keeps turning smoothly for as long as I'm on this planet."

"I'm thinking we could probably call this knitting session of ours Yarns and Yarns," Tony quipped, "because we're going to be swapping a lot of stories in the next few hours. I really want to tell you about my last conversation with the ELF, Dad, because it is as important to you as it is to me.

"I need to warn you, though," Tony continued, holding his knitting needles up to the light to be sure he had cast on his stitches correctly, "that this story may hurt a little when I tell it. I resisted facing this particular part of my life for thirty years because I didn't want to deal with the pain, but the ELF convinced me that if I didn't face it, I could never have a truly happy life."

Tony took a few breaths, sent out a silent plea to the ELF for help if he got stuck, and then plunged in.

First, he told Luca about what happened on his eleventh birthday, and how he had decided that night that something was wrong with him if he wasn't good enough for his own mother to love. When tears started to roll down Luca's cheeks, Tony reached over and held his hand. "Just stay with me, Dad. In just a moment, you'll understand why it doesn't matter anymore."

Then Tony revealed his mother's story just as the ELF had told it to him.

Luca was visibly shaken. Realizing Helen had kept something hidden from him, he also instantly grasped that if what he was hearing was true, the strange outcome of their marriage had been virtually predetermined before they had even met. In that case, his only sin—if he still believed himself capable of committing sin—was that he had made her so happy she couldn't believe she deserved it.

Once they felt clear to let go of those sad memories, the two men began to talk about happier things.

They compared the very subtle difference between practicing their A-B-Cs and cooperating with the Law of Attraction. They also discussed what they had learned about the importance of being grateful. Tony told Luca about Mike Palmieri, 'The Grateful Realtor,' and what the ELF had taught Tony about the difference between being grateful "to" and grateful "for." Luca asked Tony to share this with Molly later on.

"She's funny about that 'Rampage of Appreciation' thing," Luca said, chuckling. "She uses it especially when she gets scared. We were coming home on the subway one night from a concert in town, and a guy on the train was talking to himself and behaving really weird. The next thing I know, I can hear Molly under her breath listing all the things she's grateful for. It reminded me of when my mother used to say the rosary in the middle of a thunderstorm."

Then he added, shaking his head, "You know what I always say, Tone. Whatever works."

They talked at length about why there were so many names for

God. Luca had always blamed his dislike for the Catholic Church for his separation from God. He decided to try out the name Eternal Life Force in place of God and to work with the concept that the Force was always with him.

Tony drew him an iceberg to explain how Luca and his Inner Being were simply extensions of God, or the Eternal Life Force. Luca admitted that when he had read in Abraham that he and his I.B. were directly connected to God, or what they called All There Is, he hadn't been willing to accept it.

"After seeing that drawing, though," Luca said, "maybe I can believe it. I've heard of people who needed superhuman strength and got it. A one-hundred-twenty-pound man pulled a three-hundred-pound woman out of the way of a subway train last month, right down the street from here. No way could he have done that without calling on something more powerful than he is. The newspapers made a big thing about it, but no one had any real explanation. Even the doctors said it would be hard for him to have that much additional adrenaline running through his body at one time. Things like that make you think, ya know?"

When they got up to take a break, Tony considered it curious that he had been his father's teacher for the past hour and a half, a strange role reversal from the past. But he also felt like a student, because every time he had repeated one of the ELF's teachings to Frankie and now to his father, it became clearer and clearer in his own mind. Then he remembered having read somewhere that no one ever fully learned something until he or she also taught it to someone else. Suddenly Tony was rewarded with a flood of good feelings.

When they went back to their knitting, Tony told Luca about *MIND Is Your Own Business*, particularly about the affirmations the ELF had said would help him replace all those old 'not good enough' feelings.

"Can I buy those DVDs, too, Tony?" Luca asked. "They sound

like something great for Molly and me to watch together."

"Sure, Dad, I'll give you the website so you can order them anytime." Then, because he had memorized the affirmations, he gave Luca his white card and they repeated the affirmations together several times.

"I really like these, and I like calling God the Eternal Life Force," Luca said. "It's a funny thing about this kind of stuff, isn't it, Tony? Once you start learning it, you never seem to be able to get enough. It's like you've been starving for it all your life."

They looked at their scarves and were pleased to see that each was about two-thirds completed. "I think we can finish them tomorrow, Tone," Luca said. "But right now, we need to shower and change for our dinner with Molly."

Molly, Tony thought. *I've never even known one Molly before, let alone two. I guess I'll have to call them 'New York Molly' and 'Florida Molly' to keep them straight.* But a little voice inside of him said, *'Your Molly'* and *'My Molly'* will work just as well.

Dinner with Luca's Molly was so enjoyable for all of them that she invited them to her condominium the next night for dinner so she and Luca could exchange Christmas presents. Tony could see why his father liked her; she was really fun to be around.

Luca and Tony were on their way to Connecticut. Tony had never ridden on a train before, and had never been in a place like Grand Central Station. The many trains, tracks, levels, people, and the announcements coming over the PA system had made him almost dizzy. But Luca, now accustomed to riding subways and the confusion of New York City, had led them straight to the train Frankie had suggested.

Only when they were on the train did Luca tell Tony this was also the train he had taken several times to visit Helen during the first few months he was in New York City.

"But I knew that continuing to visit her wasn't helping me, and it wasn't helping her, either, so I stopped going," Luca continued. "It's a chapter of my life and hers that is closed for me, Tone. My mind and heart are honestly focused on my good life now, and my future, too."

"Molly said she and her sister were coming down to visit you in Florida, Dad."

"They are. In March. The condo next to us is usually for rent, except for January and February. So I wrote to the owner and found out it was available in March. Molly and Sally rented it on the spot. Molly loves to dance, so we're looking forward to going to tea dances at the Coliseum, and to swing night at the Gulfport Casino. In fact, we plan to waltz and swing our way through the month of March."

"I remember when you taught me to dance in the living room of our house," Tony said. "You rolled up the rug, turned on your stereo, and swung me right across the floor. I didn't know my feet could move that way. I thought I'd never learn to lead you, though, but I did. Maybe my Molly and I can go dancing with you and your Molly once in a while when you're in Florida."

Then, realizing what he had just said, he grinned shyly. "I guess it's time to tell you about my Molly, Dad. I'm thinking she might be becoming important."

"I'd like to hear," Luca said.

Tony told him about Molly and a little about how she kept popping into his mind on this trip. "I didn't realize how much she was starting to matter, Dad, probably because no other woman ever has mattered much at all, until now."

"Then she must be different from anyone you've ever known before," Luca said. But he didn't press it. "I'll look forward to meeting her, and especially to trying out all of her desserts when we get down to Florida in January."

Giving Tony that familiar affectionate cuff to the side of his temple, Luca leaned his head back on the seat to take a nap.

Tony spent most of the rest of the trip enjoying the Connecticut scenery and trying his best to stay in the moment. The snow on the pine trees, houses, and hills reminded him of a panoramic Christmas card that went on and on. It had an air of something almost unreal about it. Still, it was beautiful, and the falling snow made the whole experience seem like a movie or a dream.

Frankie was waiting for them at the train station in Madison, and as he drove them back to his uncle's farm, he brought them up to date on how his visit with his uncle had gone. He was bursting with news about all the things they had done in the past three days that he had never done before. Frankie and Anna obviously were enjoying this trip very much.

It's almost like a second honeymoon for them, Tony thought. *Only this time, they brought lots of other people with them.*

Among other things, Frankie told them about Cornelia, his uncle's Old English Sheepdog, and her puppies. He clued them in that later that evening, his Uncle Lawrence and Aunt Millie intended to give Anna one of the puppies for Christmas.

"But you gotta keep it a surprise, now," Frankie cautioned. "She's been playing with the puppies almost nonstop since we got here, but she thinks they've all been sold and their owners will be picking them up tonight or tomorrow. In fact," he went on, "puppy '1' will be picked up today and puppy '3' tomorrow. But Uncle Lawrence kept puppy '2' for Anna, because he is Anna's favorite."

"How many numbers—uh, puppies—are there?" Tony asked with amusement.

"Just 1, 2, and 3," Frankie answered. "My uncle doesn't like to name them. He leaves that to their new owners."

“I thought you were going to wait until you bought a new house before you got a dog,” Tony said.

“We were, and Anna still thinks we are. But you gotta see her with this puppy, Tony. You would never allow anything to separate them from each other if you could help it.”

“Anna has a way of getting right into your heart,” Tony explained to his father. “Even I have a hard time denying her anything. She’ll wrap herself around your soft heart in a nanosecond. You just wait and see.”

“Oh, I don’t know, Tone. I’m no pushover for a pretty face, you know,” Luca said, winking at his son to see if he could get a rise out of Frankie.

“You’re a goner, Mr. Celentano,” Frankie said with a grin. “Don’t even try to fight falling in love with Anna, because it simply can’t be done.”

“So puppy ‘2’ is going home with us in the car, then?” Tony asked.

“Yup. Uncle Lawrence and I bought the kennel and food and dishes and blankets and collar and leash and toys already. The little thing doesn’t weigh five pounds yet, but its luggage weighs at least twenty. It’s all stowed in the barn so Anna won’t see it.”

As they pulled into the driveway of the farm, Frankie tooted the horn. “I told Anna I’d let her know as soon as we pulled in so she can come out to meet you,” he explained.

But Anna didn’t come out.

The men carried their bags inside and set them down in the hallway as Frankie called to Anna. Still no answer. Neither did anyone else answer as he walked through the house, Tony and Luca following. When they got to the back door, they saw all the lights on in the barn, and many footprints in the snow going to and from the house.

“Something’s up,” Frankie said, as all three men started trotting toward the barn. When Frankie opened the door, they saw his uncle’s horse, Princess, lying on the floor in a big open stall. Lawrence and

Millie were huddled together close to Princess, and Anna seemed to be busy down at the tail end of the horse.

Gently, Frankie put his large, firm hand on his uncle's thin shoulder. "What's going on?"

"Oh! Hi, Frankie. Boy, I'm glad you're here. I came out here to feed Princess and found her lying down. I ran back to call the vet but couldn't get him, so Anna came out with me to see what she could see."

"She says Princess is going to have a baby," Millie said, a tone of distress in her voice. "Now, we didn't even know she was pregnant! Oh dear, we haven't done anything to take care of her while she was in this condition. I hope she's going to be all right!"

Frankie walked around to where Anna was sitting on the straw and crouched down beside her. "You okay?"

"I'm fine," she answered, reaching out to squeeze his hand. "There isn't much we can do but comfort her. So far, she's doing well, but this is a one-step-at-a-time process."

"Anything I can do?"

"Yes, maybe. I think she would be comforted if your aunt and uncle could get up near her head and talk to her, and it will give them something to do, too. This has been quite a shock, and they're awfully scared. Could you make a place for them to sit beside her so they can pet her while she goes through this?"

Frankie signaled Tony, and together they brought a couple of bales of hay up near the horse's head. When Millie and Lawrence sat down, Anna told them to stroke Princess's face gently and speak to her in soothing voices. After just a few minutes, the sound of their loving words calmed everyone down a bit, and heartbeats around the stall began to settle back into their natural rhythms.

Tony and Luca brought two more bales of hay so they could sit and watch, too, and Frankie went back to be with Anna.

"Anything else?" he asked, wrapping his arms around her shoulders in a supportive gesture.

"Maybe. I'd like you to stay here with me. I don't expect to have to help Princess, but if for any reason she can't push the foal out by herself, I may have to help her. It's possible I might not be strong enough to do it by myself, so if that happens, maybe you can help me position my body so I can do whatever I need to do."

"I'll be right here, sweetheart. Just tell me what you need and when you need it," Frankie said, dropping a few soft kisses on her neck to let her know he was all hers.

"It would also help if someone rubbed her side in gentle circles through every contraction, just to stimulate the baby a little. Do you think Tony would do that?" Anna asked Frankie.

"I'll find out," Frankie said. He wondered if his and Tony's teenage oath to do anything for each other, forever, no matter what, actually included rubbing a female horse's side while she gave birth.

At the suggestion Tony briefly jolted, but at the same time, he felt a pull to help if he could. So he knelt at Princess's side and waited for instructions.

"When she has a contraction, just rub your hand firmly but gently around her side in wide circles," Anna said in a voice that somehow reminded Tony of some Army drill sergeants he had seen in movies. Tony did exactly as he was told, and Luca exchanged an amused look with Frankie.

But the minute Tony felt the intensity of the contraction beneath his hand and felt the little foal move slightly, his senses heightened, as did his awareness that he was suddenly a part of a very awesome experience. His desire to help Princess was so intense that he automatically turned to the ELF for help, asking for guidance to do whatever Princess required to help birth her foal. His hands then seemed to find their own rhythm as he gently stroked the old mare's belly through each long, slow contraction.

I wonder if I really helped them? Tony asked himself as he settled back on his heels to wait for the next contraction.

As if he had asked the question out loud, Princess turned her head to look at Tony, her deep brown eyes registering a mix of emotions, one of which Tony sensed as genuine gratefulness. When he leaned forward to stroke her face, she pushed the side of her head into his hand and rested it there for a moment.

"Thanks, ELF," Tony said, feeling a warm, happy feeling spread throughout his body.

"Do you have a lot of experience birthing babies?" Frankie asked Anna.

"A fair amount," Anna said. "Before I was a nurse practitioner, I worked in OB-GYN for three years and assisted in some births when the doctors were very busy. But none of those babies had four legs, so I'm a little bit out of my comfort zone here."

"You're doing fine, sweetheart. You're doing just fine," Frankie said, so proud he almost couldn't stand it.

I guess when I told you I wanted us to really experience what it was like to live on a farm, you took me very seriously, didn't you? Frankie said silently to the ELF.

Because Princess must have been in labor for several hours before Lawrence found her, it took just a little under an hour for the foal to be born. Too precious for words, she looked like a ditto mark of her mother.

All five people attending her birth were stunned by the enormity of the experience.

Princess did a very careful job of licking and cleaning her little filly. Anna had never revealed her fears that the foal might be weak or dangerously small, and she was glad she hadn't. She could see that all was well, and she squeezed Frankie's hand as they watched Princess nudge the foal to get up and move into nursing position.

"They'll be fine now," Anna said after a few minutes, sensing it was time for them to leave. "I'll check them every few hours through the night to be sure, but we need to give them time now to get to know each other in this world. It is very important that they have time to bond without anybody else around. And I can't speak for any of you, but I'm ready for a bath and some food. I feel like I've just worked a double shift."

They all patted her on the back and congratulated her as if she had just given birth. Then she went happily in search of soap and water, and a few minutes alone to savor the miracle in which she had just participated.

When Lawrence had come running into the house in a frenzy saying that Princess was down, Anna had waited to be asked if she could help. It didn't take long, because Lawrence had no idea what to do. When she had looked at Princess, she had known immediately that the mare was in the throes of labor, although she could see that the news was a big surprise to the owners. The foal had apparently been in a position that didn't cause its mother's abdomen to show much swelling, and Anna had to admit that standing up, Princess probably would not have looked obviously pregnant.

If Millie and Lawrence hadn't been so upset, Anna might have panicked a little. Instead, she had begun to prepare the barn as if it were an operating theater, sending Frankie's aunt and uncle on various trips to the house for strong soap, clean towels, plastic gloves, and a band to tie around her head to hold her hair away from her face.

Then she had drawn on all her previous obstetrical experience as well as what she had learned from Abraham. In one of the CDs she had listened to recently, a doctor had asked Abraham how she could hold on to thoughts that a disease could be cured when she had seen so much evidence to the contrary. Abraham instructed the doctor to go to the Internet and gather all the information she could about those who had been cured of that disease, and to focus only on that. So Anna had affirmed that she wanted this baby horse to be born easily and naturally, and that both the mare and foal would be fine. Then, one by one, she had replayed in her mind every successful birth she had ever witnessed—and there had been many.

Finally, she had asked the angels to be with the little foal as it went through the birth process, and to be with her, too, until it arrived. Right after that prayer, Anna had seen a flash of light in the mirror above the sink where she was scrubbing her arms and hands. The light had then circled her head and pulsated just slightly before fading away.

From then on, Anna had been able to approach Princess with a new sense of calm. Except for doing all she could to make the mare comfortable in the process, Anna had let the angels take it from there.

This is turning into a very special Christmas indeed, Anna thought as she dressed for her first Christmas Eve as Mrs. Frankie Doerrer. With a new husband, new family, and new baby animals all over the place, Anna couldn't remember ever having been happier.

When Anna came downstairs wearing a red velour jumpsuit that skimmed her curvy little body very attractively, all four men salivated simultaneously. This did not escape Millie's observant eye.

"Quite a woman you've got there, Frankie," she said, chuckling as they all gathered around the dinner table. "She can deliver a filly one minute and drop four men to their knees the next."

Frankie planted a possessive kiss on the back of Anna's neck as he pulled out her chair to seat her at the table. Then he exchanged a delighted glance with Tony and sighed contentedly.

"We really didn't give you much of a welcome when you arrived," Lawrence said to Luca and Tony. "But we sure are glad you were here."

"On the contrary, Mr. Doerrer," Tony answered. "I think you gave us a spectacular welcome."

"I can't wait to tell my brother about this," Luca said. "He'll probably not believe a word of it, but I don't care, because I got to witness a real miracle tonight. It was a great experience."

"You really didn't have a clue Princess was pregnant?" Tony asked.

"No," Lawrence answered. "Stupid on my part, of course. We

boarded a neighbor's stallion for a few weeks a little while ago, but I didn't think to keep them in separate pastures. Princess is eighteen years old, for Pete's sake. I never figured she'd be in the mood."

Anna and Millie both giggled. "Never count an old girl out," Millie said, nudging her husband and winking at him suggestively.

"Believe me, my dear," Lawrence said, turning an attractive shade of pink. "I'll never make that mistake again."

CONCEPT VII

Realizing . . .
Life doesn't have to be so hard

CHAPTER NINETEEN

They all sat around Millie and Lawrence's gracious Christmas dinner table, still feeling warm and fuzzy after the birth of the foal.

"Will you raise this new filly yourself, Uncle Lawrence?" Frankie asked.

"Well, I haven't had time to talk to Millie about it yet, or to the man who owns the sire to see if he wants her. But I thought we might make her a Fillies and Colts filly. Princess and the sire both have good bloodlines. She'll grow into a fine mare just like her mother."

"How does that work, making her a Fillies and Colts filly, I mean?" Luca asked.

"Well, as soon as she is weaned, a young boy or girl will be chosen by Fillies and Colts to receive her. Generally, these kids can't afford to own a horse, and Fillies and Colts gives them a lot of training on how to care for a growing horse.

"For the first five years, we will help with the expenses of food and medical care. Then when she is old enough to breed, a suitable sire will be found through the Fillies and Colts circuit. She can be bred as many times and as often as it is safe to do so, but the first female she gives birth to will be given to another Fillies and Colts child to raise. That's one of the ways they keep the program going.

"I'll call the owner of Princess' boyfriend tomorrow and tell him he's a new grandfather. I'm sure he will be as amazed as I am about this whole event, but he's our age and I doubt he'd be interested in taking on a little filly to raise, either. So if it's okay with you, Millie, I'll call the Fillies and Colts people on Monday so they can start looking for the perfect candidate to receive her."

"I think that's a good idea, Lawrence. This is no time for us to take on another long-term commitment. We have other plans, don't we?" she said, winking at him.

"Plans?" Anna asked.

"Princess had a brother, a twin brother we called Prince," Lawrence explained. "They were both born here on the farm. Prince died about a year ago, and Millie and I decided we would care for Princess until she dies, too. It could be a couple of more years yet, but she's beginning to slow down. Or at least we thought she was," he added, scratching his head and looking bemused. "But when she dies, we plan to sell the farm and move to a warmer climate."

"We didn't know where exactly. But now that we have a family," Millie added, smiling at Frankie, "we've decided it will be somewhere near St. Petersburg."

"How cool," Anna and Frankie said at the same time.

"You're going to love Julie and Mike, and little Andy, too," Frankie told them. "Do you think you will live in a house or a condominium when you retire?"

"I don't know," Millie said. "I won't miss the winters in Connecticut, but I will miss my chickens."

"You don't have to," Frankie offered. "There are some areas in suburban St. Pete where the zoning will allow you to raise chickens."

"And Old English Sheepdogs," Anna offered.

"Wow. That would be just swell," Lawrence said. "We might come down for a visit this winter and look around, but we're committed to letting Princess live her life out here on the farm. She's never lived anywhere else."

"Well, just plan to stay with us if you come to visit," Anna said without consulting Frankie. "We'll be in our new house by then, and we'll have plenty of room."

Tony chuckled at Anna's optimism. "I can see you're expecting your house to sell…"

"Oh," Frankie interrupted. "In all the excitement, we forgot to tell you. Mike sold our house."

"He did?" Tony said in amazement. "But I thought it wasn't even on the market yet."

"It wasn't, officially, but we had signed the listing before we left. A couple came in that Mike said literally described our house when he asked them what they were looking for, so he showed it to them. They loved it and made us a full-price offer. And you know what we figured out, Bro?"

"Uh, no."

Frankie and Anna answered together, "It's because things always work out for us!"

"Oh, yeah," Tony smiled, recognizing one of the affirmations they were repeating every day, and winking at Luca, who also had caught Frankie's meaning. "I almost forgot about that for a minute. So when do you have to move?"

"In two weeks," Frankie answered. "We're going to sell most of my furniture, because Anna politely describes my personal decorating style as 'eclectic.' We'll move into Anna's old apartment until we find our new house. We had planned to sublet her apartment in January until the lease ran out in July, but we probably won't need to do that now."

"And we'll start looking for our new house as soon as we get back," Anna said. "I'm so excited! I have a list of features I want that's at least a mile long."

When dinner was over, Millie's Christmas roast of pork, sweet potatoes, and scalloped apples left everyone happy and thoroughly stuffed. Millie suggested they sit by the Christmas tree to open presents and come back later for dessert. Protests about being too full to ever eat again started until she said, "I made German chocolate cake just for Frankie, and a Lebkuchen with whipped cream for my husband."

"Well, then," Frankie said, chuckling. "I'll just have to run around the house a few times to make room for it. Want to join me, Uncle Lawrence?"

As they moved into the living room, Anna asked Millie if roast pork was a traditional German Christmas dinner choice.

"In one form or another," Millie answered. "Years ago, my family roasted a whole pig and served it with bratwurst and a special kind of macaroni salad, but my mother stopped doing that long before I became chief cook and bottle washer. The Lebkuchen, though, is traditional in my family, and it played a part, years ago, in winning Lawrence's heart. It's a warm ginger cake mostly associated with Christmas dinner, and he waits all year for it.

"Funny," she said to Anna in a conspiratorial tone, "I made it for him as a surprise one time in July, and he said it just didn't taste the same."

They all settled companionably around the tree. Lawrence poured a snifter of cognac for anyone who wanted one, and then they began the present exchange.

Anna felt as if she had been divinely guided to the perfect gift when Lawrence and Millie opened their first present: a beautifully framed and numbered print of an original painting by Christopher Still, a nationally recognized Florida artist whose work Anna dearly loved. She and Frankie had specifically chosen a scene of sunset on the beach at Caladesi Island because it was a special place where they loved to spend a quite day together. Obviously, they had no idea when they chose the gift that Florida was to become their Aunt Millie and Uncle Lawrence's new home.

"We are big believers in the power of visualization," Lawrence said as he rose to remove the painting above their living room fireplace. With Frankie's help, he hung the new picture in its place.

"We will sit here by the fireplace every morning drinking our coffee together and looking at this beautiful picture. Can't you just picture us on that beautiful beach together, Millie?"

"I can absolutely see us on that gorgeous beach together," she said with a grin. "This just makes our dream seem a little more real and a great deal closer."

"Caladesi is a beautiful place to explore," Frankie said. "It's very private. You have to take a ferry to get to the island."

Then reaching under the tree, he drew out a smaller package. "We brought you a book, also, that tells the story of the island," Frankie said, handing the package to his aunt. "It was written by the daughter of the man who homesteaded the island in the late 1800s. She writes wonderful stories about her life on the island when she was a little girl. She calls her book, *Yesteryear I Lived in Paradise*, and Caladesi Island is still a little bit of Paradise. When you're sharing your morning coffee every day and picturing you and Aunt Millie there, Uncle Lawrence, go ahead and picture Anna and me on the beach with you. We love spending a day there when we can find the time."

Then for fun, he added, "Come to think of it, we have a really neat friend who is a chef. Actually, she's a closer friend to Tony than she is to us, but maybe we can convince her to step into this imaginary beach scene and bring a tasty picnic basket for us."

"She's gonna need me to come with her to carry the basket," Tony said, good-naturedly joining in Frankie's game. "Be sure you don't leave me out of this visualization."

"And what am I, chopped liver?" Luca said, grinning. "I want to come to this beach party, too. I've heard about this chef, and I understand some melt-in-your-mouth brownies might be involved."

"This may be the most fun picture anyone has ever owned," Millie said, laughing. "But don't be surprised if it isn't too long before we're all standing on that beach together remembering back to this Christmas Eve in Connecticut. Our visualizations usually come true, so you might all want to stock up on some extra suntan lotion when you get back to Florida."

Frankie and Anna gave Tony a one-year subscription to the Abraham CDs. "And I'm throwing in a bonus present for you, Bro," Frankie said to Tony. "When my crew goes in to clean the Fillmore lobby every week, they'll clean your new office, too."

"Wow, that's cool," Tony said, surprised and touched because it was such a big bonus. "That's just really cool."

For Luca, Frankie and Anna had ordered a gift certificate, via the Internet, for Ted Peters Famous Smoked Fish, so he and Fred could have smoked mullet when they came to Florida the next month.

"We'll even take you there," Frankie said, sending Anna a sly smile. "It's one of our 'special places.' In fact, it was at Ted Peters that Anna tricked me into marrying her. But that's a long story, and we haven't got time for me to tell it right now."

In the most ladylike way possible, Anna stuck her tongue out at Frankie as she began opening her Christmas present from Tony. Tony had knit matching vests for Frankie and Anna, both in a rich milk chocolate and heavy cream blend of boucle yarn. The vests were lined in a soft, dark brown fleece and zipped down the front with wide, bronze-colored zippers. Each zipper had an embossed charm on the end—a Mickey Mouse charm for Frankie and a Minnie Mouse charm for Anna.

The vests were spectacular, and Millie, who was delighted to learn that Tony and Luca were knitters, was extremely impressed. "They look like they should have designer labels, Tony. I've never, ever in my life seen handwork of this quality, or seen knitted yarns used so imaginatively."

"These are designer originals," Anna said. "They are Tony Celentano originals." She slipped her vest on over her jumpsuit and walked over to Luca so he could see it more closely.

"Yeah, that's beautiful work, Tone," Luca said, proudly admiring his son's workmanship.

Frankie grinned. "Ain't he somethin'?" he asked his aunt and uncle, noticing that somewhere along the line he had begun to feel proud of Tony's knitting instead of embarrassed by it. But Frankie no longer questioned the changes continuing to take place inside him. Now when he recognized them, he gave thanks, because they were all "feel good" changes.

It seemed like a good time for Tony and Luca to give Lawrence and Millie their scarves.

"We only invited you three days ago," Lawrence said in amazement. "Do you two knit in your sleep?"

Luca told Lawrence he had knit his scarf with the teal stripe down the middle, and Tony had knit Millie's. He also told them how his friend Molly and her sister held Stitch and Bitch knitting parties, and that Tony had named their knitting time Yarns and Yarns, because they had talked to each other all the way through the time they were knitting. Both father and son agreed they had a great deal of fun making these particular presents, because never before had they taken that much time to talk to each other.

Millie's new scarf was the same steel-grey color of her hair, and it looked stunning on her. She especially loved the deep teal fringe that Tony had created to finish it. She draped her scarf artistically around her neck and walked over to Tony. As she gave him a sweet kiss on the cheek, she picked up the gift certificate he had received for the Abraham CDs. Studying it a moment, she then went over to her bookshelf, took down two books, and handed one to Tony and the other to Frankie. One was titled *New Beginnings I* and the other *New Beginning II*, both by Abraham-Hicks.

"You know about Abraham, Aunt Millie?" Frankie asked in genuine surprise.

"These were Abraham's first two books," Millie explained. "I started reading them about twenty years ago. We had just bought the farm and I was trying to grow vegetables. I was watching the weather and fussing with my garden, seeking out only the highest quality seeds, experimenting with various kinds of fertilizer, and constantly checking the acidity in the soil. Even so, my garden was pitiful. Our next door neighbor invited me over for coffee, as people in Connecticut tend to do once they're convinced you're here to stay. I looked out the window at her kitchen garden, and it was beautiful.

"'What do you do to make your vegetables grow like that?' I asked her.

"'I just plant the seeds, make sure they have plenty of food and water, and start thinking about all the ways I'm going to cook the vegetables when they're ready to be picked. I let the universe handle all the rest,'" she told me. Then she showed me this first book and asked if I wanted to borrow it.

"We've had great vegetables, healthy animals, a thriving business, and everything we want for our home ever since. The only thing we ever wanted that we didn't seem to be able to manifest was a family, and now I know it's because we had convinced ourselves that family had to mean having our own children.

"When your wedding announcement came," she said, smiling at Frankie and Anna, "we realized what we had been doing wrong. We had placed a condition on what we had asked for and our Inner Beings couldn't help us. In their eyes, we already had a family. We just weren't recognizing it.

"So right away, we started asking for a family to love for the rest of our lives, and we removed all conditions. And now our beloved farm house is filled with our family this Christmas Eve. New life has come to us tonight in many ways, and it is just magical," she said, moving over to where Lawrence was and taking his hand in hers. "Simply magical."

Then turning to Luca, who was the one person in the room she wasn't sure would understand, she said, "I hope I haven't offended you, Luca. I know everyone doesn't believe in the things we do, but it works for us, doesn't it Lawrence?"

"Better than I ever dreamed possible," Lawrence said. "But let's change the subject now. Luca, we consider you a very special friend, and we never want you to feel uncomfortable in our home. Since Frankie and Tony are adopted brothers, it makes you a part of our family, too."

Luca grinned. "I'm comfortable in your home, Lawrence, and that's probably because I'm a big fan of Abraham, too. Now ain't that just some kind of amazing?"

"I had no idea so many people knew about this stuff," Frankie said, "but I'm thinking we might have all had some help in finding each other right now. Do you think?"

"No, I don't think," Millie said, smiling. "I know. And my, oh my, am I grateful."

"It looks like the only presents left under the tree are from us," Lawrence said, handing Tony and Luca each a present obviously shaped like a bottle.

Tony opened his present first and found himself holding a bottle of Cabernet Franc with a label that read Doerrer Vineyards, Madison, Connecticut - 1990.

"Tomorrow," Lawrence explained, "I'll take you all out to the rear of our property to look at our vineyards and our little winery. We're not in production at this time of year, of course, but even so, you'll be able to see quite a bit of what we do here. We grow two acres of grapes to make chardonnay—that's what your bottle is, Luca—and three acres of cabernet blanc each year.

"Our proximity to the Atlantic Ocean and Long Island Sound creates an ideal climate for grape production. It's very much like the climate that produces the best grapes for the better known French wines. Connecticut isn't extremely well known for its grape production, but we think the wines we produce can hold their own proudly with the more famous California wines."

"Do you run the winery yourself, Uncle Lawrence?" Frankie asked.

"Millie and I both did for years," Lawrence answered, "but a few years ago, we realized we didn't want to work that hard anymore. Because it is so seasonal, it's really a part-time job, but it is intense. We hired an experienced wine maker who runs it for us. If it stops snowing, I'll call him and ask him to come to the winery tomorrow so you can meet him. He's a really interesting guy. His name is Hans Schmidt, and his family still owns vineyards on the Rhine River in Germany."

"How do you market your wines?" Tony asked, causing Frankie to chuckle deeply.

"We don't, really," Lawrence explained. "We're well known in the area, and our wines are used by most of the better restaurants in southern Connecticut. We also place some of our stock with the local wine merchants, really more to educate tourists to the fact that there are Connecticut vineyards than to boost our profits. Our subscription customers are the backbone of our business. We ship wines all over the world for the private cellars of wine connoisseurs, and they tell others about us. Word of mouth is enough to provide us with a profitable business. Our wine cellar is always full but seldom overflowing. We're a very small operation, but I like to think we're a high-quality one."

"I have a very special occasion coming up soon, Mr. Doerrer," Tony said, "and I am really going to enjoy making this bottle of wine a part of it."

Frankie and Anna looked at each other with the same question on their mind. *What on earth is Tony talking about?* But instead of pursuing it, they shrugged their shoulders as Lawrence got up and headed toward the back door.

"Now, we have one more Christmas surprise before we have our dessert," Lawrence announced.

"I hope this doesn't take too long," Frankie said, grinning at Millie. "The pork roast has moved on by now and I'm ready for my favorite dessert."

"Close your eyes, Anna," Millie said softly.

"Me?" Anna asked. But she did as she was told.

Lawrence brought in puppy '2,' all dressed up for Christmas Eve with a big red bow around his neck, and put him down in Anna's lap.

"Oh, is it time for him to leave?" Anna asked, opening her eyes as soon she felt his soft fur. Embracing the little ball of fluff and burying her face in his soft thick hair, she parted the hair over his eyes. "I'm really going to miss you, but the people who are adopting you will surely love you, too, so you be good now." She started to hand the puppy back to Uncle Lawrence.

"You and Frankie are the new owners, Anna. Puppy '2' is our Christmas present to both of you," Lawrence said with a smile.

"Oh, no, we can't have a puppy until we buy our new house, Uncle Lawrence," Anna said emphatically. "I would love this puppy more than any other puppy in the whole world, but..."

Frankie moved over and sat on the arm of her chair. "Oh, I think we can accept this special present, sweetheart," he said softly. "In fact, I know we can. I called your old landlord, and for a small pet deposit, he's willing to let this puppy move in with us when we close on our house."

Anna burst into tears. Then, partially recovered, she hugged Frankie, and then Uncle Lawrence and Aunt Millie."Oh, I don't know who to thank first," she said, cuddling the puppy and letting herself be puppy-kissed all over her face.

"Oh, you're gonna be mine," she said to the puppy, squeezing him again. "And I know just what we should name him, Frankie. Would it be all right if we called him Madison, after the place where he was born?"

"I think that would be a wonderful name for him," Frankie said, taking the puppy out of Anna's arms and letting Madison nuzzle his neck. "Hello, Madison. Welcome to the Doerrer family. Do you know that you're about to become the most loved puppy in the state of Florida?"

Tony came wide awake on Christmas morning. Amazingly happy in his strange but comfortable farmhouse bed, he was still tucked under the warm duvet with his head on a feather pillow when he opened one eye and looked at the clock. Ten o'clock. He got up, padded barefoot to the window, and looked out in amazement at the almost untouched blanket of white covering the ground as far as he could see.

Snow had fallen all night and was still gently falling. Deeply set into the snow drifts were dark green trees, a faded red barn, and partly buried vehicles. A stately iron buck with a full rack of antlers stood guard at the front of the farm house. More than picturesque, it was just what Millie had called it the night before: magical.

Noticing the path of big and little footprints running between the house and the barn, Tony smiled. No doubt everyone else had been up for hours, and had been out visiting Princess and her filly. He wondered if his father had gone to watch Anna milk the cows at six o'clock this morning.

He'd find out soon enough. But first, he crawled back into his warm bed, propped up the pillows, picked up his cell phone, and punched in the numbers.

"Hey, Molly. It's Tony."

"Oh, Tony, Merry Christmas! I'm so glad you called. Are you having fun?"

"I'm having at least a hundred times more fun than I expected," he told her. "There's so much to tell you, it will take a couple of hours when I get back. I won't be back until either late Tuesday or sometime Wednesday, but I wondered if maybe we could have dinner together Wednesday night so I can tell you all about it."

"I'd really like that," she said, "because I have a lot to tell you, too."

"Is Trainwreck okay?"

"Well, he's physically fine, but he misses you. Darth and I have spent a couple of hours with him every night to try to take up the slack, but he still runs to the door every time he hears the elevator, and then he walks away disappointed when it doesn't stop at this floor."

"Aw, that doesn't make me feel so good," Tony said. "But I'll just have to spoil him when I get back."

"When are you leaving New York?"

"We're not in New York. We're in Connecticut. A slight change of plans, but I'm glad we made it. Dad and I were invited to spend Christmas Eve and today with Frankie's family on their farm. It's just beautiful here, Molly. I was just looking out the window at a totally snow-covered world. I know you saw plenty of snow in Utica, but it's a whole new experience for me. I can't wait to get Frankie and Anna outside for a snowball fight this afternoon. Anna will probably win, though. She grew up in snow, just like you."

Then to answer her question, he said, "We'll leave here tomorrow and take Dad back to Brooklyn. My Uncle Fred will be back by then, so we're all going to have lunch with him in the city. Then Frankie and I will take turns driving to Savannah. A stopover in Savannah is part of Frankie's Christmas present to Anna. We stopped at Williamsburg on the way up, and we'll spend the night in Savannah on the way back.

"Oh, and there's something else that may slow us down a little. We will have an extra passenger with us for the return trip. Anna fell in love with an Old English Sheepdog puppy that was part of a litter Frankie's aunt and uncle were raising, so they gave Anna the puppy for Christmas. She was so excited, Molly. You would have loved it. She had us all in tears."

"I can't wait to see it," Molly said.

"Well, even at six weeks old, this puppy is so fuzzy it looks about twice the size of Darth Vader. But it is a cute little ball of fluff, no doubt about that. What time do you leave for the soup kitchen today?"

"I'm meeting Mary at the restaurant at eleven-thirty. Last night after the restaurant closed, we were in such a holiday mood that she and I decided to make brownies to take with us today. I called St. Vincent de Paul's and they told me they were expecting over two hundred and fifty people. It took us until about two o'clock this morning to finish baking, decorating, and packing two hundred and seventy-five brownies. Sam wasn't happy about me driving Mary home that late, so he came down and drove us both home. I'm going to walk over there soon, though, and start packing the brownies in my van."

"Those homeless people just have no idea how good they're going to have it today, do they?" Tony asked, thinking about how really kind both Molly and Mary were.

"Well, I've got a pretty good life, you know, Tony. Molly Malone's Irish Desserts is thriving, and I believe in sharing my good. After we finish serving the homeless," she went on, "Darth and I are going to Sam and Mary's to have dinner with them, and their two daughters and their families. I guess Mary has been talking about Darth, and her granddaughters want to see this tiny little dog. Darth's social life is becoming quite extensive." She chuckled.

"Oh, but don't worry, Tony," Molly added quickly. "Darth and I will spend some time with Trainwreck tonight. We bought him a new catnip toy, which I delivered this morning along with your present for him. I fed him his gourmet tuna, and I left the TV on for him all day. After all, it's Christmas."

"I wish you were here with me, Molly. I miss you," Tony said simply, his heart swelling uncomfortably. "And I don't know what to do about it, because I've never missed anyone before."

Tony heard her catch her breath. "I miss you too, Tony," she said after a slight pause."And I don't know what to do about it, either. But I've made up my mind that I'm going to ask the fairies exactly what missing you so much means. Then I'm just going to go on about my life and see what happens."

"Me, too, Baby," Tony said, trying to still the waves of emotion crashing in his stomach. "Me, too."

GO TO ELF!

When Tony came down to breakfast half an hour later wearing the new black and silver sweater his father had given him for Christmas, Luca saw something in Tony's eyes he'd never seen before. Everyone else was still in the barn, so they sat alone at the big kitchen table together.

Tony cut himself a slice of Christmas coffee cake that Millie said was called a stollen. It was filled with dried fruit and it was simply, as Luca had taken to saying lately, "to live for."

"This sure does beat fruitcake as I know it," Luca told Tony. "Someone always brought the other kind into the Times break room at Christmas time, and it would still be there in July."

"Yeah, Frankie buys one like this at the German bakery in St. Pete every Christmas, but he always serves it with the disclaimer, 'Good, but not like my mother made.' I never tasted his mother's stollen," Tony noted, "but it's hard to believe it could be better than this."

Then, unable to help himself, Luca spoke up. "You called Molly, didn't you?"

Tony looked surprised, and then remembered how well his father could read him when Tony was a kid. "Still got your radar on me, I see," Tony said, sighing and slicing himself a second piece of stollen. "Yeah, I called her, and she sounded amazing. She and one of my other customers stayed up until two o'clock this morning baking the best brownies you or anyone else has ever eaten to take to a homeless shelter today, and then they're staying there to serve the homeless people Christmas dinner. I'll never be that good if I live to be a thousand."

Luca chuckled. "Was she glad to hear from you?"

"Yes. I'd say yes. And I made a date with her for Wednesday night. You might as well know, Dad, I'm pretty sure I'm going to ask her to marry me. Words that, believe me, I never thought you would hear me say."

"I believe you, Tony. I just hope you and she wait three weeks until I get down there to see you get married, because by the look in your eye right now, you could elope by Thursday."

"I've got it that bad, Dad?" Tony asked, wide-eyed.

"Do you, Tony?"

"Yeah, I guess I have."

The outside door burst open, and Tony found himself surrounded by a crowd of people and one fuzzy puppy.

"Well, well, Rip Van Winkle is up," Frankie said, causing Luca to turn his head so Tony wouldn't see him grin.

"Good afternoon, Tony. Merry Christmas!" Anna teased.

Tony looked at them with narrowed eyes. And then he hissed.

CHAPTER TWENTY

The visitors all had a really hard time saying goodbye to Millie and Lawrence, because they were all keenly aware that they had shared a very special experience and had made wonderful memories together. Frankie drove them back to Brooklyn and he and Anna and Tony spent most of the rest of Sunday with Luca and Fred. When they finally rolled into Savannah, it was about eleven thirty on Monday morning and they were really beat. They were just a little too early to check into their rooms, but the desk clerk said he would send Housekeeping to take care of things right away. In the meantime, they left their luggage, including Madison in his carrier, behind the clerk's desk and went to the hotel dining room for brunch.

"It was hard leaving your aunt and uncle, Frankie," Anna said, patting her heart space. "I still feel a little sad."

"I know," Frankie agreed. "Who knew we could get to feel so close to them so soon?" Reaching for one of the rolls the waitress had just brought, he broke it in half.

Absently, Tony picked up the other half. "I'm glad you talked them into coming to Florida in March when my father will be there, too," he said, as he generously buttered his bread. "Dad's 'lady friend,' as he calls her, will be visiting then, and I heard him suggest to Millie that the four of them might go dancing together."

They placed their orders and then drifted into a comfortable silence. Anyone observing the three would have recognized them as weary travelers: clothes wrinkled, hair slightly disheveled, eyelids just short of droopy. They looked tapped out and much in need of sleep.

Tony broke the silence. “When I said I’d come with you on this trip, Bro, it felt like something I really should do, ya know? I just thought it was important for me to spend a little time with my father in his own space, and I didn’t think much about whether or not I would enjoy myself. So far, though, this whole trip has been just one great experience after another.

“But,” he continued, eyeing Anna suspiciously, “I don’t know about this ghost walk you have planned for tonight. You sure you know what you’re getting us into?”

“I’m pretty sure, Tony. I knew we’d want to stop for at least one night each way on this trip, and Williamsburg and Savannah are places I’ve always wanted to see. You and Frankie weren’t too sure about Williamsburg, either, but you had a good time there, didn’t you?”

“I have to admit I did, but there were no ghosts there.”

“Oh, I’ll bet there were some ghosts of settlers past with us there, too,” Anna said with a laugh. “A few years ago, my friend Crissy married Charlie. You met Crissy at our wedding, remember, Tony?”

“I do. Nice girl, and fun, too.”

“That’s just the thing about Crissy; she always finds fun things to do. Her husband’s family lives in Savannah, and while Crissy and Charlie were here visiting his parents, they all went on the same ghost tour we’re going on tonight. Savannah was a very bawdy town at one time, full of brothels and taverns and jails. Supposedly, the ghosts of some of those bad boys and girls are still lurking around town. Crissy told me about the tour when she got back to Denver, and it sounded like so much fun, I made up my mind right then that someday I’d like to take it, too.

“Then when my spectacular new husband made stopping off in Savannah part of my Christmas present,” she went on, reaching over to pat Frankie on the cheek, "he said to spare no expense. So I made us a reservation for tonight at the Olde Pink House, a five-star restaurant in the older part of town. Then I booked us for the walking tour of some of Savannah's seamier haunts.

"Oops!" she said, laughing at her own pun. "Why not just relax and let yourself enjoy it, Tony? It's all a spoof, but apparently a very well-presented one. Besides," she teased, "you're not afraid, are you?"

Adding cream to his second cup of coffee, he gave her a withering glance. "I'm not afraid of anything as old as these ghosts are supposed to be. If they get nasty, I can probably take them two falls out of three. How about you, Bro?" he asked, looking at his friend with mild amusement. "Do a few couple-of-hundred-year-old ghosts worry you any?"

"Nah, not when I have Anna to protect me," Frankie said, chuckling.

"I hope Madison will be all right in the hotel when we're gone," Anna said, suddenly fretful about her puppy. "I don't think he's ever been entirely by himself before. He's always had his mother, and then all of us with him."

"We'll take him for a good long walk before we leave and tire him out," Frankie assured her. "Then we'll feed him and set him up in the shower with his blanket and toys. He'll probably be asleep the whole time we're gone."

"Maybe I should stay in the shower with my blanket and toys, too," Tony said reflectively, "since if anything goes wrong, Anna will naturally protect you first."

Anna and Frankie both made discreet noises that sounded a lot like chickens clucking.

"Okay," Tony said with a feigned tone of annoyance. "But don't either one of you bother coming to me if your skin starts to feel prickly. It's every smart aleck for himself when things start to go bump in the night."

The clerk at the desk was true to his word, and their rooms were ready when they finished eating. They agreed to get some sleep and meet again in the lobby at seven o'clock that night.

Tony had driven the last leg of the journey that day, and he felt beat. He stepped out of a hot shower, toweled off, and fell into bed without bothering to put on his clothes. Sound asleep in two minutes, he woke abruptly in just under two hours. He had been dreaming, and he lay there a few minutes remembering the details of his dream.

He was standing at the convergence of two paths. Along the path to his right, everything was the same color: brown. The path was brown, the trees were brown, and the sky was brown. As soon as he stepped onto the path, scenes of his life began to appear in front of him, like scenes in a play. He and everything in them were brown. He was in the gym at his condo doing a vigorous workout. He was in his office meeting with a client. He was in his apartment napping with Trainwreck curled up beside him on the couch. He was eating dinner at the Fillmore Café. He was alone, both in the scenes of his life and on the path. A sign popped up bearing the words, "How do you feel?"

"I feel fine," he answered.

In the next scenes, his appearance slightly changed, he looked a little more fleshed out and quite a bit more serious. He was at a meeting of the downtown Rotary Club. He was fishing with a teenage boy who was wearing a t-shirt with the words "Big Brothers, Big Sisters" stenciled across the chest. He and Frankie and Anna were together at Andy's high school graduation. He was receiving an award from the St. Petersburg Chamber of Commerce. He was having a check-up in a doctor's office. More people were in his life now, but he was still on the path alone. A sign popped up bearing the words, "How do you feel?"

"I feel okay," he answered.

In the next scenes, older still, he had put on about thirty pounds. The hair at his temples and in his beard was beginning to turn grey. He was taking a long walk by himself. Something obviously had happened to Trainwreck, because Tony was sitting in a room he didn't recognize and petting a different cat. For the first time, he felt alone. Then, as often happens in dreams, he was back where he started, standing at a place where two paths converged.

This time he began to walk down the second path. It was bathed in sunshine. Patches of brightly colored flowers grew along both sides of the path, and leafy, green trees formed a bower of branches overhead. Birds were singing, and other music, too, floated gently around him on a soft breeze.

All the Technicolor scenes appearing before him this time included Molly. They were working on something together in his office. They were cooking together in the kitchen. They were entering a museum together. They were at a party at Frankie and Anna's house, surrounded by other friends. They were cuddling together in a movie. And now, they were also walking together on the path. A sign popped up bearing the words, "How do you feel?"

"I feel wonderful," Tony answered.

More scenes of him with Molly appeared as he walked farther. They were buying a house together. They were planting a garden. They were visiting Ireland and she was showing him her Gran's house. They were having dinner at the Yacht Club. They were entertaining friends on the patio of a house he had never seen before. They were sitting on the beach in the moonlight, pointing at the stars. They were square dancing and laughing as they tried to keep up with the caller. Another sign popped up bearing the words, "How do you feel?"

"Happy. Contented. Grateful," Tony answered.

And again, he was standing where the two paths converged, the one he could travel alone and the other he could travel with Molly.

The dream left him a little dizzy. Tony recognized this feeling as one he'd had before when he was on the brink of making a big decision. What he needed, he decided, was a cup of strong coffee. Slipping into jeans and a fresh t-shirt, he jogged down the stairs to Starbucks and ordered a grande cappuccino. Then he took the stairs, two at a time, back to his room.

He rearranged the furniture in the room just slightly so he could sit in a chair and put his feet up on the bed. He shouldn't have been surprised, then, to have a visit from the ELF. After all, hadn't he been setting the scene for it?

Sitting on the edge of the bed, the ELF looked kindly at Tony but didn't say a word.

"Did you put that dream in my head?" Tony asked.

"No, you did, Tony. You've been debating between those two paths in your mind this whole trip. Did the dream help you make your decision?"

"Almost. I know which path I want to take, but there's this nagging little voice somewhere in me that says, 'What if something goes wrong?' I know that voice isn't yours, so whose is it?"

"It's your ego, Tony. Your ego does a lot of things to make your life difficult at times, but this time, it's just trying to protect you from being hurt again."

"Can it do that?"

"No, but it would like you to think it can."

"But what if something does go wrong, and Molly and I wind up being unhappy with each other? You know what the marriage statistics are. They're dismal. Right now, we're not unhappy the way we are. Wouldn't we be risking an awful lot to change that?"

"Happy or unhappy, those are simply choices, Tony. You just left Lawrence and Millie, didn't you? How long have they been married?"

"Forty-five years, they said."

"And in that time, were they ever unhappy?"

"They mentioned a few times that life didn't go their way," Tony answered. "She said she miscarried three times, and then the doctor told them not to try again or she might die. I don't know how bad that feels to a woman, but she looked sad about it, even all these years later. And I know they very much wanted to have children of their own. They also said their house burned down about ten years ago and they thought it was the end of their world at the time, but then they built the house they live in now, and they like it even better."

"And would you say they're happy now?"

"Yes, very. And they're excited about their future together, too."

The ELF shifted his position, his colors shimmering up and down as he spoke. "Every married couple has some of what you call 'good' and 'bad' experiences, Tony. If you use the tools I have taught you and don't build yourself any boxes that keep me from giving you what you ask for, you can ward off most of the bad ones. When you don't use your tools, some things happen that you're not so happy about.

"You've already learned, though," the ELF continued, "that what makes life so interesting is that it is always changing. Good experiences replace bad ones. Abraham explains very well how those so-called bad experiences serve as contrast to help you enjoy and appreciate even more the really good experiences that follow."

"When did you know I was in love with Molly?" Tony asked.

"Well, eons before you realized it, that's for sure," the ELF said. "What do you feel when you think about Molly, Tony? Just think about Molly. Nothing else."

"I feel excited. I feel exhilarated. I feel like I want to touch her and never stop touching her. I want to hold her and never let go. I want to know everything she's ever thought about, every feeling she's ever felt. I want to explore every mental, physical, and emotional part of her. I want to take care of her and let her take care of me, forever."

"And all that feels good?"

"'Good' hardly describes it. It feels so much better than anything

I have ever felt before that I can hardly get my head around it."

"What has your dream done for you, Tony?"

"It's made the question I've been asking myself seem much clearer. Do I want to spend my life by myself, which has the potential to be okay but holds no guarantees, or do I want to spend it with Molly, which has the potential to be fabulous? Again, with no guarantees."

"That's the question. And as I always have told you, you're never given a question to which you don't already know the answer. Are you ready to listen to your heart, Tony?"

"I'm going to ask Molly to marry me as soon as I get home," Tony answered, "but first, I'm going to ask for what I want. I don't want to take any chances that I won't do this right. I want Molly to marry me, and I want our marriage to look very much like the one I saw along the sunny path in my dream. That's what I'm asking for, and now I choose to believe that you will work out the details. I'm also going to graciously collect what I have asked for, whenever, wherever, and however you decide to deliver it."

"That's exactly the right way to get what you want, Tony," the ELF said, shimmering with delight. "Just keep your mind focused on what you want and leave the rest to me."

With a wave, a shimmer, and a cheerful laugh, the ELF disappeared.

Tony looked at his watch. It was four o'clock. With no hesitation, he picked up his jacket and jogged back down the stairs to see the concierge.

Within thirty minutes, he was standing in Levy Jewelers. Selecting a two-carat, round-cut emerald surrounded by tiny diamonds in a platinum setting, he handed the salesman his credit card without a second thought. He could already picture the ring on Molly's finger, and he intended to put it there himself, just as soon as possible.

Tony barely made it back in time to change for dinner, but

when he stepped into the lobby to meet Frankie and Anna at seven o'clock, Molly's ring was in the concierge's safe and Tony was in a fabulous mood.

Frankie picked up on it instantly, and for reasons he clearly didn't understand, he felt both touched and relieved. *It's been too long since Tony and I have had time together*, he thought. *Much too long.* "I guess it's time we had a talk, Bro," Frankie said, resting his hand on Tony's shoulder while they waited for Anna to check out the hotel limousine that would take them to the restaurant and then to the ghost tour.

"As soon as we get a chance, I'll tell you about my latest conversation with You Know Who," Tony said. Then they followed Anna's wave signaling that the hotel limousine was waiting.

Tony pulled the van into Frankie's driveway at about ten o'clock Tuesday night. He got out and stretched, appreciating the warmth of the Florida night air. *Funny, a few weeks ago, I would have called this night cool*, Tony thought.

Opening the back door, he gently shook a sleeping Frankie's shoulder. "We're home, Bro," he said, trying not to startle either Anna or Madison.

"Jeez, Tony, you could have stopped at your condo so we could let you off," Frankie said, yawning. Then he gently moved Anna from under his arm and kissed her awake.

"I figured you'd need a hand unloading your luggage and getting Madison inside and settled in," Tony explained. "By that time, you'll be awake enough to run me back home."

Frankie immediately perceived that Tony wanted to talk to him alone, and his curiosity was suddenly piqued.

"You can stay the night if you want to, Tony," Anna murmured. "The guest room's all made up."

"Thanks, Anna, but I kind of want to get home to Trainwreck. Molly said he was really missing me," he explained, carrying Madison in his carrier into the house and setting them down on the living room floor.

Behind them Frankie raised an eyebrow. *I didn't know he'd been talking to Molly while we were away. Hmm...isn't that interesting?*

It didn't take long to get all of Frankie and Anna's baggage, plus the rest of Madison's trappings, into the house. Anna, now wide awake, assured them she could handle setting up a safe place for Madison to sleep. "Go home and see your cat," she said kindly, nudging Tony and her husband back out toward the van. "I just hate the thought of him missing you any longer than necessary."

As soon as they pulled out of the driveway, Frankie zoomed in. "Okay, Bro, spill it, And why do I think this conversation is going to be all about Molly?"

Tony put it simply. "I'm in love with her and I'm going to ask her to marry me."

"You're what?" Frankie almost shouted, involuntarily jerking the steering wheel and then struggling to keep the van in line. "I didn't even know you were dating her, Tony. How come you didn't tell me you were going to marry her, for Pete's sake? It's not as if we don't ever see each other."

Tony smiled to himself, remembering that he had used just about the same language a few months ago when Frankie had surprised him by saying he intended to marry Anna. I *guess neither of us ever does the big things in quite the conventional way*, he thought.

"A few huge things have happened to me since we last had breakfast together at the Dome Grill, Frankie. Without Anna, I mean. I've had three different conversations with the ELF, including the mother of all conversations where I discovered what I had done to sabotage myself for almost thirty years after my mother lost her mind. You're going to find it pretty interesting, too; I know I did. And we won't be able to talk this Saturday," he said, not bothering to keep the annoyance out of his voice, "because it will be New Year's Day and Pete's will be closed again."

Immediately feeling terrible that he hadn't made time for Tony in such a long time, or shared with him anything about his own talks with the ELF about his father and uncle, Frankie did not hesitate. "Then we'll meet for breakfast on Friday this week, because I sure don't want to wait another week to hear about it. Did talking to the ELF have anything to do with your decision to marry Molly?"

"It probably did pave the way for it, now that I think of it," Tony answered. "But the main reason I haven't been sharing with you that I was falling in love with Molly is because I didn't realize it myself. I started to understand it for the first time almost as soon as we left town. Do you remember the first day of the trip, when I was driving north from Gainesville and you had to thump me on the back to get my attention?"

"Yeah, Anna and I couldn't believe how out of it you were."

"Well, I was in the process of reliving my relationship with her since it began. That was when I realized we had been doing an awful lot of things together for quite a while. They all just fell into place so naturally that I never noticed she was becoming important to me. As soon as I got honest with myself, I had to admit we've been pretty much a couple since the night we had dinner at your house and I gave you your wedding presents."

"Did any of this coupling involve real coupling, pal?"

"No, that's just it, Frankie. I've never even kissed her, except for a peck on the cheek. Oh, I've wanted her more than once, big time. She has the most tempting round little body, and she is totally unaware of how innocent she is. She's driven me crazy plenty of times.

"But every time I had the urge to take her to bed for a few days, I would remind myself that she was a client and she lived just down the hall. Both of those things made a personal relationship with her off limits for me. So I would force myself to stop thinking of her that way. Those were the nights I was in the gym at three o'clock in the morning, working off all that sexual energy.

"And by the way, it's not that she has exactly discouraged me, either. Not having sex with her was my choice, not hers. If I had asked, I've no doubt she would have said yes. What drove me nuts on this trip, though, Frankie, was that just putting her out of my mind didn't work, no matter how hard I tried. Remember the night at Williamsburg when we were sitting on the hillside listening to the choir sing Christmas carols? Suddenly, I wanted Molly there with me something fierce. The longing was so strong you'd better believe it scared the shit out of me.

"After that, she started popping into my mind all the time, and sometimes I would actually ache for her. It was unreal. And it wasn't just sex I was missing her for, Bro. I missed everything about her. So I called her on Christmas Day and told her how much I missed her, and admitted I didn't know what to do about it because I'd never missed anyone before."

"And she said?"

"And she said she missed me, too, and she didn't know what to do about it, either. But she was going to ask the fairies what to do about it and then wait for the answer."

"So what's next?"

"I'm going to ask her to marry me. I asked her to have dinner with me tomorrow night, and I'll probably do it then. I just wanted you to know about it before I do it. I guess I'm kind of asking for your blessing, Bro."

"You know you've got it, pal. If you can be as happy with Molly as I am with Anna, I'm going to very grateful."

Frankie pulled up in front of the elevators in the parking garage of Tony's building and helped unload both of Tony's bags—the old one he had taken with him, and the new one he had bought to hold all his new things.

"I will call you either way, Bro," Tony said, giving Frankie a tight one-arm hug. "And anyway, I'll see you Friday morning at

Pete's at nine o'clock. Brace yourself for some really interesting ELF talk."

From the second he stepped off the elevator, Tony could hear Trainwreck's frantic meowing. Unlocking the door to his condo, he set his bags down in the front hall and picked up his excited cat. Trainwreck put one front paw on each of Tony's cheeks and simply wailed for a few seconds. Then he began to pat Tony's cheeks vigorously, making such serious scolding noises that Tony laughed out loud.

After he felt he'd been sufficiently told off, Tony began to talk to Trainwreck in soothing tones, explaining that everything was all right now, and he didn't plan to leave again anytime soon. The calmness of Tony's voice and the firmness of his hold eventually brought Trainwreck down from his emotional jag.

When Tony finally sat down on the couch with him, Trainwreck crawled up onto his chest and tucked his head under Tony's chin. Then he let out such a long, deep, shuddering sigh that Tony was sure Frankie and Anna could hear it at their place.

"I know just how you feel, buddy," Tony said, gently stroking his cat's back. "It's pure hell missing someone you love, isn't it?"

After a while Tony got up, still holding Trainwreck in his arms, and went upstairs to the bedroom. Putting the cat down on his bed, Tony stripped off his clothes and crawled under the covers. Seconds later, Trainwreck joined him.

"It's a good thing Molly and Darth Vader are small," he told Trainwreck, giving him an affectionate scratch. "Otherwise I'd have to buy a bigger bed. Because if I have my way, we're all going to be sleeping together here tomorrow night, and every other night from now on."

Because she had an eleven-thirty appointment she couldn't break, Molly knocked on Tony's door Wednesday morning at nine. She told herself she was just checking to see if he was home, because if not, she needed to feed Trainwreck. But if she was perfectly honest with herself, she was there because she couldn't wait any longer to see Tony.

She had put four cinnamon buns on a plate and attached Darth Vader's leash to his collar. When they had headed for Tony's apartment, Molly felt amazingly calm, considering what she was planning to do.

Tony opened the door and they stood there a few seconds silently drinking in the sight of each other.

He looks like a movie star, Molly thought, her breath catching in her throat. Wearing the black and silver sweater his father had given him for Christmas, Tony looked just fine in pair of slim-fitting jeans.

She looks like a fairy herself, Tony thought, his stomach alternately clutching and releasing in a lovesick spasm. She had on a gauzy cream-colored dress that fell from her shoulders straight to the hemline several inches above her knees. Molly also wore black tights and black suede ankle boots, her shiny auburn hair pulled back by a black velvet headband.

Jolted back to reality, Molly handed Tony the plate of cinnamon buns so she could reach down and unsnap the dog's leash. "Welcome home," she said, more steady as she straightened up and dashed a quick kiss to his cheek.

"Gee, thanks," he said, taking the plate. "Come on in and have some coffee. I'll just get another mug." Setting the cinnamon buns on the coffee table, he headed for the kitchen, hoping the activity in his stomach would quiet down.

When he came back with two mugs of fresh coffee, she was sitting in a lotus position facing him from one end of the couch, her back resting against the arm.

"Now, tell me everything you did while I was gone," Tony

said as brightly as he could manage, hoping that if they could start with some general conversation, it would help him get a grip on his nerves before he told her he absolutely couldn't live one more minute without her.

He was very interested in what she had to say, so he knew he could listen to her on two levels at the same time. Still, he was glad when Trainwreck jumped up into his lap. Petting the cat would help keep his hands busy so he wouldn't be tempted to reach out and touch her too soon.

"Well," she said, feeling delighted at how happy Trainwreck looked on Tony's lap, "I did a lot of things while you were gone. The first few days I worked all day, every day, stocking my freezers. I was moving right along until the county health inspector came in and told Sam and me we'd have to build a wall to separate our two kitchens. And he said my business will require its own health certificate, so I'm going to take a class the Monday after New Year's to become certified. Then I can apply for it.

"The inspector was a nice guy, considering the rules he has to play by, and he gave me a temporary 'stay of execution' for thirty days. He also told me my kitchen would have no trouble qualifying for the certificate. I know—things always work out for me. But it gave me quite a jolt, believe me."

"Does having to put up a wall upset Sam and Mary?"

"Well, at first, it upset us all. And of course, we had to get Mr. Ferguson's permission to build a wall. But he said it would be fine. After we let the dust settle, we decided it would be just fine with us, too. We're going to split the cost of construction, which keeps it from breaking the budget of either business.

"There will be a double door in the wall, which the inspector says we can leave open if we want. We can still talk to each other, and the wall will give us both some more storage space. For Mary, it will mean fewer steps and less time to get to her cooking supplies when she's busy. For me, it will mean there will be wall space for one or two more chest freezers, and I can have a real desk built into the kitchen. The carpenter who did my other installations is going to build the wall next Thursday and make sure it's strong enough to hold shelving and storage on both sides.

"Also, I got a new customer all by myself. Well, almost all by myself. The table cards you designed for the Café played a part. A guy who works at the bank has a sister who's a personal chef. She owns a company that provides trained chefs to cook at parties held in private clubs, private homes, corporate offices, and on yachts and private jets. When he saw the table card about my desserts, he asked Sam how his sister could get in touch with me, and Sam gave him my card.

"She called me a few days later. It seems her chefs are extremely talented at making appetizers, soups, salads, and entrées, but none of them is good at making desserts, so she's lost some customers because she wasn't doing a good job with that part of her meals.

"Sam let me set up a tasting for her in the Café, and she ordered a whole freezer full of desserts that her chefs can pull from at any time. She will order stock to refill it as needed, but she also signed a contract with me for a minimum order, once a month, of seasonal desserts. It's really a nice deal, Tony."

"That's just super," Tony said. "How are the table cards working for Sam? Is he selling any more desserts?"

"Yes. In fact, he and Mary have doubled the size of their regular order for the three desserts a day. Occasionally he orders something special just to keep his regulars interested. I made him some Bailey's Irish Cream pies for Christmas week, and he just ordered a Homeland Irish Whisky Cake for New Year's. He's serving each piece this week with a sparkler in it."

"And what's happening with the Yacht Club?"

"I've already delivered a freezer load of regular menu desserts to them, and they get the first delivery of their signature desserts tomorrow. They'll be serving them the first time on New Year's

Eve. But here's the news that will interest you most about the Yacht Club. The response they got from the e-mail reminder to members to spend New Year's Eve at the Yacht Club more than doubled their reservations. They've opened both of their smaller dining rooms, and they've still had to turn people away.

"The manager and Amelia were impressed, to say the least. Now in the coming year, she's got her eye on expanding their wedding business, so the club manager wants to talk to you about how to market those services. The more weddings they book, the more business for me, so I'm glad they're going to take that route."

"You do wedding cakes, too?"

"No, not traditional ones, but not all brides want traditional wedding cakes anymore. Recently, ice cream cakes and cupcakes have become popular substitutes. Groom's cakes are becoming popular again, too. Also, weddings generate other kinds of parties, and the Yacht Club knows that. Engagement parties, wedding showers, bridesmaid luncheons, bachelor and bachelorette parties, rehearsal dinners, and events like that are usually small but elegant. If all those events are held at the Yacht Club, there will be more business for me."

"Are you busy enough now, or will you want more customers?"

"I'm certainly not going to turn any business down if I get referrals, Tony, but I think I'll try to find a better rhythm before I go out after any more business. It will help to have a desk and a phone and a wall-size calendar right in the bakery so I can keep track of my busiest times. Then I will know where I have time to add more work. Working between home and the bakery gives me flexibility, especially at the experimental or creative end, but it also makes it hard for me to stay organized. I have to learn how to better balance the two."

"Well, you certainly worked hard while I was gone. Did you do anything for fun?"

"I did one fun thing that will surprise you. To keep Trainwreck company, Darth and I came over here every night for a few hours, and I entertained myself by watching the *MIND Is Your Own Business* DVDs. I've learned so much from them, and I was feeling so grateful for John McLaughlin, I wondered how to thank him. Then I remembered you said he lived in Clearwater. I looked in the phone book, and there was only one John McLaughlin in Clearwater.

"Just on a hunch, I packed up a box of desserts on Christmas Eve and had a messenger service deliver them to John McLaughlin at that address. I wrote a little note and put it in the box saying that if he was the John McLaughlin who was the teacher of *MIND Is Your Own Business*, three of my friends and I wanted to thank him for making such a difference in our lives. Yesterday, he called to thank me, and told me those were the best brownies he'd ever eaten. It was neat."

"That's so cool," Tony said with genuine excitement. "We were talking about him on the trip home in the car, and were wondering if we could call and ask him to have dinner with all of us. Now that he's been tempted by Molly Malone's killer brownies, maybe it will be an offer he can't refuse.

"Anything else you forgot to tell me, Molly?"

"Yes, there is one more thing that happened while you were gone, Tony," she said, setting her mug on the coffee table, folding her hands in her lap, and raising her eyes to him. "I discovered I'm in love with you."

CHAPTER TWENTY ONE

The air was electric. "Could you say that again just one more time, please?" Tony said, barely breathing as he stood up. Reaching for Molly's hands, he gently pulled her to her feet in front of him.

She put her hands on his chest as if to hold him away. "I said I love you. But don't let it worry you, Tony," she said with a tremor in her voice." It's my problem, not yours, and I'll deal with it. But you know me, I always like all the cards on the…"

Arms banded tightly around her and he drew her in with a deeply passionate kiss.

When she could breathe again, she sighed.

Reluctantly, Tony slightly broke away and cupped her face between his hands. "I love you, too, Molly, and I didn't know how to tell you," he said. "I don't know how it happened and I don't care. I just know I love you, and I want to be with you more than I ever wanted anything in my entire life."

"Just please don't go away again, Tony, at least not for a long time," she murmured between the fluttering kisses they lightly brushed on each other's face. "I've never been so lonely for anyone before. That's how I figured out I had fallen in love with you."

"Wherever I go from now on, Baby, you're going with me," Tony said. And this time, he poured into their kiss all the energy he had been building up for days. Winding her arms firmly around his neck, she freely returned his passion.

When they finally relaxed, she leaned into him and held him tightly for a few seconds. "I wish I didn't have to leave you right now, Tony, but I have to be at the bakery to accept a delivery at eleven thirty."

"I'll go with you," he said. "And since we didn't eat even one of your cinnamon buns, I'll buy you lunch at the Café. Then can you spend the rest of the day with me?"

"Yes, oh yes. And the night, too, if you'll let me."

"How about the rest of our lives, Molly? Will you marry me, grow up with me, grow old with me?"

She didn't hesitate. "I will. I will marry you, Tony, and I promise to love you every day for as long as I live."

"That's a good thing, Baby," he said. "Because I plan to love you every day for as long as I live, too."

Then, almost as if they had been tapped on the knee, they looked down to see their two little animals sitting hip to hip at their feet, staring up at them with huge questioning eyes. As if on cue, Tony and Molly leaned down together and scooped Trainwreck and Darth up into their arms in their first family group hug.

When Tony and Molly walked through the doorway of the Fillmore Café holding hands, sparks of love virtually arced between them. At the very sight of the loving couple, Sam broke into a gigantic grin.

"What are you so happy about today, Sam?" Tony asked.

"I'm smiling because I just won a twenty dollar bet, Romeo," Sam answered, still smiling. "Mary and I had a bet about how soon you two would realize you're in love. I said this trip would do it. She thought it would take a little longer. Obviously, I was right."

"Has it really been that obvious?" Tony asked, shrugging his shoulders at Molly as if the whole thing were still a puzzle to him.

"Only to someone with eyes and ears that were open."

As Tony and Molly selected a table by the window, Sam took out his order pad. "How would you like your hot turkey sandwich today, Tony?"

"No, no. Falling in love has changed me. I'm a new man, Sam," Tony said. "And since I've developed a new appreciation for all things Irish, I'm switching to corned beef and cabbage today."

Then picking up one of the table cards he had designed to promote the Café's new line of desserts, he added, "Tell me about these Irish desserts you're pushing. Are they any good?"

"Well, I'll tell you," Sam said, launching into his spiel. "These Irish desserts are so good…"

"Oh, never mind, Sam," Tony said, getting up and walking around to Molly's side of the table. "I believe I'll just taste one for myself." Lifting a surprised and giggling Molly into his arms, he kissed her squarely on the mouth. As applause erupted from the other diners in the Café, he danced with her into the kitchen to tell Mary she'd just lost twenty bucks.

While Molly was receiving her delivery, Tony walked into the lobby of the hotel and dialed directory service to get the number of Fred's Steak House at the Vinoy. Against all odds, he hoped there would still be an available reservation for New Year's Eve.

From his days of handling that account at ADPRO, Tony knew Francois, the restaurant manager at Fred's, so he punched the number in and asked to speak to Francois personally. While the extension was ringing, Tony started a silent mantra of the affirmation, "Things always work out for me."

"Tony, you're a colossal optimist, which is, of course, what has made you such a good ad man," Francois replied when Tony asked for a reservation on New Year's Eve. "And it would seem that things just continue to work out for you, my friend. We've been booked solid for two months, but not fifteen minutes ago, someone cancelled for eight-thirty. Table for two by the window overlooking the fountain. I'm putting your name on it right now."

"Well, being French and all, you'll be happy to know that I need that table for a very good reason. I'm going to give my future wife her engagement ring while we're there."

"Oh, I just love public displays of affection on New Year's Eve! I'll chill a bottle of our best champagne, then. On the house, of course. And you're right, I'm a hopeless romantic. But I'll try not to cry before the ring is safely on her finger. See you Friday, Tony!" he said cheerfully before hanging up.

Then Tony called Frankie. Not to worry, Tony told him. He had proposed, Molly had accepted, and he'd give up the details on Friday morning.

For the next day and a half, the only work either Tony or Molly made room for was the delivery of Molly Malone's Irish Desserts to the Yacht Club for New Year's Eve. Tony went with Molly to make the delivery, and while she was working with Amelia, Tony made an appointment with the club manager for the next week to discuss the promotion of weddings for the coming year.

The rest of the time, Molly and Tony spent in Tony's apartment learning everything they could think of to ask about each other. They talked about their childhoods and their adult challenges, their likes and dislikes, their hopes and dreams. Because both of them were practical and serious people, they discussed what they thought were all the big important subjects, and they found very few points of conflict.

Tony didn't want to have children and, as it turned out, Molly wasn't able to have them, anyway. They both wanted eventually to live in a house instead of a condo. They loved running their own businesses. Neither of them had much family to make demands that might upset the other. They both liked to open Christmas presents on Christmas Eve and sleep late on Sunday mornings. They both thought consulting a financial planner would be a good idea. She liked to sleep on the right side of the bed and he preferred the left. They both liked to travel, but they preferred short trips to long ones.

Although neither of them had been church-goers as adults, they both were very excited about what they were learning from Abraham and from their *MIND Is Your Own Business* DVDs, and they wanted to learn much more. Tony told Molly more about his talks with the ELF, and she explained more about her communication with the fairies.

Having so many points of agreement both surprised and delighted them, and the few things they thought differently about—the colors they would choose to paint the walls of their bedroom and whether or not to use white or colored sheets—they recognized as insignificant in the whole scheme of life.

Eventually, they made room in their getting-to-know-you time to call her parents and his father to tell them they would be getting married, and then they planned their wedding and their honeymoon. In between, they made love, day and night, until they finally agreed that they could be apart for a few hours and still believe the other would be there on their return.

On Friday morning, almost ready to leave to meet Frankie, Tony asked Molly what was on her agenda for the day.

"Well, it's New Year's Eve, you know," she said coyly, "and I have a date with the man I'm planning to spend the rest of my life with. So I thought such an occasion might be worthy of a new dress. I'm going shopping with Anna."

"Anna?"

"Uh-huh. She's got the day off because she has to work tomorrow, so we decided since you and Frankie would be together today, we'd spend today together, too."

"Did you call her?"

"No, she called me while you were in the shower this morning. I'm guessing you clued in Frankie that we're going to get married, because she wanted to let me know she was just ecstatic for both of us. Then we started to talk about where we would be going tonight, which led to what we were going to wear, which led to the idea that today would be the perfect day for us to buy a couple of really sexy dresses, because you and Frankie deserve for us both to look spectacular tonight."

"I can't wait for tonight, Baby," Tony said, looking her up and down. To him, she already looked spectacular in jeans and a turtleneck sweater.

"Do you know what they're doing for New Year's Eve, by the way?" Molly asked.

"No. I figured Frankie would tell me this morning, though."

"Well, I just think it's the sweetest thing they're doing. Because Frankie didn't have a chance to give Julie and Mike a real Christmas present, he's booked a room for them, and one for himself and Anna at The Don Caesar on the beach for tonight. Frankie and Anna are going to have their New Year's Eve dinner at sunset. Then they're going to pick up Andy and keep her with them so Julie and Mike can have a midnight supper and spend the night alone together."

"Frankie really has become an imaginative gift-giver since he married Anna, hasn't he?" Tony said with a chuckle. Then noticing the question in Molly's eyes, he explained. "Frankie would give the people he loves the moon if he realized they wanted it. But he always felt awkward when it came time for gift giving, because he never seemed to know what to choose. Anna apparently is very good at choosing just the right thing."

Then he told Molly about the print of Caladesi Island that Frankie and Anna had given to Frankie's aunt and uncle for Christmas, and how his uncle had hung it over the fireplace immediately. "They said they'd look at it every morning and picture us all together on that beach, so we'd better stock up on suntan lotion. They seem to know how to manifest what they want, and I have no doubt they'll be living down here in no time."

Tony turned and took both of Molly's hands in his. "About my having breakfast with Frankie this morning, Baby. You know that today is unusual because all the other weeks of the year we meet on Saturday morning at nine o'clock, and that's something that's just not going to change. Does that bother you?"

"Not only doesn't it bother me, Tony," she said, drawing his hands up to her heart, "but I think it's just about the nicest thing I've ever heard. And I'm going to be thinking of Frankie like my brother now, too, just the way Anna thinks of you as hers. There's no competition here, Tony. I know there's plenty of room in your heart for all of us, and in mine for all that matters to you.

"Now," she said, resisting temptation as she felt the physical pull between them grow suddenly intense again, "I need to get ready to go, because finding the perfect dress takes time and concentration. What time shall I be ready for dinner tonight?"

"I thought we'd have a champagne toast with our children here first," he said, reaching down to pat the head of both Trainwreck and Darth Vader, who seemed to gather inquiringly at the feet of their owners whenever they embraced for any length of time. "Then we can walk over to the Vinoy for dinner at eight-thirty. Fred's is just five minutes from here. Does that sound okay to you?"

"Oh, yes," she said, kissing him long and hard. "It sounds stupendous."

When Tony walked into the Dome Grill on the morning of New Year's Eve, he was surprised to find Pete a little out of sorts. In all the years he and Frankie had been having breakfast there, he'd never seen Pete quite so agitated.

"You don't look happy, Pete," Tony said with real concern. "Anything I can do?"

"Nah, it's just the holidays," Pete said. "It happens to me every year about this time. I'm just ready for them to be over. My help is unpredictable, it's hard to get deliveries on time, my regulars complain if I'm not open on the holidays, but then they don't come in if I do stay open. I'm gonna have to stay here after I close tonight and take down these stinkin' decorations, and now seeing you here this morning makes me realize that my favorite customers can't even come here on their regular day. It just annoys me, that's all."

"Ya gotta learn to go with the flow better Pete," Tony said, remembering that just a little over a month ago, the holidays used to be a thorn in his side too. "By Monday, the earth will resume its regular rhythm and all will be right at the Dome Grill again."

Frankie walked in just in time to hear the last part of the conversation. "Don't worry if Tony seems disgustingly cheerful this morning Pete," Frankie said, grinning at his friend. "He's just in love."

"Yeah? I thought he was acting a little out of character," Pete said. "It was kinda nice."

"I'm more than just in love," Tony said, making it clear he didn't intend to let either of these turkeys spoil his good mood. "Molly has agreed to marry me, and tonight I'll be giving her an engagement ring." He took the little box out of his back pocket to show them the emerald ring he had bought in Savannah.

"Holy cow," Pete said, "you're as bad as Frankie, Tony. It took you two forever to find the right women, but then all of a sudden, you fall like the dew on a daisy on a summer morning. Well, good luck from me, Tony. Whoever she is, she's getting a swell guy."

"You hear that, Frankie? Molly's getting a swell guy," Tony said.

"Yeah, with an equally swelled head," Frankie said, winking at

Pete. "What do you say we sit down and eat, Casanova?"

"You know, this is kind of fun, Frankie. Sam called me Romeo. You're calling me Casanova. I'm waiting for someone to call me Adonis next."

"Oh, just cool it, pal. I'm not sure I didn't like you better when you were sexually frustrated."

"Yeah, well thank heaven those days are over for life," Tony said, grinning. "Just think, I'll soon be a mellow fellow all the time, just like you are, Doerrer."

"A mellow Italian, Celentano? Now that does not compute."

With a silly smile on his face, Tony went to pick up their breakfast and quickly returned to the table. Frankie then suggested that Tony tell him about his conversation with the ELF that related to Tony's mother and father.

Thirty minutes later, Tony had brought Frankie up to speed on that conversation, as well as all the other ELF conversations since. He also told Frankie about Molly delivering desserts to John McLaughlin for Christmas, and then about his and Molly's wedding plans.

"We're getting married on March seventeenth," he told Frankie. "It happens to be a Saturday, and we are enjoying the irony of Molly Malone becoming Molly Celentano on that oh-so-Irish holiday. Plus, my Dad and your aunt and uncle will already be down here then, so it will be convenient for them to come to the wedding.

"We talked about lots of places to get married, but since so much that matters to us right now revolves around the Fillmore Hotel, we talked to Mr. Ferguson, and he agreed to let us be married in the lobby of the hotel under the big arch."

"You know, that could be really nice," Frankie said, thinking back to his own wedding the month before. "I guess the wedding party could come down the staircase. Should be pretty."

"Deirdre, Molly's best friend from New York, will be the maid of honor," Tony continued. "And even as we speak, Molly is inviting Anna to be her bridesmaid."

"I suppose we should be a little apprehensive about Anna and Molly getting together and talking about us," Frankie said, "but I'm just not. Are you?"

"Nope," Tony said, "although if they could overhear us right now, I bet they'd both be asking why we think all they have to talk about is us."

Grinning, Frankie nodded.

"When we called her parents to tell them we were getting married, Molly's mother had to confess that Molly's father was not well enough to travel to Florida. He's quite a bit older than her mother, apparently, and though he's not dangerously ill, whatever is wrong would make travel by plane, train, or car too difficult for him.

"I guess we'll find out more about that in March, because after the wedding, we're gonna fly up to see them. I'll tell you more about that in a minute, but I want to tell you a couple of other things first. Since her father won't be walking her down the aisle, Molly asked Sam if he would. Do you know, Frankie," Tony reported in amazement, "Sam was so touched when she asked him that the big tough guy burst out crying right in front of his customers. The three of them must have gotten pretty close since Molly's been working there, because Mary has been fluttering all over her, too, as if she were the mother of the bride. But here's the kicker, Bro. Guess who's going to perform the ceremony?"

"I don't know. Does Molly have a priest in her family?" Frankie asked.

"Not that I know of," Tony said, laughing. "But if she did, we wouldn't be asking him anyway. John McLaughlin is going to marry us."

"No kidding!" Frankie said, his fork clattering to his plate. "How in the world did that happen?"

"Molly just called him and asked him, and he said he would be delighted. He even knows exactly where the Fillmore Hotel is, Frankie. He told Molly he's lived in and around St. Petersburg since he was six years old. And he also said he would be out of town for most of the month of January, but when he gets back in February, he would enjoy having dinner with the four of us and we could work out the wedding details with him then."

"Anna will be pretty excited to hear that, and the truth is, so am I," Frankie said.

Then switching gears, Frankie sounded perturbed. "Now that you've introduced me to the whole wedding party, Tony, are you going to ask me to be your best man, or is there someone else I have to kill first?"

"Oh, sorry, Bro," Tony said, looking a little contrite. "I thought it was automatic. See, it's just that to me, you're always the best man, wherever we are."

Something about the way he said it touched Frankie to the bone.

"Okay, now you've made me sloppy, and I hate this," Frankie said, reaching for his handkerchief. "I'm sorry to be so sensitive, Tony. It's just so hard for me to get a grip these days. Can you even begin to think about all that's happened to you and me in just a little over two months? You talked to the ELF for the first time, then I asked Anna to marry me, then I began talking to the ELF, then Anna and I got married, and now you've asked Molly to marry you. And those are just the highlights."

Hoping he was back in control of his emotions, Frankie blew his nose. But as they continued to talk about all they had learned at what Frankie called soap-opera speed from the ELF, Abraham, and John McLaughlin, tears ebbed and flowed from both men for at least another ten minutes.

"It's a good thing neither of us is embarrassed about crying in public," Tony said as he wiped away the last of his tears for the time being. "So moving forward, let me tell you about our honeymoon. It won't be quite as kitschy as your Disney World deal, but it looks like it's gonna be close. Since we're going to New York anyway, Molly confessed to me that when she was a little girl, she absolutely loved to look at all the billboards around Utica with pictures of happy couples honeymooning at Niagara Falls. She once promised herself that someday she would spend her honeymoon in Niagara Falls.

"You know me, Bro," Tony continued. "As long as Molly and I go on this honeymoon together, I couldn't care less where we go, so Niagara Falls is as fine with me as any other place.

"So I called a friend of mine in the New York office of ADPRO who comes from Niagara Falls, and I asked him if he could tell me how I could honeymoon in Niagara Falls with a little class.

"He told me about an upscale bed and breakfast at the edge of the city. I looked it up on the Internet. It really does look very nice, so I booked us there for three nights. Then he had me call his cousin Vinnie, who does private tours, and Vinnie's working out a personal guide for us to show us some beautiful views of the falls, even some nighttime views that the average tourist never sees.

"And that's about it, pal," Tony told Frankie as they both finished their third mug of coffee.

"You driving?"

"No, it would take too long, and I don't want to work that hard. I'd rather save my strength for other honeymoon activities. We'll fly to Utica, rent a car, and drive to Niagara Falls for three days. It's only a three-hour drive. Then we can come back to Utica, return the rental, and see her parents again before we fly back to St. Petersburg."

"You and Molly have accomplished a lot in a day and a half, Bro. But Anna and I made all our wedding plans in one day, too. I don't get these people who take six months to plan a wedding, do you?"

Then Frankie leaned over and put his hand on Tony's arm. "I just have one question, Bro. When you did all that talking together, were there any red flags about your relationship you're not telling me about?"

"No, there weren't, Frankie, and I don't think I'm just so blinded by love that I wouldn't recognize them. I've been too scared of the idea of marriage for too long not to be awake to something that could mess up me or Molly."

Then a smile crossed Tony's face.

"Okay, what was that about?"

"Well, Molly did say one thing that cracked me up," Tony said. "I asked her to give it to me straight, you know? What kind of man had she always thought she would like to marry? She thought about it a while and then she said, in all seriousness, 'What I want most is to marry a man who will take care of me while I'm being independent.'"

Tony expected Frankie to laugh out loud, but he didn't.

Frankie sat there thinking about it the way Molly had. "You know, Molly's right on target there, Bro. I guess we all want that. You know, if I ever let myself think about getting married before I met Anna, I was so afraid of losing my independence—being stifled, you know—it scared me skinny. But with Anna, I not only haven't lost anything, I've gained stuff I didn't know I was missing.

"I come in at night, tired and sore," Frankie continued, "and Anna doesn't ask any questions. She just starts massaging my shoulders, and those little hands just dig in there and smooth out those kinks in a few minutes. And I gotta tell you, climbing into a made-up bed every night on sheets I didn't have to wash, finding my shirts washed and dried and hanging in the closet when I want them, and having Anna offer to make me a sandwich at ten o'clock at night—those things make my life just better than you can imagine. She really does take care of me while I'm being independent.

"But on the other side of the coin, when it starts to thunder in the middle of the night and she scoots over to me for protection, as if I could ward off the storm single-handed, and then falls right back to sleep, that touches my heart, you know? And when I see her stroking her car after she discovers I washed and polished it without even telling her, or when I reach up and pull something down from a shelf she can't reach, I can tell she feels taken care of, and she likes it, too. I think Molly hit on exactly what makes it so perfect to be married to someone who loves and respects you as much as you love and respect them.

"You'll see, Bro. You'll see," Frankie said as they walked out of the restaurant together.

Tony wanted to hear about Frankie's talk with his Uncle Lawrence, but it was time to walk Madison, so they went back to Frankie's house. "I'm not so sure having a puppy is any less trouble than having a kid," Frankie said, "except that this one never sasses me back."

They walked the dog, and then settled down on Frankie's back patio with a couple of glasses of iced tea. "I'll tell you briefly what Uncle Lawrence told me about the family in Germany," Frankie said. "It seems that when my father and Lawrence were twelve and ten, their parents got a divorce. My grandmother took Lawrence and they went back to live on her parents' farm, where Lawrence said he was raised in a healthy and loving environment.

"She would have taken my father too, but he had asked to go live with his father. That probably wasn't my father's best choice, though. Because my grandfather grew into a hard and cruel man who beat my father every day and told him constantly, though Lawrence doesn't know why, that if he had never been born, there never would have been a divorce.

"When they each were around eighteen, both Lawrence and my father came to America, although for a number of years neither knew the other was here. By the time they met, Lawrence was married to Millie and they had just bought their first farm in Connecticut. My father and mother were also married. Julie was about two, Lawrence said, and my mother was pregnant with me. My father was working for an insurance company here in St. Petersburg and apparently doing very well, but then something went wrong. My father was fired because the company he worked for said he never should have sold a policy that wound up costing them a lot of money.

"My father was scared he wouldn't be able to support us, so he tracked down some other Doerrer relatives here in the United States, and eventually found Uncle Lawrence in Connecticut. My father went to see him and asked to borrow money until he could find another kind of work.

"Uncle Lawrence cried really hard when he told me this, Tony," Frankie said, his own voice shaking as he remembered it. "I just have to believe he was giving me the straight story, even though there is a part of me that still would like to hear my father's side.

"Anyway," Frankie continued, "Uncle Lawrence explained that he had just plowed every cent he had and all of Millie's inheritance into the farm, and had no money to lend my father. Apparently my father didn't believe him, or didn't want to believe him, and he said some really awful things to Lawrence before he left and came back to Florida.

"Uncle Lawrence told me about some sort of informal network that used to exist between the German immigrants in this country that made it possible for them to turn to each other for help if someone was in trouble. Uncle Lawrence tapped into that network and got in touch with someone here in St. Petersburg who knew someone who owned an insurance company, a competitor to the one that fired my father. They offered my father a job, and he kept that job until he died.

"Apparently though, memories of his childhood really haunted my father, and he started drinking heavily.

"Lawrence said that he and Millie came down twice to St. Petersburg to try to mend the fences between him and his brother when I was still a toddler, but when they saw how the very sight of Lawrence only upset my father more, they went away and didn't come back. Considering the families we were born into, Bro, it's a wonder either of us turned out sane, isn't it?" Frankie asked, rubbing the back of his neck to relieve the tension that had built up as he told the story.

"Yeah, I guess we come by our hang-ups naturally, don't we, Bro?" Tony agreed. "You must have been plenty torn up about this story. Did you 'Go to ELF!' about it?"

"I did 'Go to ELF!' almost immediately. After I finished talking to Uncle Lawrence, I took a walk out to the pasture where the cows were grazing and had a private conversation with the ELF about my father. I didn't expect to see the ELF, but then suddenly, there he was on the fence rail next to me. He started talking right away, and he was very direct about what he had to tell me.

"He said, 'I know what Lawrence told you was hard to hear, Frankie, and I think it was important for you to understand why your father behaved the way he did, just as it was important for Tony to understand why his mother behaved the way she did. But now I'm going to tell you the kindest thing I can ever tell you. It's even more important for you to forget this sad story as soon as possible. Share it with Anna and Tony if you want to, but then just let it all go and shift your focus to what is happening now.'

"He could see I didn't really get that, I guess, so he explained. 'When you dwell on a sad story like that, it only makes you feel unhappy, and those unhappy feelings are there to alert you that you are thinking about something you don't want. When you think about things you don't want, you just create more things you don't want.

"'The past was real once, but now it is just an illusion, Frankie. The only real moment you ever truly experience is the one you are living right now. Unfortunately, most physical beings waste more than half of their human lives reliving past experiences that simply don't exist anymore. I know you don't want to be one of those people.' He said it with the same kind expression on his face he had back in Sherwood Forest.

"'Be at peace, Frankie. Trust me. Your parents are both just fine here with me, and your grandparents are, too. They've all moved on to new experiences. They never think about the past, and neither should you. Experience your life as it is happening, Frankie. This time, this place, this moment in your life is the most exciting moment there is.'

"So I asked him right out, Tony. 'Besides forgetting about the past and not worrying about the future, what are the most important things I need to know to live a happy life?'"

"What did he say?"

"Well, right away he got all shimmery like he does when he likes what he's hearing, and he said, 'I'm so glad you asked me that, because I think you are really ready to hear it, Frankie. The rules for living a happy life are as easy as 1-2-3. All you have to do is remember these three things:"

"'One, you are never alone. I am you and you are me, everywhere and always.

"'Two, the answer to any question you have is already written on your heart.

"'Three, if you have two paths to choose from, always choose the one that is the most fun.'

"And then," Frankie said, scratching his head, "I looked over at a big black cow in Uncle Lawrence's field that I could have sworn was nodding her head in agreement, and when I looked back, the ELF was gone."

"That's it?" Tony asked.

"That's it," Frankie answered. "I wrote those three things down as soon as I could so that I wouldn't forget a word of them. Here's your copy, Bro. I've read them a thousand times since then, and I gotta tell you, they make a lotta sense.

"The secret to getting everything I want is as easy as A-B-C. The secret to living a happy life is as simple as 1-2-3. And that's what the ELF has been telling us all along, Tony. It's kind of a kick to figure out that life doesn't have to be hard unless we make it that way, isn't it?"

Driving home to shower and dress for his New Year's Eve date with Molly, Tony was very conscious of the emerald ring in his pocket and how much he was looking forward to seeing Molly's face when he put it on her finger. He knew it would make her happy. And there is no sight in the whole world more beautiful, he thought, than Molly's face when she is happy.

"I'm asking, ELF," Tony said out loud. "I'm asking because I want to know for myself. Are those three things that you told Frankie all I really need to know to be happy? Can the secret to a happy life really be as simple as 1-2-3?"

Instantly the dream he had in Savannah popped into his mind. *When I was walking down the Technicolor path with Molly, I was happy,* he remembered. *We weren't thinking about the past or the future. Molly and I were just enjoying how beautiful everything around us was at that moment.*

Back in the present, a sign popped up in Tony's mind that read, "How do you feel?" At the same moment, Tony felt, and then saw, the ELF shimmer into the seat next to him.

"I guess you want to know how I feel," Tony said.

"I know how you feel, but I want to hear you say it out loud," the ELF said with a happy grin.

"Okay," Tony said, surprised by the words forming in his heart. "I feel loved. I feel loved by Molly and Frankie and Anna, and by my father and Trainwreck, and that's very exciting. But I also feel something bigger than that. I feel loved by you, and that makes every unpleasant thing that happened to me in the past very unimportant by comparison."

"Well, then," the ELF answered, shimmering with delight, "now that you remember that I really love you, and that I am with you everywhere and always, you are ready to live the life you came here to live, Tony. So let me just give you a little glimpse of how good your future can be."

And to Tony's absolute delight, the whole world, for as far as he could see in all directions, was filled with brilliant, shimmering rainbow light. Awestruck by such unearthly beauty, Tony turned to look back at the ELF, but he was gone.

"Ah, but you're not really gone, are you?" Tony said to the ELF. "Because you are me and I am you, everywhere and always."

Tony parked his car. As he pushed the button in the elevator that would take him upstairs to Molly, he felt a little shimmer of delight run through his body. Yeah, I get it, he admitted to himself. *Now that I remember that I am loved inside and out, my life is about to get a lot more interesting, isn't it?*

EPILOGUE

March 17 was an exquisitely beautiful day in St. Petersburg. The mood was light as Tony and Molly's friends and family gathered in the gracious lobby of the Fillmore hotel. Standing around in small groups, they talked to one another about how they happened to know the two people who were to be married there a short time later.

In one of the guest rooms on the second floor, Mary Casey played the role of mother of the bride. Deirdre, Molly's maid of honor, and Anna, Molly's surrogate sister, had just declared Molly "ready, set, go." Her hair and makeup looked gorgeous. Her beautiful empire style wedding dress was new, her grandmother's emeralds were old, and the tiny, blue enamel fairy pin Mary had just attached to Molly's sleeve was "something borrowed and something blue" all in one. Mary kissed Molly lightly on the cheek.

When Tony tapped on the door, Anna opened it. "You're not supposed to be here," she said gently, successfully blocking his view into the room as she listened to what he had to say. Then she asked Molly, "Do you want to let Tony see you before the wedding? He says he has a very important surprise for you."

"Of course, I do," Molly said to the women who were tending her so lovingly. "We still have half an hour before the wedding starts. Do you mind giving us a few minutes alone?"

"Not a bit," Mary said, shaking her head. "It will give me a chance to see how Sam is holding up. He's even more nervous about walking you down the aisle than he was about our own daughters."

"I know what you mean," Anna agreed. "I thought having breakfast with Tony this morning at the Dome Grill would settle Frankie down, but the last time I saw him, he was a weepy mess. Come on, Deirdre. Let's go give my sentimental husband a shot of much-needed support."

Tony took a minute simply to admire his beautiful bride. "Hi, Baby. I missed you last night," he said, kissing her lightly on the nose so he wouldn't smear her makeup. "But now, I have a surprise for you."

"Should I close my eyes?"

"Oh, no, not for this surprise. You're going to want to have your eyes wide open," he said, gently drawing Molly down onto the little settee that faced the bed.

In seconds, she saw a little light flash on the bedspread, and the ELF appeared right in front of her.

"Oh, my goodness," she said, one hand rising to clutch at her throat.

"You have a lot of goodness, Molly, and so does Tony," said the ELF. "I asked him if I could come and give you my blessing today."

"Oh, my, yes," Molly said, mesmerized by the way the ELF's body shimmered with colors more intense and beautiful than she had ever seen.

"I know there's something you want to ask me, Molly. I can feel your thoughts. Go ahead, don't be shy."

"Oh, my," she said again. Then getting a grip on herself, she explained. "I've been wondering if there is some tool we can use or something Tony and I can practice to help us stay as happy for the rest of our lives as we are today."

"Indeed, there is. It's one of my favorites," the ELF said, grinning at her. "I call it the marriage model. It is an exercise you both can practice if you ever get out of sorts with each other. Would you like me to teach it to you?"

"Oh, yes, we would, wouldn't we, Tony?" she asked excitedly.

"We would, and we would like to share it with Frankie and Anna, too," Tony said.

"Well, here's my promise to you both on the morning of your wedding," the ELF said joyfully. "If you go on your honeymoon and promise to have the most fun you can possibly have while you're gone, I will meet with all four of you when you get back and teach you how to use the marriage model. But if you just can't wait," he added, "ask John McLaughlin to tell you about it. I taught him how to use the marriage model over twenty-five years ago.

"Now, I don't want you to be late for your own wedding, and you two have one more interesting discovery to make before it starts. So I'll leave you alone to find out what it is. If you need anything while you're at Niagara Falls, remember, just 'Go to ELF!'" With a happy wave, the ELF shimmered out of sight.

"What do you think he might be talking about, Baby?" Tony asked, turning toward Molly so he could look directly into her eyes.

"You mean what she might be talking about?"

"She?"

"Yes, the ELF," Molly said. "She is beautiful in a way I never saw beauty before. Seeing her was a lovely surprise, Tony."

"The ELF you saw was a she?"

"Of course, she was a she. With killer high-heeled shoes."

"Shoes?" Tony wasn't sure he believed what he was hearing. "Describe her for me, please, Molly. I want to know everything about the ELF that you saw."

"Okay," Molly said, frowning. Why was he asking her this? After all, he'd been right there, too. "She had a sweet face and soft grey hair, little round glasses, and rosy cheeks. Her face was framed in the prettiest, whitest collar I've ever seen. Her blue hat exactly matched her blue eyes, and her rainbow body was just too magnificent to describe. Then there were those killer blue shoes."

Tony's face registered something like shock, and panic raced though Molly's body. "What's the matter, Tony?" Oh, my, maybe I'm dreaming. Maybe I didn't just talk to the creator and sustainer of all life. Maybe I'm not getting married today. Maybe there is no Molly Malone's Irish Desserts. Maybe I never moved to Florida at all and I'm asleep in my bed in New York. I must be going completely over the edge.

Molly reached over and pinched Tony.

"Ouch!" he yelped, snapping out of his nearly catatonic state. "Why'd you do that?"

"Well, I'm sorry, but you scared me, Tony. I thought for a minute that I hadn't really seen the ELF, and maybe I was just dreaming you up, too. So I pinched you to see if you were real."

"Oh, Baby, I'm so real. And I'm so sorry," Tony said kissing her nose again. "It was just such a jolt to me to find out that you saw the ELF as a female."

"You mean…well, what did you see?" Molly asked, taking a deep breath and feeling comforted that her pulse rate was returning to normal.

"I saw the same ELF I always see," Tony told her. "He's a happy little guy, the kind you feel like you've known for your whole life. He's about three feet tall with the same kind of shimmering body you are describing, and he has grey hair and round glasses, but he also has a grey beard, vivid green eyes, and a purple hat. And I never saw him wearing any shoes."

Then came a joint epiphany.

"Of course!" Tony exclaimed. "Why should we be so surprised to discover that the ELF appears different to each of us? Your ELF is the ELF in yoursELF, and my ELF is the ELF in mysELF."

"The clue is in the affirmations," Molly said, mirroring his insight. "If there is no other person exactly like me in physical form, then it figures that there is no other person exactly like me in non-physical form, either."

"Oh, my, Tony," Molly said. "Life with you is always going to be interesting, isn't it?"

"You see, there are no opposites in Spirit. There is no right and wrong, good and bad, tall and short, black and white, little and big, in and out, up and down, high and low or any other such contrasts. Those opposites, along with heaven and hell, belong only to the human experience."

The ELF

RESOURCES

Ask and It is Given – Abraham-Hicks
Available at Amazon.com

MIND is Your Own Business
9 DVD Home Study Course
Available at Amazon.com

Affirmations for Your Spiritual Awakening
2 CD set - audio and subliminal
Available at Amazon.com

ABOUT THE AUTHOR

Lauren McLaughlin is part of a team of thousands of teachers on the planet at this time, whose purpose is to remind those who wish to remember that they are deeply and dearly loved by the creator and sustainer of all life, that the answers to the most important questions they have are carefully stored in their own heart, and that they deliberately chose the human experience for the sheer fun of it. Lauren is a writer, speaker, and retreat facilitator who is currently living happily-ever-after with her husband, John, in Clearwater, Florida.